DISABLED CHILDREN IN BRITAIN

Disabled Children in Britain

A RE-ANALYSIS OF THE OPCS DISABILITY SURVEYS

David Gordon
Roy Parker
Frank Loughran

with

Pauline Heslop

London: The Stationery Office

Applications for reproduction should be made in writing to The Stationery Office Limited, St Crispins, Duke Street, Norwich NR3 1PD.

The information contained in this publication is believed to be correct at the time of manufacture. Whilst care has been taken to ensure that the information is accurate, the publisher can accept no responsibility for any errors or omissions or for changes to the details given.

Contact details:
School for Policy Studies, University of Bristol, 8 Priory Road, Bristol BS8 1TZ, United Kingdom
Tel: (+44) (0)117 954 6755 Fax: (+44) (0)117 954 6756 e-mail: dave.gordon@bristol.ac.uk

A CIP catalogue record for this book is available from the British Library

First published 2000

ISBN 0 11 702394 9

Printed in the United Kingdom by Albert Gait Ltd., Grimsby.
TJ001433 c6 04/00 9385 12661

Contents

PART TWO: YOUNG CHILDREN

PART THREE: DRAWING THE THREADS TOGETHER

Preamble

In 1984, the Department of Health and Social Security commissioned the Office of Population Censuses and Surveys (OPCS), now the Office for National Statistics (ONS), to undertake a survey of disability in Great Britain as part of the review of social security. It was the most extensive inquiry into disability ever mounted in this country (costing £2.47 million) as well as being one of the largest social surveys in any field. The results were published during 1988 and 1989 in six reports but, necessarily, a great deal of data remained unanalysed.

The survey was divided into four parts: studies of adults in private households, studies of adults in communal establishments and studies of children in the same two settings. Given our long-standing interest in children with special needs we were anxious to exploit the material provided by the children's surveys more fully than had been possible for OPCS. We obtained permission to use the data and were given financial support from the Department of Health.

In light of the costliness of collecting data of this kind, we were convinced that the fullest possible use should be made of it. That entailed not only secondary analysis but also the additional interpretation of results. Nonetheless, some may wonder why we spent so much time and effort in these further explorations of the data when OPCS had already reported on a good deal of it in their publications. The reasons are twofold. The first is that we believed that the application of a different methodology could overcome some of the limitations of the OPCS approach, especially in the treatment of multiple disabilities. Of course, what OPCS did remains valid in its own terms, but there is a virtue in seeing what might be achieved by tackling the analysis somewhat differently. The second reason why we wanted to go beyond what was already published was in order to concentrate in more detail upon the provision of health and social services and to examine the influence of socio-economic factors upon the notion of 'need' and upon the distribution of services.

Of course, it might be argued that data which were gathered in the mid-

1980s are hardly worth more detailed study and analysis. We do not believe this to be the case, for four principal reasons. First, these surveys of disabled children were the largest and most comprehensive ever undertaken. The size of the sample enables conclusions to be drawn with considerable confidence over a whole range of issues: the results are the most statistically reliable that we have. Secondly, the last decade has witnessed major changes in policies for disabled children and in the services that both they and their parents might reasonably expect to receive. What the OPCS data provide, therefore, is a bench-mark against which the current state of provision and the circumstances of disabled children and their families can be compared. What has changed and what has remained unaltered? The third reason for our believing that these data from the 1980s are still extremely relevant is that their analysis highlights a number of key questions which we know remain of the utmost importance; the significance of others remains to be established. Finally, we would argue that in engaging in this additional analysis of the OPCS data we have adopted a system based on the medical classification and grouping of the children, a system which is of importance both methodologically and in offering one way of understanding better the patterns of their disability.[1]

However, the work has not been straightforward. Some of the computational problems have been enormous and taken a great deal of time to resolve.[2] Furthermore, the original designs of the two children's surveys were different; in particular, whereas the data from the communal establishments study applied only to children between 5 and 15 years of age, the data from the private households inquiry covered all children under 16. Over and above this, however, OPCS devised different measurements (for example, of the severity of disability) for the under-5s from those that were employed for the older children. These factors made it difficult to draw direct comparisons between the children living in private households and those living residentially; they also made it difficult to combine results for these two principal age groups. For this reason, we have kept the discussion of the under-5s separate from that concerned with the other children in much of what follows.

Should anyone look at the whole range of data that was collected in the surveys, they will be mesmerised by its volume and extent. In its published analyses, OPCS had to be selective: the same necessity has constrained us. We could not do everything and have omitted to discuss such important matters as the provision of transport. However, these very omissions underline the richness of this treasure chest of data, a chest that deserves even further exploration than we have been able to undertake.

NOTES TO PREAMBLE

[1] As a result of this somewhat different approach to the analysis of the data, it will be noted that, from time to time, our figures vary a little from those to be found in OPCS publications. Small discrepancies arise from our use of slightly different versions of the data; for example, the age of the child at the time of the interview instead of the age of the child at the time that the sample was drawn, or the use of unweighted, rather than weighted, figures.

[2] In particular, the SPSS system file containing all the data from the OPCS blue and yellow schedules relating to the private households survey and all the derived variables associated with these data, had no variable descriptions or value labels attached. It took many months to 'reverse engineer' what OPCS had done and over 3500 lines of computer code to re-attach these missing labels.

Acknowledgements

We have received generous assistance from many quarters in undertaking this work. The research was facilitated by a grant from the Department of Health and supported throughout in a patient and understanding manner by Dr Carolyn Davies, our liaison officer. We are most grateful to her. Thanks are also due to the staff at OPCS, and particularly to Howard Meltzer, for their help in unravelling questions about the design and conduct of the original surveys; to the Economic and Social Research Council (ESRC) Data Archive for permission to use the data tapes and to the University of Bristol Computer Centre for a generous allocation of file space. We would like to give particular thanks to Helen Anderson for her heroic efforts in interpreting the schedule file of the private households survey which contained no variable descriptions or value labels. Without her painstaking efforts to re-attach these labels and her careful editing work, this report would not have been possible. We would also like to thank especially Yvonne McCann and Patricia Lees for their meticulous aid in typing the material and the Dartington Social Research Unit for providing valuable facilities.

We alone are responsible, of course, for any errors or misunderstandings that may have crept into our analyses and interpretations.

1 | General introduction

1. The background to the OPCS surveys

Between 1985 and 1988 the Social Survey Division of OPCS undertook a series of major surveys for the (then) Department of Health and Social Security to assist them in planning benefits and welfare services policies for people with disabilities. The surveys aimed to produce estimates of the number of people in Great Britain with disabilities[1] and to explore their social and financial circumstances. They covered both adults and children and included those living in private households as well as those in residential establishments. The four surveys, together with the year in which they were conducted, the number interviewed and the weighted base sample sizes, are listed in Figure 1.1.

Figure 1.1
Basic details of the four OPCS surveys

1985 Adults (16 years and over) in private households
11,035 interviews *(Base = 10,000)*

1985 Children (0–15 years) in private households
1359 interviews *(Base = 1200)*

1986 Adults (16 years and over) in communal establishments
3533 interviews *(Base = 4000)*

1988 Children (5–15 years) in communal establishments
1019 interviews *(Base = 1000)*

Adults and children with disabilities living in private households were identified from an initial screening of 100,000 addresses in Great Britain.[2] For the other two surveys, interviews were conducted in 858 communal establishments sampled from 18,982 eligible units identified in preliminary screening exercises.[3]

The results of the surveys appeared in six reports published during the late 1980s (Martin *et al.*, 1988; Martin and White, 1988; Bone and Meltzer, 1989; Martin *et al.*, 1989; Smyth and Robus, 1989; Meltzer *et al.*, 1989). The basic data were deposited in the Economic and Social Research Council's (ESRC) Data Archive at the University of Essex and became available to academic researchers for secondary analysis at the end of 1990. This report draws upon these data and builds on our previous studies of children with disabilities living in communal establishments (Loughran *et al.*, 1992; Gordon *et al.*, 1994) and in private households (Gordon *et al.*, 1996). As a general rule, the data in the tables and figures relate to Great Britain as a whole; if they refer to only part of Britain, the area is specified in each instance.

The criticisms of the OPCS studies

However, at the outset, it is important to note that a number of criticisms have been made of the OPCS data. The first of these centres on the methodology. Walker (1991) argues that, in attempting to clarify such 'complex and ill-defined areas' as the extra expenditure that results from disability, a small-scale study using semi-structured interviews would have been more appropriate. Such a study would have enabled supplementary questions to have been asked and points which arose in the interview to be clarified – so providing a more sensitive, thoughtful and accurate response to the topics being examined. Likewise, the large-scale OPCS surveys using structured interviews were, the Disablement Income Group (1988) and Disability Alliance (Walker, 1991) argued, inaccurate in that they asked about hypothetical situations (for instance, what proportion of heating costs were incurred because of a person's disability) and assumed that it was possible to quantify (without time being given for much thought) the 'extra costs' associated with disability. It was maintained that hidden costs, in terms of lost opportunities for disabled people and their families, were ignored.

The second kind of criticism levelled at the OPCS surveys was that they were centred on the notion that functional limitation could be investigated without regard to the different social and environmental aspects of people's lives (Abberley, 1992). Today there is, arguably, a much greater appreciation of the social implications of disability and of the interactions between the individual and his or her family and the environmental milieu. Depending upon their social circumstances, those with particular kinds and degrees of impairments may be more or less restricted in their activities to a widely variable degree. The OPCS surveys, it has been argued, failed to take account of this. We have endeavoured to redress the balance.

The third, and perhaps the most fundamental, criticism of the OPCS disability surveys has been a conceptual one: namely, that the definition of disability employed was too medical and focused solely upon the individual. Disability was thus regarded as an individual phenomenon reflecting a person's identified impairments. This approach has been challenged by 'social model' theorists and by a number of disability groups including the British Council of Organisations of Disabled People. Disability, according to this school of thought, is mainly a function of the actions or behaviour of other people which impose disadvantages on those with impairments, thereby excluding them from the mainstream of social activities. Following this line of analysis, Abberley (1996) argued that the OPCS surveys were inadequate because they investigated the wrong thing as a result of the way in which they chose to define disability, thereby focusing incorrectly on individuals rather than structures.

Whilst being sympathetic to the social model of disability for the insights that it has provided, we believe that the kind of data that OPCS collected have their place and can be effectively utilised in the interests of disabled children and their families. We have, however, given thought to our use of language in the report. Since the concept of disability employed by OPCS was impairment-focused (as we shall see in the next section), we have used the term 'children with disabilities' to reflect the medical emphasis that this implies. However, in our more general discussions incorporating both medical and social (or only social) considerations, we have preferred the term 'disabled children'.

The concept of disability employed by OPCS

The concept of disability that was adopted for the OPCS surveys may be captured in the words of two of the authors of the original reports. Disability was, they explained, viewed as: 'any restriction or lack of ability to perform activities considered normal for a person of similar age, which has resulted from the impairment of a structure or function of the body or mind' or, put more simply, the focus of the surveys was on 'what people cannot do, without regard to the cause of their disability' (Martin and Elliot, 1992). This definition of disability is closely related to that used in the International Classification of Impairments, Disabilities and Handicaps (ICIDH), which utilises three different concepts to describe 'disablement' (WHO, 1981; Bradley, 1987; Wood, 1980, 1987, 1989; British Association for Community Child Health and the Department of Health, 1994; Schuntermann, 1996; Barolin, 1997; Bickenbach *et al.*, 1999). These concepts are elaborated in Figure 1.2.

Figure 1.2
*Concepts of
'disablement' used in
the International
Classification of
Impairments,
Disabilities and
Handicaps*[4]

Impairment	Any loss or abnormality of psychological, physiological or anatomical structure or function.
Disability	Any restriction or lack of ability (resulting from an impairment) to perform an activity in the manner or within the range considered normal for a human being.
Handicap	A disadvantage for a given individual, resulting from an impairment or disability, that limits or prevents the fulfilment of a role (depending on age and sex as well as upon social and cultural factors) for that individual.

However, an important difference between the ICIDH and the OPCS definitions of disability is that the one used by OPCS was age-related when applied to children. This modification was found to be essential if meaningful measures were to be obtained for children at different stages of development.

Initially, DHSS had asked OPCS to design a method of assessment for the surveys based on the 'loss of faculty' approach used in adult Industrial Injuries and War Pensions schemes. In these schemes, a medical officer identifies a loss of faculty attributable to an industrial injury or disease, or to service in the armed forces, assesses the disabilities resulting from the loss of faculty and then arrives at a percentage of disablement on the basis of which a benefit is awarded. However, OPCS considered that assessments of 'loss of faculty' or 'impairment' were not appropriate for use in its surveys because they required clinical examinations, tests and judgements. It was not considered feasible to arrange for all those in the surveys to be medically examined. Moreover, disabled people themselves, and organisations representing their interests, generally found questions about disability more relevant than questions about impairment. The general reaction at the pilot stage was that informants could not see the point of being asked questions about impairments that did not result in disability. Furthermore, such impairments would not necessarily be mentioned if they were not considered to be relevant (Martin and Bone, 1986).

Thus, the focus of the OPCS surveys was on disabilities rather than on specific impairments that *may* result in disabilities or on the handicaps that *may* arise for a person with a disability in relation to certain factors in their milieu. However, information was collected about the conditions causing specific impairments as well as about handicaps (disadvantages experienced by the individual or their family) but these data were not used in constructing the measure of severity that OPCS employed.

Two important consequences of the choice of definition that OPCS made, especially in relation to definitions used in earlier surveys, were that impairments that did not lead to disabilities were *excluded* but behavioural and emotional difficulties were *included* as disabilities whether or not they were associated with any specific psychiatric or organic disorder.

The significance of the definitions employed in the children's surveys is considered later, but the examples in Figure 1.3 illustrate what would be covered by the three different ICIDH concepts of disability and the effect that the exclusion of 'impairment' and 'handicap' would have had upon who was included or left out (Shaar and McCarthy, 1994).

Figure 1.3
Examples of the application of the three ICIDH concepts of disability

Example 1
A child with epilepsy which was controlled by drugs to such an extent that the child had not had a fit for two years would have an *impairment* but would not be considered to have a *disability* in this area.

Example 2
A child who was short-sighted would have an *impairment* but would not have a *disability* if their vision was corrected sufficiently by spectacles to allow them to recognise somebody they knew across a road. If the child's parents were unable to afford spectacles, or would not allow the child to wear them, these *handicaps* would cause the impairment to become a visual disability.

Example 3
A child with lung damage would have an *impairment* which would give rise to a locomotion *disability* if breathing problems led to the child having difficulty walking a quarter of a mile on level ground.

Example 4
A child who was confined to a wheelchair following injury to their legs would have an *impairment* and a *disability*. If there were no access ramps at the school, this would also become a *handicap*.

Example 5
A child who had severe behavioural and emotional problems which had no organic basis would have a *disability* arising from an *impairment* of psychological function.

The areas of disability that were assessed

OPCS assessed each child or adult included in the surveys for the presence of disability in 13 areas. These were developed from the groupings proposed by the ICIDH. They are listed in Figure 1.4 with examples of the types of behaviours and activities that were covered by each of them.

Figure 1.4
*Areas of disability
assessed by OPCS
(their descriptions)*

Locomotion	Walking, running, steps and stairs, bending and straightening, falling and balancing.
Reaching and stretching	Reaching in front and behind, stretching above the head.
Dexterity	Picking up objects, gripping, turning.
Seeing	Recognising known people close to and at a distance, following a TV programme.
Hearing	Following a TV or radio programme, hearing a door bell, using a telephone.
Personal care	Independence/dependence in a range of daily activities such as bathing, dressing, eating.
Continence	Enuresis, encopresis, the use of devices to manage bladder or bowels.
Communication	Being understood, understanding others (relatives, friends and strangers).
Behaviour	Aggressive, withdrawn or self-destructive behaviour; peer relationships.
Intellectual functioning	Reading, writing, numeracy, memory, the ability to concentrate.
Consciousness	Fits and convulsions.
Eating, drinking and digestion	The need for minced or liquidised food.
Disfigurement	Scars, blemishes and deformities.

The common severity scale and the overall measure of the severity of disability

OPCS developed a new measure of severity because none existed that utilised the ICIDH concept of disability (Martin and Elliot, 1992). For the purposes of their surveys, severity was defined as: 'the extent to which an individual's performance of activities is limited by impairments' (Bone and Meltzer, 1989). The severity of disability was assessed in all of the 13 areas covered in the studies. For this purpose, OPCS developed a severity scale that could be applied without modification in each of the areas. This allowed severity in different spheres to be compared so that, for example, it could be determined whether (and to what extent) children who could not feed themselves without help had a more severe disability than those who were only able to walk a few steps.

A further new development in the OPCS surveys was the construction of an overall measure of severity which allowed judgements of relative severity to be made between individuals with different types, numbers and combinations of disabilities. This measure assigned each individual to one of ten overall severity categories (category 1 being the least severe and category 10 the most). Thus, it enabled assessments of the relative severity of disabilities to be made between, for example, an adult with visual, intellectual functioning and continence disabilities and a child with locomotion, hearing and behavioural disabilities. The development and application of the common severity scale and the overall severity measure are described and discussed further in Chapter 2.

2. The children's surveys

The two children's surveys that OPCS conducted remain by far the largest exploration of childhood disability ever undertaken in Great Britain.[5] One unique feature was the inclusion of children who were resident in communal establishments; another was the size of the samples and the range and complexity of the questions that were asked.

The identification and sampling of children with disabilities living in private households

Since there is no comprehensive list of all people with disabilities from which a sample can be drawn, OPCS undertook a major screening exercise (Bone and Meltzer, 1989). First, as we have mentioned, a large sample of 100,000 addresses throughout Great Britain was used to identify people with some form of disability. This was done with the help of a short questionnaire, the information from which provided the basis for a smaller number of fuller interviews. These were conducted with those people – or, in the case of children, with their parents – who were potential candidates for inclusion in the eventual sample. Some, of course, were excluded because their disabilities did not conform with the definition or reach the threshold of severity that OPCS had set.

For fairly obvious reasons, somewhat different questions were asked about children than about adults, both at the point of initial screening and in the later interviews. Furthermore, there was some variation in what was asked about children under 5 and about those between 5 and 15 years. As we have noted already, this difference created a problem in making comparisons between the two groups and explains why a separate part is devoted to the under-5s later in this report.

The information about the children (and to a lesser extent about their families) was collected by means of structured interviews with, where possible, the child's mother, or else with the father. In the absence of either parent, the person who 'was responsible for the child' was interviewed, typically a foster carer or grandparent. Interviews were obtained for 84% of the children in the final private households sample, a total of 1359, weighted down to a base figure of 1200 in most of the analysis.

The identification and sampling of children with disabilities living in communal establishments

In order to obtain a representative sample of establishments that catered for children with disabilities, OPCS first had to determine how many there were. This information was obtained from various registers held by central government departments, from a variety of year-books and by contact with all local authority social services and education departments, with all health authorities and with the headquarters of the major voluntary and charitable child-care organisations. A total of 517 authorities (a 95% response rate) provided information about 3421 establishments in Great Britain that offered any form of residential care for children.

A census of these establishments was carried out in order to discover which of them contained children who were eligible for inclusion in the survey. This initial screening exercise produced a 79% response rate. From these data, 687 establishments were identified, a quarter of those that had returned the census forms. The remaining establishments were excluded for one or more of the following reasons: because they had no children resident who were under the age of 16; because none of the children met the residence criteria (see below); because they contained no children who met the disability criteria (see below); or because they catered for fewer than four children.[6]

All the establishments looking after 11 or more children with disabilities were selected for the survey, with the smaller units being sub-sampled. Some establishments were later excluded, mainly because they were found not to contain any children who met the residence criteria. The ones omitted were 'predominantly those where the children's stay at the establishment was relatively short term, for example, children in hospital for the treatment of acute illness, or in community homes on a voluntary short-term basis or in respite care' (Bone and Meltzer, 1989).

One important issue was the way in which OPCS allocated children either to the private households sample or to that covering the communal establishments. In order to be eligible for inclusion in the communal establishments survey, the children had to meet each of three criteria that concerned the presence of one or more disabilities, residential status and age. The residential status criteria were designed to exclude children whose residential stays were either very short or where their home was considered to be somewhere other than the establishment in which they were then residing. This interpretation depended upon whether the children visited their parental home less than once a fortnight on average. The effect of this was to exclude all children receiving respite care (Geall *et al.*, 1991) as well as most children who were weekly or termly boarders at residential schools. These children were included in the private households survey. This should be borne in mind when we come to examine the services received by the families of children with disabilities. However, two other groups at boarding school were included in the communal establishments survey. They were children who resided there all year and those who stayed at another residential unit during the vacations.

The question of the allocation of the children to one or other of the survey groups was further complicated by the decision of OPCS that even though certain children in residential establishments met the 'fortnightly-visiting-home' criterion they should not be treated as if they were living at home. These were children who were in the care of a local authority on a compulsory basis; that is, children who had been committed to care by a court. Despite this caveat, the general result of the OPCS decision to allocate some of the children who were cared for most of the time in residential establishments to the private households sample was to under-play the significance of the residential experience in the care careers of many children with disabilities.

The final criterion for being allotted to the communal establishments survey concerned the age of the children. Originally, all children under the age of 16 were to have been included. However, OPCS decided that those under five years of age should be excluded because the initial census had found so few who met the residential criteria (about 150) and because they were widely dispersed.

Interviews were eventually conducted therefore with the carers of 1019 children between 5 and 15 (95% of those eligible) in 288 establishments. For the purposes of analysis, this total was weighted down to a base figure of 1000.

The interviews and the interview schedules

On the basis of the data gathered in interviews, the children aged 5–15 were assigned a severity scale score in one or more of 11 of the 13 areas of disability originally chosen by OPCS. In the event, the areas of 'digestion' and 'disfigurement' were omitted because they provided insufficient information to produce severity scales.[7] Descriptions of the minimum and maximum points of the scales that were used in each of the 11 areas are reproduced in Figure 1.5 for the children aged 5–15. The maximum and minimum points of the scales for the ten areas chosen for children aged five are shown in Figure 1.6 (the area of 'intellectual functioning' being omitted).[8] The severity scores of children under five were related to those of children aged five by means of a modelling exercise that took account of the 'normal' ages and rates at which young children develop (see Chapter 14 for further details).

3. The prevalence of disability discovered

The OPCS surveys (Bone and Meltzer, 1989) estimated that, overall, there were 360,000 (±22,000) children under the age of 16 in Great Britain who had one or more disabilities (and 327,000 in England and Wales). This represented a little over 3% of the population in that age range (a rate of 32 per 1000). This is a much lower rate than those obtained by most other surveys of childhood disability that have been undertaken in the last 30 years which produced estimates ranging between 3% and 16%. Table 1.1 (updated from Bone and Meltzer, 1989) shows how the prevalence rates in the OPCS disability surveys compare with those obtained from other studies.

Of course, any estimate is a reflection of the way in which disability is defined. The earlier surveys tended to focus upon impairments rather than upon the disabilities that they *may* cause. The Isle of Wight survey, which produced the highest estimate, included psychiatric disorder in its definition of 'handicap' (Rutter *et al.*, 1970). The 1991 census is the only survey to have produced a lower prevalence rate than the OPCS surveys. However, it probably underestimated the prevalence of limiting long-term illness in children. For instance, 12% of adults were enumerated as having a limiting long-term illness whereas the 1991 Census Validation Survey found a rate of 14% (Heady *et al.*, 1996). Similarly, interviews conducted in the 1989 Post-Enumeration Survey (the census test) also discovered an adult prevalence rate of 14% (Pearce and Thomas, 1990); and the 1987 Autumn Wording Test of the Census Questions found an adult prevalence rate of 16% (Pearce *et al.*, 1988; Thomas, 1989). Unfortunately, none of

Figure 1.5
Maximum and minimum points on the severity scales for children aged 5–15 years (OPCS wording)

Locomotion	*Maximum*	Cannot walk at all.
	Minimum	Can only walk for a quarter of a mile without stopping or without severe discomfort.
Reaching and stretching	*Maximum*	Cannot put either hand up to smooth or ruffle hair.
	Minimum	Can put one hand up to smooth or ruffle hair but not the other.
Dexterity	*Maximum*	Cannot pick up and carry a tennis ball with either hand.
	Minimum	Can pick up and carry a small can of drink with one hand but not the other.
Hearing	*Maximum*	Is totally deaf in both ears.
	Minimum	Does not hear if name is called in the street.
Seeing	*Maximum*	Cannot tell by the light where the windows are.
	Minimum	Cannot see well enough to recognise someone they know across a road.
Communication	*Maximum*	Finds it impossible to understand anything their family says to them.
	Minimum	Is difficult for people outside his family to understand because the child stammers or stutters, or their words are unclear.
Continence	*Maximum*	Cannot usually control bowels.
	Minimum	*Is aged 5–10* and wets self during the day at least once a month or *is aged at least 11* and wets bed at least once a month, but does not wet self by day.
Personal care	*Maximum*	Cannot feed self without help.
	Minimum	Cannot bath self without help.
Intellectual functioning	*Maximum*	*Is aged 5–7* and cannot count up to 10 or *is aged 8–15* and cannot recognise own name if written down.
	Minimum	*Is aged 5–7* and cannot count and calculate well enough to make small purchases and give or receive correct change or *is aged at least 8* and has difficulty writing but can write a short thank you letter without help.
Behaviour	*Maximum*	Is aggressive, violent-tempered or destructive or screams and shouts *most of the time* every day.
	Minimum	Is *sometimes* miserable, afraid or worried about lots of different things but less than once a week.
Consciousness	*Maximum*	Has fits both during the day and night and loses consciousness during a fit and experiences more than one fit a day.
	Minimum	Has experienced 1–4 fits during the past year but did not lose consciousness.

Figure 1.6
Maximum and minimum points on the severity scales for children aged under five years (OPCS wording)

Locomotion	*Maximum*	*Is aged 5* and cannot kick or move legs at all.
	Minimum	*Is aged 5* and can walk upstairs with alternating feet without help but cannot manage as many as 12 stairs.
Reaching and stretching	*Maximum*	*Is aged 5* and cannot stretch *either* arm out to reach for something in front of self.
	Minimum	*Is aged 5* and can hold out *one* arm to put into the sleeve of a jacket but not the other.
Dexterity	*Maximum*	*Is aged 5* and cannot hold a small building brick with *either* hand.
	Minimum	*Is aged 5* and cannot unscrew a lid.
Hearing	*Maximum*	*Is aged 5* and is totally deaf in both ears.
	Minimum	*Is aged 5* and cannot hear if own name is called in the street.
Seeing	*Maximum*	*Is aged 5* and cannot tell by the light where the windows are.
	Minimum	*Is aged 5* and cannot see well enough to follow a TV programme sitting at a normal distance from the TV set.
Communication	*Maximum*	*Is aged 5* and cannot understand words such as 'bye-bye' and 'no! no!'
	Minimum	*Is aged 5* and can talk in sentences but people outside the family cannot understand what is meant.
Continence	*Maximum*	*Is aged 5* and cannot usually control bowels.
	Minimum	*Is aged 5* and wets self during the day at least once a month.
Personal care	*Maximum*	*Is aged 5* and cannot feed self without help.
	Minimum	*Is aged 5* and cannot bath self without help.
Behaviour	*Maximum*	*Is aged 5* and is aggressive or destructive, has temper tantrums or screams and shouts *most of the time* every day.
	Minimum	*Is aged 5* and is aggressive or destructive, has temper tantrums or screams and shouts *sometimes* but less than once a week or is awake for much of the night or is unable to settle at night *often* at least once a week; or *is aged 1* and screams and cries for long periods during the night often at least once a week.
Consciousness	*Maximum*	Has fits every day.
	Minimum	Has fits at least once a year but less than four times.

Table 1.1 Estimates of the prevalence of limitations in children under 16

Source	Type of limitation (as described)	Percentage of children with limitation
Rutter et al., 1970 (Isle of Wight study in 1964 of 9–11-year-olds)	Handicapped	16
Weale and Bradshaw, 1980 (based on the 1974 GHS)	Severe and moderate handicap	3
Court, 1976	Severely and moderately handicapped (excluding psychiatric handicaps)	9
General Household Survey (OPCS, 1985)	Limiting long-standing illness	6
OPCS disability surveys, 1985 and 1988	Disabled	3
1991 census	Limiting long-standing illness	2.6
1995 Health Survey for England (10–15-year-olds) (Prescott-Clarke and Primatesta, 1997)	Disabled (locomotion, personal care, seeing, hearing and communication, but excluding continence)	5

these surveys attempted to measure the accuracy of the 'limiting long-term illness' prevalence rate for children in the census.

The age of the different surveys may also have affected the prevalence rate of childhood disability that they obtained. There is some evidence that the prevalence rate may well have increased gradually over the past 30 years, although the reasons for this apparent increase may be complex (Sturgis, 1999; Thomas, 1999). Figure 1.7 shows, for example, the change in the rates of 'limiting long-term illness' in children as recorded in the general household surveys between 1974 and 1995.

Thus, although there has probably been an increase in the prevalence of disabilities in childhood since the 1970s, this is unlikely to explain completely the differences in the estimates produced in the different surveys listed in Table 1.1. These are, in part at least, the consequence of the different definitions of disability that were employed or of the variable use of the concepts of 'impairment', 'disability' or 'handicap'. What should be borne in mind, however, is that the results obtained in the OPCS surveys are at the lower end of the range, thus suggesting that their definition of what was or was not to be considered childhood disability was fairly restrictive.

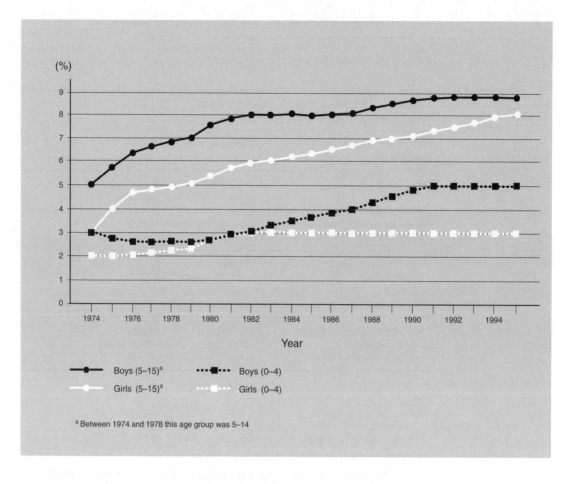

Figure 1.7

Changes in the limiting long-term illness rates for children between 1974 and 1995 (smoothed General Household Survey data)

The problems of defining childhood disability make international comparisons of prevalence fraught with difficulty. Eurostat (the European Statistical Office) and Directorate-General V – Employment, Industrial Relations and Social Affairs (Integration of Disabled People) of the Commission of European Communities have attempted to produce some comparative statistics for member states (Eurostat, 1995). Table 1.2 shows the estimated prevalence rates for disability amongst children and young people in 1991 or 1992.

The UK appears to have the second highest prevalence rates for childhood disability in Europe, with only The Netherlands reporting higher rates. However, the prevalence rates in Table 1.2 need to be interpreted with caution since direct estimates of disability rates by age group were only available from surveys carried out in Germany (ex-FRG) in 1981, Spain in 1986, France in 1980/81, The Netherlands from 1986 to 1988 and the UK in 1985, 1989 and 1990. There were no survey data available by age group from Belgium, Denmark, Greece, Ireland, Italy, Luxembourg or

Table 1.2 Estimated prevalence rates of disability for children and young adults in 1991 or 1992 from censuses and national surveys

Country	Age 0–4 (%)	Age 5–9 (%)	Age 10–14 (%)	Age 15–19 (%)
Belgium	0.9	1.1	1.5	1.9
Germany	0.8	1.1	1.4	1.9
Greece	0.6	0.8	1.0	1.3
Spain	1.4	1.8	2.3	3.0
France	1.0	1.3	1.6	2.0
Italy	0.8	1.0	1.3	1.7
Netherlands, The	1.8	2.3	2.8	3.4
Portugal	0.9	1.2	1.5	2.0
United Kingdom	1.5	1.8	2.3	2.8

Note: There is no information on childhood disability prevalence rates available from Denmark, Ireland or Luxembourg. Prevalence estimates for Belgium, Greece, Italy and Portugal are derived from statistical modelling not direct survey measurement.

Portugal. The prevalence estimates were calculated by extrapolating the observed relationship between disability and age from regression analysis and applying this relationship for countries without specific age group data. It was also assumed that the observed relationship between age and disability did not change over the 1980s. The definition of disability varied between countries, and Eurostat noted that the member states used a terminology that often deviated from the International Classification of Impairments, Disabilities and Handicaps (ICIDH) (Eurostat, 1995).

NOTES TO CHAPTER 1

[1] Similar surveys were carried out in Northern Ireland during 1989 and 1990. The results of these surveys were published in a series of reports (McCoy and Smith, 1992; Smith *et al.*, 1992; Smith *et al.*, 1993; Duffy, 1995a, 1995b; Monteith *et al.*, 1997; Zarb and Maher, 1997).

[2] The addresses were selected from a geographically stratified sample of the Postcode Address File.

[3] To be eligible for inclusion in the survey, an establishment had to have four or more residents, at least one of whom had to have been identified as having a disability during the initial screening exercise.

[4] The ICIDH was developed by the World Health Organisation. The concepts of disablement it employs draw upon the work of Wood (WHO, 1981; Wood, 1980). See also, and more specifically, British Association for Community Child Health and the Department of Health, 1994.

[5] The previous OPCS surveys of disability did not include children (Harris *et al.*, 1971, 1972; Buckle, 1971). The Committee on Child Health Services had to compile its own estimate of the national prevalence of childhood disability from the results of several local studies (Court, 1976). Two studies based upon the General Household Survey did include children but not those living in communal establishments, and the samples were much

smaller than in the OPCS inquiries (Weale and Bradshaw, 1980). Prior to the OPCS surveys, the most comprehensive study of childhood disability was that mounted by Rutter and his colleagues on the Isle of Wight (Rutter *et al.*, 1970). The great strength of this study was that it was based upon individual medical, psychiatric and psychological examinations; however, because of its restricted geographic and age coverage (9–11-year-olds), general conclusions could not be drawn with confidence.

[6] These small units could have been included in the private households survey, although none actually appeared in that dataset.

[7] Nevertheless, a weight was added to take account of them (if they applied) when the overall severity of a child's disability was assessed.

[8] However, the under-5s did receive a severity score if they had, or will have had, severe difficulty learning or a mental handicap.

PART ONE

5–15-year-olds

2 The classification of disability

5–15-year-olds in private households and communal establishments

1. The severity scale devised by OPCS

One of the main aims of the OPCS disability surveys was to construct a scale that could be used to measure the severity of a person's disability whatever the type, number or combination of those disabilities. So, for example, it was intended that the same system would provide a 'severity score' for someone who was unable to walk as well as it would for another who was partially deaf and blind. Each would receive a score that located them on a shared gradient of severity. In the event, OPCS divided this gradient into ten levels, and individuals were allocated a level according to their severity score. Level one contained the least and level ten the most severely disabled.[1]

This approach enabled prevalence rates of the ten different levels of severity to be calculated for the whole population, thereby fulfilling one of the purposes of the surveys: to provide a means of gauging the emerging costs of benefits that were varied according to the severity of a claimant's disability. However, as we shall see, this is not such an appropriate approach if the purpose is to assist in the planning of welfare services. Before we consider this issue, it is necessary to explain rather more fully how OPCS devised the severity scale. The procedure adopted was, to say the least, complicated. However, parts of what follow later in the book cannot be understood without explaining some of that complexity. In the next few paragraphs we do our best to do that.

OPCS began by assembling panels of independent assessors[2] who were then provided with several sets of cards on each of which certain disabling conditions were described. Each set covered a particular area of disability such as locomotion, communication or seeing. Armed with these cards, the judges were then asked to assess the relative severity of what was described and taken through five different stages of the process.

First, they were required to locate each of the descriptions in each set of cards on an 11-point scale;[3] that is, for each area of disability. More than one card could be placed at a point on the scale and not all the points had to be used. Various measures of agreement between the assessors were calculated, the ratings of the few that were out of line with the majority being excluded. The averages of their combined ratings were then used to assign a score to each of the disabilities described on the cards.

The *second* stage of the procedure required the judges to decide upon the relative severity of the various descriptions *between* the different types of disabilities. This was done by allocating the most and the least severe examples in each area of disability on a new 15-point scale covering all the areas combined.

Once this was done, the *third* step was for the new mean scores for the most and least disabling descriptions of all types to be used to place the remaining cards on the so-called *common* 15-point severity scale. Having done this, however, a lower threshold of severity for all the areas of disability was set; below this level, people would not be considered to be disabled for the purposes of the survey.[4]

After the common 15-point severity scale had been constructed, the *fourth* stage was for each person to be assigned a score for each area of their disability. The score they were given was the rating that had been accorded to their most serious limitation in that area of disability. If someone had a severity score for only one type of disability, that became their rating on what was called the measure of *overall* severity.

However, this left the problem of giving an overall severity score to those with more than one type of disability. In order to deal with this possibility, a *fifth* procedure was invoked. Each assessor was given a set of 84 representative profiles of combinations of disabilities, broadly grouped by type (physical, mental and sensory) and by severity (appreciable, severe and very severe). As before, the profiles were rated on a 15-point scale and any outlying assessments discounted. A regression analysis was then undertaken to model the processes used by the assessors in order to arrive at severity scores for the examples of multiple disabilities that had been considered. It was found that the judges had hardly ever taken account of more than three disabilities in reaching their assessments.[5] That being so, it was decided that, where multiple disabilities occurred, the individual's overall severity score would take only three into account.

When all this was completed, every individual in the surveys could be given an *overall* severity score.[6] It was these scores that were then divided into the ten bands of severity that we described in the first paragraph of this chapter.

However, there is one further note to make. The disabilities associated with fits and convulsions (consciousness) and disfigurement as well as with problems of digestion had to be omitted from the assessment exercises, although they were reflected in the calculation of the overall severity scores.[7]

This complicated series of judgement exercises and scoring methods was developed originally for use with the data from the adult surveys. When it came to the children, certain adjustments had to be made in the way the panels made their assessments. In the main, this involved asking the assessors to rate the severity of the two specific card descriptions that were common to all ages on (another) 15-point scale, with respect to whether it was an adult, a child of 6–15 or a child of 5 who experienced the disability. The mean scores derived from this exercise were then used to relate the children's scales to those of the adults by re-calculating the scores of all the *other* card descriptions to bring them into line with the results obtained from the two-card rating procedure.

Over and above this, the rating of combinations of disabilities was repeated for the children in order to check that the assessments had been made in the same way as they had been for the adults. However, it was found that 'the adult model fitted the results of the children's exercise poorly' (Bone and Meltzer, 1989, p. 60). Despite this, the adult model was applied to the children because of the overriding need to develop a single, universal scale of severity that could be applied to everyone.

Readers certainly deserve our sympathy for being asked to pick their way through this (simplified) description of the extraordinarily complicated way in which OPCS arrived at its ten categories of severity. However, it *is* important to appreciate how these were derived, and to recognise that it was the requirement that OPCS produce a single scale that could be used to allocate people, with all types and combinations of disability, to a particular level of severity (and thus determine levels of benefit payments) that created such a technical nightmare.

2. An alternative approach to classification

The limitation of the OPCS classification of disabilities being based upon a single severity scale led us to consider an alternative approach that would be more appropriate for the planning of welfare services. We were also anxious to produce a system that could be easily repeated. For various reasons, this is not possible to do with respect to the OPCS scheme because not all the necessary details have been published. Furthermore, the need for large panels of expert judges would make their system expensive to replicate.

In the light of these drawbacks, we sought a classification that would take into account and make more visible the type, severity and combination of *all* the disabilities experienced by a child. This was clearly a task more suited to computer analysis than to human sorting skills. Indeed, when the potential range of combinations of disabilities is contemplated, it is not surprising that the judges used by OPCS could take into account only the three which they regarded as the most severe.

The group of techniques that is most appropriate for such a task is cluster analysis. A fuller explanation of these and of the particular method that we used is to be found in Appendix I. Put simply, cluster analysis provides a means of grouping together those cases in a population that have the most similar characteristics, having sorted through the available data. Of course, this process can be continued until there are more and more categories which are more and more distinct; however, the number in each cluster then becomes smaller and smaller, making it less and less useful for practical purposes. There is, therefore, an 'optimum solution' which creates enough different clusters to be useful, but not so many that there is a confusion of only slightly different possibilities.

The data that we relied upon were, of course, borrowed from the OPCS surveys. For the purposes of the cluster analysis we decided to use four items from this source. They were: the number of disabilities that each child had; the type of each disability (for example, problems of locomotion or hearing); the severity of each disability (based upon the OPCS scores); and, where a child had more than one disability, the way in which they were combined.

Since it was not possible for children under five to have as high a severity score in the different areas of disability as children who were older, their disabilities were effectively being measured on different scales of severity. For this reason, we felt obliged to undertake two separate cluster analysis exercises for the children in private households. The first, described below, for children aged 5–15 and the second (described in Chapter 14) for the children younger than five. Similarly, a separate analysis was carried out for children in communal establishments in order to elucidate the similarities and differences between them and their peers living in private households; but that is included later in this chapter.

3. The clusters of children aged 5–15 in private households

All the 'solutions' between 2 and 15 clusters were examined. This seemed the practical range. Although each of these solutions was highly significant, that which gave 11 clusters was chosen as the best for our purposes. With more clusters than this, the groups could only be separated by small differences of severity; with fewer, the clusters began to merge into unduly heterogeneous groups.

It should be emphasised that we did not aim to produce our own classification of the severity of disabilities. We relied, as we have said, on the scale devised by OPCS and the measures obtained from it; but only as one of the factors to be included in the cluster analysis. However, as will be seen, when our 11 clusters were ranked on items that could be taken to indicate levels of overall severity, they fell into an ascending order. Thus, the clusters from 1–11 can be regarded as reflecting increasing degrees of severity.

One of our problems was to give labels to each of the 11 clusters. What should they be called? Titles had to be short but also convey the kinds of disabilities that each cluster contained. What we chose is evident in Table 2.1, although we are far from satisfied with the list, especially with respect to Clusters 9, 10 and 11. The difficulty is that, whereas the conventional descriptions of different disabilities have tended to concentrate on the principal condition or diagnosis, these clusters take account of more complicated combinations. For this reason, as will be seen, we have included a synopsis of the kinds of disabled children who were gathered together in each of the clusters; but first we present the general results of the cluster analysis. These are displayed graphically in Figure 2.1, the 11-cluster solution appearing at the foot of the dendrogram.

Clusters 1, 2 and 6, containing, respectively, 141, 262 and 146 cases, are by far the largest groups. As will be discussed in more detail later in this chapter, Clusters 2 and 6 are characterised by children who typically suffer from behavioural and some other disabilities. The children in Cluster 1 have relatively mild disabilities. Had we chosen fewer clusters, this cluster would have been associated with Clusters 3 and 4, which are typified by children with disabilities of incontinence and fits, respectively. By contrast, Clusters 7, 9, 10 and 11 cover children with much more severe disabilities, particularly those concerning personal care. Most of the children in Clusters 10 and 11 have at least six different disabilities. Clusters 5 and 8 are characterised by children with hearing and other disabilities.

One way of showing the differences between the 11 clusters is by calculating the average number of disabilities suffered by the children in each group. The results of doing this are displayed in Figure 2.2. The mean number of disabilities is shown on the vertical axis and the clusters are shown along the bottom. The horizontal line represents the mean for the whole sample, and the lines above and below it the 95% confidence interval. The dots (•) mark the mean number of disabilities for children in each cluster. Thus, the average number of disabilities experienced by the children in private households was 2.6. However, children in Clusters

Figure 2.1 *Dendrogram of 5–15-year-old children with disabilities in private households*

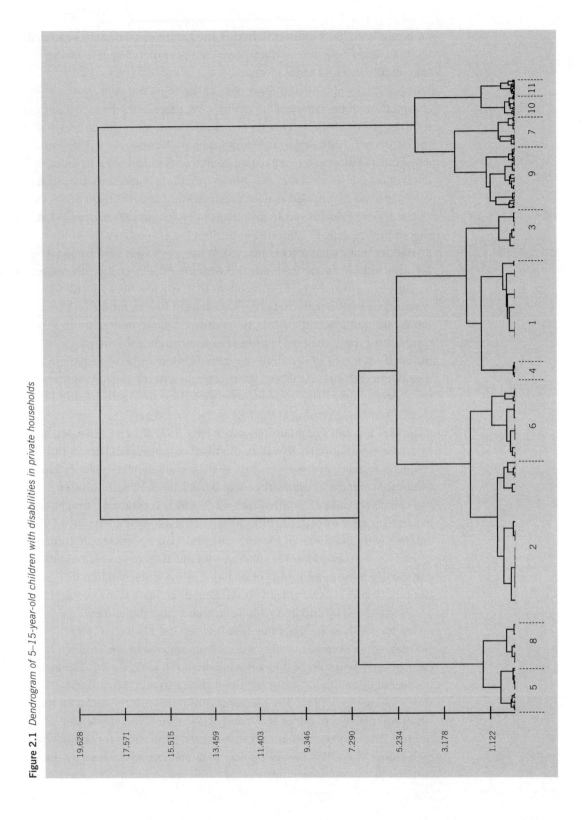

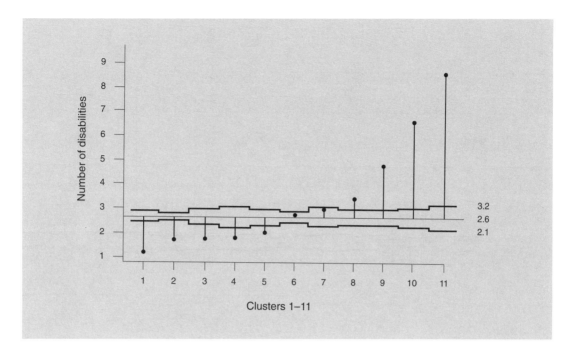

Figure 2.2

Average number of disabilities of 5–15-year-old children in private households, by cluster

1–5 experienced fewer disabilities than the average, whilst those in Clusters 8–11 experienced more. Table 2.1 gives the details represented in Figure 2.2.

A broadly similar pattern and rank order of clusters emerges if the total severity scores (obtained from the OPCS scale) in each are examined. Figure 2.3 shows the means of these scores analysed by the clusters, and Table 2.2 gives the details. As one would expect, the children in Cluster 1 (who, as

Table 2.1 Mean number of disabilities per child in each cluster (children aged 5–15 in private households)

Cluster	Description	Number	Mean number of disabilities	Standard deviation
1	Mild disabilities	141	1.1	0.51
2	Behaviour	262	1.6	0.86
3	Incontinence	79	1.7	0.94
4	Fits	43	1.8	1.00
5	Hearing and communication	71	2.0	1.01
6	Communication and behaviour	146	2.7	1.26
7	Personal care	52	2.9	1.09
8	Hearing and behaviour	73	3.4	1.06
9	Multiple disabilities	81	4.8	1.47
10	Multiple and severe	52	6.6	1.21
11	Multiple and very severe	28	8.6	1.07
All		**1028**	**2.6**	**1.98**

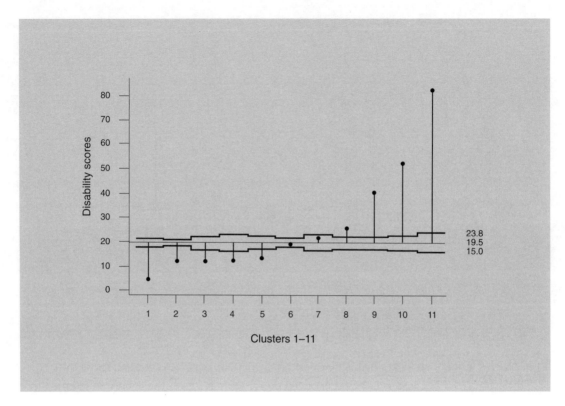

Figure 2.3
Average total OPCS disability scores for 5–15-year-old children in private households, by cluster

Table 2.2 Means of the total OPCS severity scores for each cluster (children aged 5–15 in private households)

Cluster	Description	Number	Mean of the total disability score	Standard deviation
1	Mild disabilities	141	4.2	3.43
2	Behaviour	262	11.9	6.02
3	Incontinence	79	11.6	6.99
4	Fits	43	11.6	4.55
5	Hearing and communication	71	12.7	7.06
6	Communication and behaviour	146	18.6	9.68
7	Personal care	52	21.2	7.99
8	Hearing and behaviour	73	25.5	9.00
9	Multiple disabilities	81	39.8	14.53
10	Multiple and severe	52	52.2	11.58
11	Multiple and very severe	28	82.1	11.83
All		**1028**	**19.4**	**17.9**

we have said, typically had only relatively mild disabilities) had the lowest average score whereas the children in Clusters 9, 10 and 11 (who had multiple disabilities) had very high scores.

When the clusters were analysed by their mean scores on the OPCS *common* severity scale for each *area* of disability (Table 2.3), it was found that, in most of these areas, as with the total scores, severity again increased from Cluster 1 to 11. Likewise, the frequency of different disabilities in each category of disabilities mounted in a similar way (Table 2.4). As well as noting these trends, it is helpful to draw attention to the patterns of disabilities that these two tables expose. For example, in Table 2.4, all the children in Cluster 2 had behavioural disabilities, as did almost all of those in Clusters 8–11 (notably high rates are picked out in bold type in both tables). Or, looking at it somewhat differently, one sees, for instance, that the great majority of the children in Cluster 10 had disabilities of behaviour, communication, personal care and locomotion, and that many others faced problems of intellectual functioning, dexterity and continence. By contrast, few had disabilities of seeing, eating, drinking or digestion.

Table 2.3 Mean scores on the OPCS common severity scales for each cluster in each area of disability (children aged 5–15 in private households)

Area of disability	Cluster										
	1	*2*	*3*	*4*	*5*	*6*	*7*	*8*	*9*	*10*	*11*
Behaviour	0.4	**9.1**	3.7	1.9	..	**6.9**	1.1	**9.0**	9.4	10.4	9.9
Intellectual functioning	0.9	1.0	..	0.1	0.6	2.2	0.5	1.4	4.4	**5.2**	8.6
Communication	0.1	0.3	0.2	0.7	3.7	**6.8**	0.8	**5.0**	6.2	8.6	12.2
Continence	0.6	0.3	**6.6**	0.4	0.2	0.7	0.3	0.8	3.6	2.8	9.1
Personal care	..	..	0.1	–	0.3	0.1	**9.3**	0.1	9.7	9.9	11.0
Locomotion	1.3	0.7	0.9	..	0.3	0.8	3.9	0.9	4.2	4.6	10.7
Seeing	**0.9**	..	0.2	0.1	0.1	..	0.5	0.3	0.3	0.4	3.3
Consciousness	0.1	0.6	..	**7.9**	0.3	0.1	0.6	0.5	1.6	2.0	3.7
Dexterity	–	–	–	–	–	0.9	2.5	–	0.2	4.5	7.0
Reaching and stretching	..	–	–	–	–	..	1.4	–	0.5	0.5	4.4
Hearing	..	–	–	0.5	**7.3**	0.2	0.2	**7.6**	0.2	3.6	2.1
Base	*141*	*262*	*79*	*43*	*71*	*146*	*52*	*73*	*81*	*52*	*28*

Notes:

a .. = less than 0.1.

b The possible range of scores on the OPCS severity scale for each area of disability was:

Locomotion	1.3–12.5	Continence	0.8–10.2
Reaching and stretching	0.7–7.3	Personal care	2.3–11.2
Dexterity	0.9–7.7	Intellectual functioning	0.8–12.6
Hearing	1.4–12.5	Behaviour	1.3–13.6
Seeing	2.3–12.0	Consciousness	0.5–12.5
Communication	3.3–13.6		

Table 2.4 Frequency of different types of disability by cluster for children aged 5–15 in private households (%)

Area of disability	Cluster										
	1	2	3	4	5	6	7	8	9	10	11
Behaviour	14	100	39	33	3	73	23	100	91	98	89
Intellectual functioning	18	19	3	5	11	38	12	29	62	79	96
Communication	1	5	3	14	51	93	14	58	64	89	100
Continence	28	11	100	7	7	19	12	19	59	52	96
Personal care	1	2	5	–	6	4	94	3	100	98	100
Locomotion	28	17	17	2	13	21	52	19	56	81	100
Seeing	15	–	3	5	1	1	8	6	6	10	36
Consciousness	4	9	1	100	6	1	8	6	20	23	46
Dexterity	–	–	–	–	–	16	39	–	4	71	100
Reaching and stretching	1	–	–	–	–	1	31	–	10	17	68
Hearing	1	–	–	12	99	4	4	100	4	46	29
Disfigurement	4	2	1	5	–	3	14	1	16	10	25
Eating, drinking and digestion	1	2	1	–	–	–	–	–	5	4	18
Base	141	262	79	43	71	146	52	73	81	52	28

Although, as we have said, both the severity and the frequency of disabilities increases as one goes from Cluster 1 to Cluster 11, there are exceptions with respect to the separate areas of disability. For the sensory disabilities of hearing and seeing, neither the mean severity scores nor the proportions experiencing these disabilities showed a clear gradient across the clusters. There are also single peaks in both Tables 2.3 and 2.4 in the case of disabilities of behaviour, continence and communication, variations that are discussed later in this chapter.

4. The eleven clusters of the children aged 5–15 in private households, described more fully

CLUSTER 1: Children with a variety of mild disabilities

n = 141 (14% of total)
population estimate = 40,000; mean age = 10.0 years

This, the third largest cluster, groups together children with a range of disabilities, all of them relatively mild. Eighty-five per cent of this group have just one disability. All the other clusters contain children typically having either moderate or severe disabilities.

Over a quarter (28%) of this group have a *locomotion* disability, the fifth highest level of all the clusters. Most of their disabilities in this area are grouped at the mild to moderate end of the scale, although a few children have more severe difficulties. Only one child uses a wheelchair; 5% use other mobility or walking aids. There are very few other motor problems in this cluster (two children have mild reaching and stretching disabilities).

The same proportion (28%) have a *continence* disability, again, the fifth highest level of all the clusters. All but one of the children with this disability receive the same score because they wet the bed every night (and are aged 5–10). Nearly a quarter (24%) use some form of incontinence aid.

This cluster has the second highest proportion (15%) of children with *visual* disabilities. The spread of scores is in the mild to moderate range, with the majority receiving a score at or just above the mid-point of the scale. Nearly a quarter of the cluster (24%) need glasses or contact lenses. This cluster also has the highest usage of other visual aids (5%).

Of this cluster, 18% have a disability of *intellectual functioning*, with a spread of scores on the mild to moderate range of the scale.

This cluster has the second lowest level of *behavioural* difficulties (14%) and the second lowest mean score on this scale.

CLUSTER 2: Children with behavioural disabilities, sometimes combined with other mild disabilities

n = 262 (25% of total);
population estimate = 74,000; mean age = 10.6 years

This is the largest cluster, accounting for a quarter of the total. All the children have behavioural disabilities. For just under half (47%) this is combined with other mild disabilities, most frequently of intellectual functioning (19%), locomotion (17%) or continence (11%).

The scores on the *behavioural* disability scale are in the moderate to severe range. This distribution is skewed towards the severe end, with over a quarter of the group (26%) receiving the maximum rating (for being aggressive, violent-tempered or destructive most of the time every day) and 62% scoring above the mid-point of the scale.

This group of children has a similar level and severity of disabilities of *intellectual functioning* as those in the first cluster.

Although 17% of the cluster have a *locomotion* disability, this group has no other motor problems. Most of the disabilities in this area are grouped at the mild to moderate end of the scale although a few children have rather more severe difficulties. Only one child uses a wheelchair; a further 2% use walking aids.

Eleven per cent have a *continence* disability, mainly for bed wetting, and 12% use some form of incontinence aid.

CLUSTER 3: Children with continence disabilities, with a significant minority who also have a behavioural disability

n = 79 (8% of total);
population estimate = 22,000; mean age = 9.6 years

All the children in this cluster have moderate or severe continence disabilities, and for almost two-fifths this is combined with behavioural difficulties. Apart from a group with locomotion difficulties, only a few children have scores on any of the other scales.

The *continence* disabilities are in the moderate to severe range of the scale (but far less severe than those experienced by the children in Cluster 11). Almost a quarter (23%) score the maximum as they have little or no control of their bowels. Forty-four per cent of the group soil at least once a month and 11% are doubly incontinent at least once a week. Four per cent use a device to manage their bladder and 3% to manage their bowels. Almost three-fifths (59%) use other incontinence aids.

The scores of the children in this cluster with *behavioural* difficulties (39%) are grouped in the moderate to severe range of the scale.

Although 17% of the cluster have a *locomotion* disability, this group has no other motor problems. Their locomotion disability ratings are widely spread across almost the entire range of the scale. Five per cent of the cluster use mobility or walking aids, and this figure includes two children who also use a wheelchair.

This cluster has the lowest proportion (3%) of children with a disability of *intellectual functioning*.

CLUSTER 4: Children with consciousness disabilities, with a significant minority who also have a behavioural disability

n = 43 (4% of total);
population estimate = 12,000; mean age = 10.5 years

All the children in this cluster experience fits, and the majority have at least one other disability, most frequently behavioural difficulties.

Both the frequency and the severity of the *consciousness* disabilities found in this group of children are much greater than in any of the other clusters. The great majority of their scores are grouped a little above the mid-point on the scale, although a few children have more severe disabilities in this area.

One-third of the cluster has *behavioural* difficulties, mostly rated within the mid-range of the scale.

This is the first cluster to contain a notable group of children (14%) with a disability of *communication*. These are mild disabilities, all the scores being on the first few points of the scale.

Twelve per cent of the cluster have fairly mild *hearing* disabilities, with 5% wearing hearing aids. Only 5% of the cluster have visual disabilities but 35% needed glasses or contact lenses, the third highest proportion of all the clusters.

Although only 7% of the group have a score (moderate) on the *continence* scale, 23% wet or soil occasionally (possibly as the consequence of a fit) and 5% use some form of incontinence aid.

CLUSTER 5: Children with hearing disabilities, with half also having a communication disability

n = 71 (7% of total);
population estimate = 21,000; mean age = 9.6 years

Almost all (99%) of the children in this cluster have a hearing disability; for just over half, this is combined with a communication disability. This cluster is also notable for having the lowest frequency of behavioural disabilities of all the clusters, just 3% (all scored on the lowest point of the scale).

The children's *hearing* disabilities are in the moderate to severe range, with 82% placed in the top half of the scale. None of the children in the private households survey was found to be totally deaf and assigned the top score, but 28% of this group were placed on the next point down. Almost a quarter (24%) use or need a hearing aid.

This is the first cluster in which the majority (51%) of children have a *communication* disability. The scores are fairly widely spread but heavily skewed to the milder end of the scale, indicating that for most of the children the problems are concerned with communication outside the family. Their disabilities in this area are less severe than for the children in Cluster 8, who have a similar level and severity of disabilities of hearing. Six per cent of the cluster use some means in addition to speech in order to communicate.

Although 13% of the cluster have a *locomotion* disability, this group has no other motor problems. Disabilities in this area are grouped at the milder end of the scale, and none of the children uses any form of mobility or walking aid.

Despite their hearing and communication disabilities, only 11% of children in this cluster have a disability of *intellectual functioning*, with a fairly even spread of scores in the mild to moderate range. In this respect, the group differs markedly from Cluster 8 children who have a similar rate and severity of hearing disabilities.

CLUSTER 6: Children with communication and behavioural disabilities, a minority of whom also experience a range of other disabilities

n = 146 (14% of total);
population estimate = 42,000; mean age = 10.9 years

This is the second largest grouping. Most of the children have a communication disability and almost three-quarters have behavioural difficulties. Unlike the previous cluster, however, only a few of these children (4%) have a hearing disability. The disabilities found in this group range across all 11 scales, and it is the first cluster to contain a significant group with multiple disabilities, with the mean number being 2.7. This is also the first cluster to contain a significant group with a disability of intellectual functioning. Significant minorities have locomotion or continence disabilities.

Communication disabilities (93%) are far more frequent and severe in this group of children than in the previous cluster. The scores are spread across the complete range of the scale, and the majority of these children have difficulties communicating within as well as outside their families. Fourteen per cent of the cluster use some means in addition to speech in order to communicate.

In this cluster, 73% have *behavioural* difficulties, with scores skewed towards the severe end of the scale; nearly a fifth (19%) of the group receiving the maximum rating.

Nearly two-fifths (38%) of these children have an *intellectual* disability, with scores mostly in the moderate range. A few have a more severe disability in this area and may have a mental impairment.

Just over a fifth (21%) of this group have a *locomotion* disability. Most of the disabilities in this area are grouped at the mild to moderate end of the scale. Only two children use a wheelchair; 3% use other mobility or walking aids.

Although only one child has a reaching and stretching disability, this is the first group to have a notable proportion (16%) with *dexterity* disabilities. It is one of only five clusters to include children with this disability. The scores on this scale fall mainly in the moderate to severe range.

Almost a fifth (19%) have *continence* disabilities, with the scores skewed to the mild to moderate end of the scale. Most of the scores are for wetting. Only two children use any incontinence aids.

CLUSTER 7: Children who require a high level of personal care and have a wide range of other disabilities; just over half have a disability of locomotion

n = 52 (5% of total);
population estimate = 15,000; mean age = 9.4 years

The disabilities found in this cluster range across all 11 scales, with a mean number of 2.9. This is the first cluster in which the majority of the children have motor disabilities. Just over half have a locomotion disability, almost two-fifths have problems of dexterity and nearly a third have difficulties with reaching and stretching. However, the most distinguishing feature of this cluster is the very high level of disabilities of *personal care*. Ninety-four per cent of the children are so affected, with scores heavily skewed to the severe end of the scale. Just over half (52%) receive the maximum rating as they are unable (amongst other things) to feed themselves. This high need for personal care is not readily explained as their other disabilities are not as severe as those found in the later clusters (9, 10 and 11) where high levels of personal care disabilities are also found. One possible explanation may be in the combination of motor disabilities among a sub-group of this cluster.

The *locomotion* disabilities experienced by over half of the cluster (52%) are grouped in the moderate to severe range of the scale, and 12% of the group receive the maximum score as they cannot walk at all. Fifteen per cent use a wheelchair and a further 12% use other mobility or walking aids.

This is the first cluster to have a significant minority (39%) with a disability of *dexterity*. The scores are skewed to the more severe end of the scale with 6% being assigned the maximum. It is also the first cluster in which a significant group has a disability of *reaching and stretching*, being one of only four clusters containing a significant number with this disability. It has both the second highest frequency (31%) and the second highest mean severity score for this disability after Cluster 11. The scores on this scale are fairly evenly spread, with 12% of the cluster being assigned the maximum.

Less than a quarter (23%) of this cluster have a *behavioural* disability; those who do were assigned scores in the mild to moderate range of the scale.

Only 12% of the children in this cluster have a disability of *intellectual functioning*, with scores grouped in the mild to moderate range. This is in marked contrast to the other three clusters (9, 10 and 11) in which children have high levels of motor disability and a need for personal care but have much higher frequencies and mean severity scores on the intellectual scale. It is worth noting that, although many of these children have multiple disabilities, this cluster has the third lowest mean severity score on the intellectual functioning scale.

Fourteen per cent of this group have mild or moderate *communication* disabilities.

Twelve per cent have *continence* disabilities, with the scale scores skewed to the mild to moderate end of the scale. All of the scores are for wetting. One child uses a device for management of the bladder and 10% use other incontinence aids.

This is the first cluster to have a notable proportion (14%) of children whose parents consider that they have a *disfigurement* which severely affects their ability to lead a normal life.

CLUSTER 8: Children with quite severe hearing and behavioural disabilities; over half also have a disability of communication

n = 73 (7% of total);
population estimate = 73,000; mean age = 10.6 years

The children in this cluster have a similar frequency (100%) and severity of hearing disabilities to those in Cluster 5. The major difference between the two clusters is that, whereas Cluster 5 has by far the lowest frequency of all the clusters for behavioural disabilities, all the children in this cluster have behavioural problems which are often quite severe. Over half have communication disabilities, and significant minorities have disabilities of intellectual functioning, continence and locomotion.

The scores on the *behaviour* scale for this cluster are spread across the moderate to severe range but skewed towards the more severe end of the scale. Nearly one-fifth of the group (19%) are assigned the maximum score.

The children's *hearing* disabilities are in the moderate to severe range, with 85% placed in the top half of the scale. None of the children in the private households survey was found to be totally deaf and assigned the top score, but 32% of this group were placed on the next point down. Almost a third (32%) use or need a hearing aid; the highest proportion of any of the clusters.

Over half (58%) of this group of children have *communication* disabilities which are more severe than those found in Cluster 5. The scores are widely spread across the scale, but there is a significant sub-group (19%) who score on the top three points of the scale as they have great difficulty communicating within their family. Nearly a quarter (22%) of the cluster use some means in addition to speech in order to communicate.

Twenty-nine per cent have a disability of *intellectual functioning*, with scores fairly evenly spread across the mild to moderate range of the scale. Both the frequency of this disability and the mean severity score are more than double those of Cluster 5, in which similar proportions of children have hearing and communication difficulties.

Although just under a fifth (19%) of the cluster have a *locomotion* disability, this group has no other motor problems. The locomotion disability ratings are mostly grouped in the mild to moderate range of the scale. None of the children uses a wheelchair and only one uses a mobility aid.

Almost a fifth (19%) have, mainly moderate, *continence* disabilities. Most of the scores are for wetting and 10% of the cluster use incontinence aids.

CLUSTER 9: Children with multiple disabilities, who have quite severe behavioural disabilities and who require a high level of personal care; significant majorities have disabilities of communication, intellectual functioning, continence and locomotion

n = 81 (8% of total);
population estimate = 22,000; mean age = 9.9 years

All the children in this cluster have multiple disabilities, with over 80% having four or more. All 13 disability types are present. This is the first cluster in which the majority of the children have a disability of intellectual functioning. All the children have a disability arising from a high need for personal care but, in contrast to Cluster 7, most of them also have quite severe behavioural problems and much higher frequency and mean severity scores for disabilities of intellectual functioning, communication and continence.

On the *personal care* scale their scores are heavily skewed to the severe end, with 44% assigned the maximum rating as they are unable (amongst other things) to feed themselves.

Ninety-one per cent of this cluster have a *behavioural* disability, with their scores skewed towards the severe end. Almost a third (32%) are assigned the maximum score, with two-thirds placed within the top half of the scale.

Over three-fifths (62%) of these children have a disability of *intellectual functioning*. Their scores are fairly evenly spread across the moderate to severe range of the scale. Some children in this cluster are likely to have a mental impairment. Fifteen per cent were assessed as having the highest severity score for their age range.

Almost two-thirds (64%) of this group have *communication* difficulties, with the scores skewed towards the more severe end of the scale. Thirty per cent of the group are placed on the top three points of the scale, indicating very severe limitations on their ability to communicate with their family. Five per cent are unable to speak at all and almost a third (32%) use some means instead of or in addition to speech in order to communicate.

Nearly two-fifths (59%) of the children in this cluster have *continence* disabilities. The scores are spread across the full range of the scale, but 31% of the group are covered by the top four points, with 16% receiving the maximum score as they have little or no control of their bowels. Thirty-one per cent of the group soil at least once a month and 17% are doubly incontinent at least once a week. Six per cent use a device to manage their bladder and 37% use other incontinence aids.

Over half (56%) of the children have *locomotion* disabilities which are grouped in the moderate to severe range of the scale. Five per cent of the group receive the maximum score as they cannot walk at all, 15% use a wheelchair and a further 15% use other mobility or walking aids. Although the children in this cluster have a similar rate and severity of locomotion disabilities to those in Cluster 7, they have a much lower rate and severity of other motor disabilities. Only a few children have any difficulties with dexterity; 10% have, mainly moderate, disabilities of reaching and stretching.

A fifth of the group experience fits, with their scores on the *consciousness* scale fairly evenly spread across the moderate to severe range.

Sixteen per cent of this cluster have a *disfigurement* which their parents thought severely affected their ability to lead a normal life.

CLUSTER 10: Children with multiple and severe disabilities

n = 52 (5% of total);
population estimate = 15,000; mean age = 9.5 years

In many of the areas of disability this cluster differs from Cluster 9 only by degree. The main difference is in the much greater severity of the disabilities of dexterity and hearing. In proportional terms, there are also higher levels of disabilities of behaviour, intellectual functioning, communication and locomotion. All 13 disability types are present in this cluster, with a mean number of 6.6 disabilities.

Almost all the children (98%) have *behavioural* difficulties, and this group has the highest mean score of all the clusters on the behaviour scale. Over a third (35%) were assigned the maximum score.

Almost all the cluster (98%) have a disability arising from their high level of need for *personal care*. Nearly two-thirds (65%) of the group received the maximum score as they are unable (amongst other things) to feed themselves.

Eighty-nine per cent of this group have a *communication* disability. The scores are heavily skewed to the top end of the scale, with 30% being placed on the top two points. Eight per cent are unable to speak at all and a third use some means in addition to or instead of speech in order to communicate.

The children in this cluster have a slightly higher mean severity score on the *locomotion* scale than the children in Cluster 9, but a far higher proportion (81%) have this disability. The scores have a wider spread than for Cluster 9 but are still skewed to the moderate to severe end of the scale. Six per cent of the group receive the maximum score as they cannot walk at all, 10% use a wheelchair and a further 12% use other mobility or walking aids.

This cluster of children has a similar, low, mean severity score on the reaching and stretching scale to Cluster 9 but has a much higher frequency and severity of problems of *dexterity*. They have the second highest mean severity score and the second highest frequency (71%) for this type of disability after Cluster 11. The children's disabilities are quite severe, with most of the scores near the top of the scale. A far smaller proportion (17%) have any disability of *reaching and stretching*, unlike the other two clusters (7 and 11) that also have high frequencies of disabilities of dexterity.

Over three-quarters (79%) of this group have a disability of *intellectual functioning*. There is a wide spread of scores on this scale but they are mainly grouped in the moderate to severe range. Fifteen per cent received the maximum severity score for their age range. Many of the children are likely to have mental impairments.

Just over half (52%) of the children in this cluster have *continence* disabilities. The scores are spread across the full range of the scale, with 8% receiving the maximum score as they have little or no control of their bowels. Nineteen per cent of the group soil at least once a month and 17% are doubly incontinent at least once a week. Twenty-nine per cent use incontinence aids.

A little under half (46%) of the cluster have a *hearing* disability, with the scores on this scale spread in the moderate to severe range. Just under a fifth (19%) use or need a hearing aid. One in ten of the children has a *visual* disability, the scores on this scale being grouped in the mild to moderate range. Thirty-seven per cent wear glasses or contact lenses, the second highest proportion after Cluster 11.

The children in this cluster have a slightly higher frequency (23%) and severity of *consciousness* disabilities than those in the previous cluster. Similarly, their scores on this scale were fairly evenly spread in the moderate to severe range.

One in ten of this cluster has a *disfigurement* which their parents thought severely affected their ability to lead a normal life.

CLUSTER 11: Children with multiple and very severe disabilities

n = 28 (3% of total);
population estimate = 8000; mean age = 10.3 years

This, the smallest of the clusters, contains the children with by far the most profound disabilities. The disabilities ranged across all 13 types, with a mean number of almost nine. This cluster has the highest mean severity scores on all but three of the scales (behaviour, consciousness and hearing). All the children have disabilities of communication, personal care, locomotion and dexterity, and all but one child also has disabilities of intellectual functioning and continence. This was the only cluster to have sizeable proportions of children with disabilities of seeing, disfigurement and eating, drinking and digestion.

These children's motor disabilities are far more severe than in any of the other clusters. All the children in the group have a *locomotion* disability, with the scores heavily skewed towards the severe end of the scale. Fifty-seven per cent of the group received the maximum score as they cannot walk at all, with three-quarters of the cluster scoring on the top three points of the scale. Over three-fifths (61%) use a wheelchair; nearly all the rest (32%) use other mobility or walking aids.

All the children in this cluster have severe *dexterity* disabilities, and for over two-thirds (68%) this is combined with severe disabilities of *reaching and stretching*. The scores are very heavily skewed towards the severe end of the dexterity scale, with 43% receiving the maximum score and 89% being at the top three points. Half the group were also assigned the maximum score on the reaching and stretching scale.

As would be expected, all the children in this cluster have a disability arising from their very high need for *personal care*. All but two of the group (93%) were assigned the maximum score.

All the children in this cluster have *communication* disabilities which are far more severe than for any of the other clusters. Just under half (46%) were assigned the maximum score, with 89% rated on the top three points, indicating that they have extreme difficulties communicating with their families. Over a third (36%) are unable to speak at all and 89% use some means instead of or in addition to speech to communicate.

Almost all the children in this cluster (96%) have disabilities of *intellectual functioning* and these are far more profound than in any of the other clusters. Seventy-one per cent have the maximum severity score for their age group and most of these children are likely to have severe mental impairments.

Nearly all the children (96%) in this cluster have *continence* disabilities, and these are far more severe than in any of the other clusters (including Cluster 3). Over two-thirds of the group score the maximum on this scale because they have little or no control of their bowels. All but one score on the top four points of the scale. Nearly two-thirds (64%) are doubly incontinent every day; three-quarters soil at least once a week. One child uses a device for management of the bowels and almost two-fifths (79%) use other incontinence aids.

Although a smaller proportion (89%) than in Cluster 10 received a score on the *behaviour* scale, for those who did the problems were often far more severe. Over two-fifths of the cluster (43%) were assigned the maximum score (because they were 'aggressive, violent-tempered or destructive or screamed or shouted most of the time every day'). However, the profound nature of the disabilities of some of the children in this cluster would have meant that they would be physically unable to present many behavioural problems.

This cluster had the second highest frequency (46%) of *consciousness* disabilities. The scores on this scale were mainly moderate, with a few children having more severe disabilities.

This is the only cluster in which a significant proportion (36%) have a *visual* disability, the scores on this scale being skewed to the severe end. Forty-three per cent of the group need glasses or contact lenses (the highest proportion of any of the clusters) and 4% use low vision aids. Twenty-nine per cent have a *hearing* disability, although none have a hearing aid. (In view of their very severe communication disabilities it seems likely that it would be very difficult to assess the value of such aids.)

This is the only cluster to have a significant proportion (25%) with a *disfigurement* which their parents thought severely affected their ability to lead a normal life. Similarly, it is the only cluster with a sizeable group (18%) whose problems with *eating, drinking or digestion* also affect their ability to lead a normal life.

5. Results of the cluster analysis for children aged 5–15 living in communal establishments

The cluster statistics for all solutions between 2 and 15 clusters were examined. Although each of these solutions was highly significant, the ten-cluster solution was chosen as optimal for our purposes; that is, one cluster fewer than for children aged 5–15 in private households. Above ten, the clusters could only be separated by small degrees of severity on some of the scales; if fewer than ten were used, distinct clusters began to merge into more heterogeneous groups.

It was our intention to produce a classification of types of disability that took account of the severity of individuals' disabilities; we did not set out to produce an alternative measure of overall severity. However, as will be seen, when ranked on items which could be said to be indicative of overall severity, the ten clusters fell into the same order. The cluster labels adopted (Cluster 1 to Cluster 10) can be said to indicate a broad measure of increasing overall severity.

The cluster analysis results are displayed in the dendrogram in Figure 2.4. The ten-cluster solution is shown at the base of the dendrogram.

It can be seen that Cluster 1, with 418 cases, is by far the largest group. As will be discussed in more detail elsewhere, this cluster is characterised by

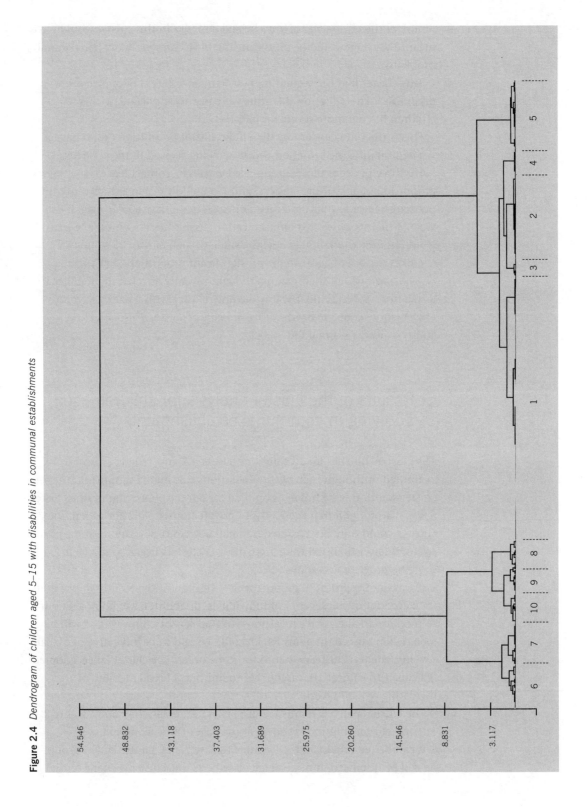

Figure 2.4 *Dendrogram of children aged 5–15 with disabilities in communal establishments*

children typically suffering from behavioural disabilities alone. Cluster 1 is associated with four other clusters (Clusters 2, 3, 4 and 5) which are typified by children with behavioural and one or two other disabilities. By contrast, Clusters 6–10 group together the children with much more severe disabilities: typically they have scores on at least five different scales.

The differences between the ten clusters can clearly be seen from the one-way analysis of means of the number of disabilities of a child by cluster displayed in Figure 2.5. As before, the mean number of disabilities is shown on the vertical axis and the clusters along the bottom axis. The three horizontal lines represent the global sample mean with its 95% confidence interval. The diamonds (♦) mark the mean number of disabilities for each of the ten clusters.

The average number of disabilities experienced by children in communal establishments was 3.3 (compared with 2.6 for children in private households). Children in Clusters 1–5 experienced fewer disabilities than the average, whereas children in Clusters 6–10 experienced far more. Table 2.5 gives the details represented by Figure 2.5.

Figure 2.5
Average number of disabilities of 5–15-year-old children living in communal establishments, by cluster

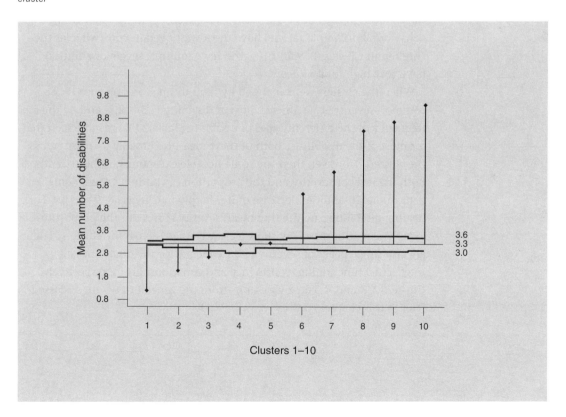

Table 2.5 Mean number of disabilities per child in each cluster (children aged 5–15 in communal establishments)

Cluster	Description	Number	Mean number of disabilities	Standard deviation
1	Behaviour	418	1.1	0.43
2	Intellectual and behaviour	142	2.1	0.32
3	Incontinence and behaviour	41	2.6	0.92
4	Fits and behaviour	31	3.1	1.14
5	Communication and behaviour	108	3.2	0.94
6	Multiple disabilities	65	5.4	1.30
7	Multiple and severe	70	6.4	1.30
8	Multiple and very severe	38	8.2	1.04
9	Multiple and extreme	37	8.6	1.36
10	Multiple and very extreme	50	9.4	0.85
All		**1000**	**3.3**	**2.81**

A similar pattern and rank order of clusters emerges when the total severity scores are examined. These are the scores summed across the 11 disability scales. Figure 2.6 shows a one-way analysis of means of the total disability score by cluster; Table 2.6 gives the details. As would be expected, the children in Cluster 1 (who, as we have seen, typically suffer from behavioural disabilities alone) have the lowest overall score, whereas the children in Clusters 8, 9 and 10 (who have multiple severe disabilities) have very high total scores.

When the clusters were analysed by their mean scores on the OPCS common severity scale for each area of disability (Table 2.7) and by the frequency of the different types of disability (Table 2.8), it can be seen that for most of the disabilities both of these measures broadly increase across the clusters. However, there are some notable exceptions to these trends. Both the level of severity and the proportion of children experiencing behavioural disabilities decrease quite sharply in Clusters 8, 9 and 10. For hearing disabilities, neither the mean severity scores nor the proportion experiencing this disability show a clear gradient across the clusters. There are also single peaks of severity and frequency for the disabilities of intellectual functioning, continence and consciousness in, respectively, Clusters 2, 3 and 4. These variations from the general trend are discussed later in this chapter.

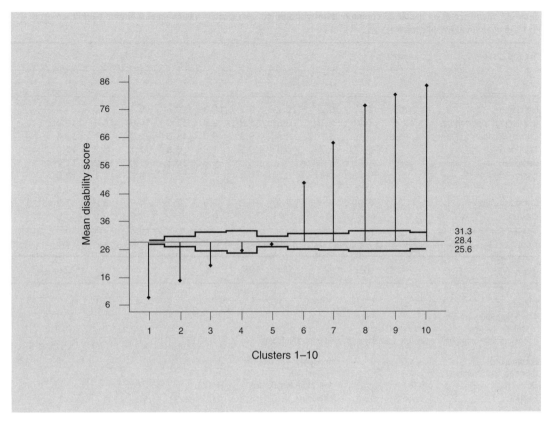

Figure 2.6
Average total OPCS disability scores for 5–15-year-old children living in communal establishments, by cluster

Table 2.6 Means of the total OPCS severity scores for each cluster (children aged 5–15 in communal establishments)

Cluster	Description	Number	Mean of the total disability score	Standard deviation
1	Behaviour	418	9.0	3.84
2	Intellectual and behaviour	142	14.6	3.40
3	Incontinence and behaviour	41	19.7	7.69
4	Fits and behaviour	31	24.9	8.81
5	Communication and behaviour	108	26.9	7.60
6	Multiple disabilities	65	48.5	12.55
7	Multiple and severe	70	62.9	11.63
8	Multiple and very severe	38	76.2	11.93
9	Multiple and extreme	37	79.9	13.73
10	Multiple and very extreme	50	83.1	9.00
All		**1000**	**28.4**	**26.62**

Table 2.7 Mean scores on the OPCS common severity scales for each cluster in each area of disability (children aged 5–15 in communal establishments)

Area of disability	Cluster									
	1	2	3	4	5	6	7	8	9	10
Behaviour	**8.5**	**8.7**	**9.2**	**10.1**	**9.2**	**10.3**	**10.6**	8.3	6.1	4.0
Intellectual functioning	..	**5.7**	2.2	3.6	**5.8**	**9.9**	**11.0**	**10.9**	**10.4**	**10.7**
Communication	..	–	1.1	2.8	**9.3**	**9.0**	**11.5**	**12.7**	**9.7**	**13.3**
Continence	..	..	**6.7**	0.3	0.2	1.8	**8.8**	**7.7**	**8.2**	**10.0**
Personal care	..	–	–	–	..	**9.5**	**10.1**	**11.0**	**11.2**	**11.2**
Locomotion	0.1	–	0.4	0.2	0.4	2.6	5.5	**8.6**	**12.1**	**12.0**
Seeing	..	0.2	..	0.2	..	1.0	1.4	3.5	3.0	**4.6**
Consciousness	–	–	–	**7.9**	0.2	2.5	2.2	4.4	**5.2**	**7.2**
Dexterity	–	–	–	–	0.2	0.1	–	**7.0**	**6.5**	0.9
Reaching and stretching	..	–	–	–	0.1	0.2	0.2	0.3	**6.3**	**6.7**
Hearing	0.1	–	–	..	1.6	1.5	1.6	1.8	1.2	**2.6**
Base	418	142	41	31	108	65	70	38	37	50

Notes:
a .. = less than 0.1.
b Notably high mean scores are in bold type.
c The possible range on the severity scale for each area of disability was:

Locomotion	1.3–12.5	Continence	0.8–10.2
Reaching and stretching	0.7–7.3	Personal care	2.3–11.2
Dexterity	0.9–7.7	Intellectual functioning	0.8–12.6
Hearing	1.4–12.5	Behaviour	1.3–13.6
Seeing	2.3–12.0	Consciousness	0.5–12.5
Communication	3.3–13.6		

6. Details of the ten clusters of children in communal establishments

The dendrogram (Figure 2.4) clearly shows how the ten clusters divide into two broad groups of five, which eventually merge at the two-cluster level. These two higher order clusters can be characterised as one larger cluster (74% of the sample) containing children with a dominant behavioural disability, either alone or in combination with a few other disabilities that were rarely of a 'physical' nature, and one smaller cluster (26% of the sample) containing children with multiple severe disabilities.

When the characteristics of the ten clusters were examined, and the pattern of cluster mergers at higher levels traced, other broad groupings could be discerned. Clusters 2, 3 and 4 contain children with a dominant behavioural disability and, typically, one other characteristic disability (intellectual functioning, continence and consciousness, respectively). These three clusters merge by the eight-cluster level and join with Cluster 1

Table 2.8 Frequency of different types of disability by cluster (%) for children aged 5–15 in communal establishments

Area of disability	Cluster									
	1	2	3	4	5	6	7	8	9	10
Behaviour	**100**	98	96	**100**	97	**100**	96	80	70	47
Intellectual functioning	1	**100**	44	53	80	96	**100**	**100**	98	96
Communication	..	–	16	31	**100**	81	**100**	**100**	82	**100**
Continence	2	2	**100**	8	4	35	99	82	89	**100**
Personal care	..	–	–	–	..	**100**	99	**100**	**100**	**100**
Locomotion	2	–	11	9	13	44	60	**91**	**100**	**100**
Seeing	3	7	2	6	2	26	33	**81**	61	88
Consciousness	–	–	–	**100**	2	33	24	54	66	74
Dexterity	–	–	–	–	3	2	–	**100**	**91**	95
Reaching and stretching	1	–	–	–	3	2	5	15	**98**	**98**
Hearing	2	–	–	3	20	16	19	24	14	41
Disfigurement	3	..	–	3	7	6	13	27	39	37
Eating, drinking and digestion	1	–	–	6	–	3	8	25	24	32
Base	418	142	41	31	108	65	70	38	37	50

Notes:
a The disabilities of disfigurement and of eating, drinking and digestion were not used in the cluster analysis.
b Notably high rates are in bold type.

(in which the children have a behavioural disability alone) at the five-cluster level.

Clusters 6 and 7 merge at the six-cluster level. They both contain multiply disabled children who have severe mental impairments and locomotion disabilities but who generally have a greater degree of mobility than the children in the clusters with multiple and very severe disabilities – groups with which, in the analysis, they eventually merge.

Cluster 5 contains children with a very mixed pattern of disabilities. Some of them will have mental impairments and, in common with Clusters 6 and 7, there is a very high frequency of severe communication disabilities. However, this cluster eventually merges with the other 'behaviour' clusters at the three-cluster level.

The children in the last three clusters (8, 9 and 10) all have multiple severe disabilities and, for the most part, these groupings were separable only by the degree of severity. High levels of disability in the areas of sight, consciousness, reaching and stretching (Clusters 9 and 10) and dexterity (Clusters 8 and 9) set them apart from the other seven clusters. Nearly all the children in these groups were likely to have had a severe mental impairment. These clusters were the only ones to contain significant groups of children who had disfigurements or a disability arising from eating, drinking or digestion problems. Clusters 9 and 10 merge at the seven cluster-level, and this grouping merges with Cluster 8 at the four-cluster level.

A significant number of children in the last three clusters were found to be too profoundly disabled for assessments to be made in several of the areas of disability, especially behaviour, hearing and sight. The method OPCS used to score these children on the scales for which it was impossible to assess them varied between the disability areas. For disabilities of behaviour and consciousness, children who could not be assessed received no score; for disabilities of sight, they were assigned the minimum score; for disabilities of reaching and stretching and hearing, they were assigned scores at about the mid-point of the scale; for disabilities of dexterity and communication, they were assigned the maximum score. (All the children were able to be assessed for disabilities of intellectual functioning, continence, personal care and locomotion.) The high rate of non-assessment among the children in the last three clusters can make comparison with the other clusters rather misleading. It also accounts for some of the reductions (or lower than might be expected figures) in the severity and frequency of certain disabilities for these clusters: in particular, behaviour and hearing; and, for slightly different reasons, which are discussed later, dexterity.

All the children in Clusters 6–10 have multiple disabilities, and the cluster labels (multiple disabilities; multiple and severe; multiple and very severe; multiple and extreme; multiple and very extreme) have been chosen to try to convey the increasing level of severity across these clusters. They have also been chosen to facilitate comparisons with the children aged 5–15 in the private households cluster analysis. However, it must be stressed that the children in Clusters 8, 9 and 10 in communal establishments are so profoundly disabled that even many professionals who work with disabled children will rarely have encountered any who require such a high level of care. The simple, one-line cluster labels cannot adequately describe the details of such disabilities.

In the following, more detailed, descriptions of the ten clusters, the results on the behaviour disability scale have been treated in a different way from the other areas of disability. First, in comparison with the other disability scales, behaviour is the least 'linear' and relies more heavily on the subjective judgement of the carers. Although, for example, it is reasonably straightforward to rate encopresis as a more severe disability than enuresis, or an inability to run as less severe than being unable to walk, it is much harder to determine the difference in the severity of behaviours such as daily outbursts of aggression or daily bouts of depression. The difference in severity between these two behaviour patterns is likely to be heavily influenced by the effect that they have upon the carer.

Secondly, the definition of 'disability' adopted by OPCS required the severity scales to measure the disabilities as experienced by the child; however, in so far as it was always the carers who were interviewed, the ratings must be influenced by their perceptions. This would seem a particularly important consideration when assessing the results on the behaviour scale. It was the carers rather than the child who were asked if the child was aggressive. Viewed in this way, the behaviour scale is as much a measure of the behavioural *difficulties* confronting the carer as a measure of the child's behavioural *disabilities*.

The third reason for presenting information derived from the behaviour scale differently arises from the way in which the results on individual items combine to form distinct patterns of behavioural difficulties that vary markedly between the clusters. Three groupings emerge: problems of conduct, of behaviour indicative of depression, and of 'risk-to-self' behaviour, which could be either intentional (self-injury) or unintentional (lacking a sense of danger).

7. Descriptions of the ten clusters of children in communal establishments

CLUSTER 1: Children with behavioural disabilities only

n = 418 (42% of the total);
population estimate = 2350; mean age = 13.5 years

Ninety-one per cent of this group have only a *behavioural* disability. The other 9% have low scores on a range of scales rather than on any one in particular. Despite the high rate of behavioural disability, very few (1%) experience sufficient learning difficulties to receive any score on the intellectual functioning scale.

The behavioural problems presented by this group are largely those of conduct and delinquency, although a significant minority showed signs of depression. Twelve per cent were assigned the maximum severity score on the behaviour scale. The children in this cluster are those most likely to take part fairly regularly in some form of substance abuse (getting drunk, taking drugs or sniffing glue). Just over a fifth (21%) engage in such activity at least once a month. Nearly half (47%) are involved in lying or stealing at least once a week (the second highest proportion among the clusters). Just over a third (36%) have outbursts of violent temper or aggression at least once a week, and a similar proportion are described as overactive and usually unable to concentrate. Just under a third (32%) are described as being miserable, afraid, or worried most of the time every day, and this group has the second highest rate of threatened or attempted suicide (8% at least once per month).

CLUSTER 2: Children with behavioural disabilities and moderate disabilities of intellectual functioning

$n = 142$ (14.2% of total);
population estimate = 800; mean age = 13.2 years

This group has a similar mean maximum behaviour score to the first cluster but, in addition, all the children have some degree of *intellectual functioning* disability. Very few (9%) have scores on any of the other scales. The severity scores on the intellectual functioning scale were grouped in the lower (more moderate) half of the scale, with 86% rated below the mid-point. A very small minority may have a mental impairment.

This cluster's mean score on the behaviour scale was almost the same as that of the first cluster, and the pattern of behaviour was also similar. However, higher proportions have outbursts of violent temper or aggression (48%) and are described as overactive (56%). They have only slightly lower levels of lying and stealing (45%) and substance abuse (19%). They are almost as likely as the first cluster to be described as being miserable, afraid or worried (31%) but have much greater difficulty than these children in making friends (30%).

CLUSTER 3: Children with disabilities of behaviour and continence, with a significant minority also having a disability of intellectual functioning

$n = 41$ (4% of total);
population estimate = 250; mean age = 12 years

These children all have a *continence* disability as well as quite severe behavioural disabilities. Their continence problems are relatively mild in comparison with the majority of the children in the last four clusters (7, 8, 9 and 10). However, 90% have some degree of enuresis, with 32% wetting daily, and 41% have some problems with soiling, with just over a quarter doing so at least once a week. Half of the children in this cluster have scores on more than two scales. A significant minority (44%) have moderate intellectual functioning disabilities and 16% have communication disabilities. Apart from 11% who have mild locomotion disabilities (problems of balance) these children have no motor problems.

The children in this cluster also have high levels of conduct problems, but show far more evidence of both depression and overactivity than the first two clusters. They are the most likely of all the clusters to have engaged in lying and stealing activities (49%) and they also have high levels of violent or aggressive outbursts (40% weekly, including 19% who are described as being violent or aggressive every day). After Cluster 4, these children appear to be the most depressed. Over two-fifths (42%) of the group are described as being miserable, afraid or worried most of the time, every day, and nearly a quarter (24%) are reported to be withdrawn for much of the day. Over a third (37%) have difficulty in making friends. Nearly half (47%) are described as overactive or usually unable to concentrate, and just over a third (34%) have difficulty sleeping on a regular basis (at least once a week). More than a quarter of the cluster (27%) are said to do peculiar or embarrassing things at least once a week (the highest proportion, apart from Clusters 6 and 7 in which nearly all the children have mental impairments).

CLUSTER 4: Children who have severe behavioural disabilities and who also experience fits; over half have a disability of intellectual functioning and nearly a third have one of communication

n = 31 (3% of total);
population estimate = 200; mean age = 12.5 years

All the children in this group have behavioural and *consciousness* disabilities. In addition to obtaining scores on these two scales, 61% of them have scores on other scales: most commonly because of disabilities of intellectual functioning (53%) and communication (31%). Some of these children will have 'mild' mental impairments. Apart from 9% who have minor walking disabilities, these children have no motor problems. Although only 8% have a score on the continence scale, just under a third wet occasionally (possibly as a consequence of a fit). Only 6% have a score on the seeing scale, but 37% have glasses or contact lenses, the highest proportion of any of the clusters.

This cluster was notable for having the highest proportion of children presenting behaviour indicative of depression. Nearly half (48%) are said to be miserable, afraid or worried every day, with a fifth threatening or attempting suicide at least once a month. A third of the group was described as withdrawn for much of the day. They also have high levels of overactivity: 38% have difficulty sleeping at least once a week and nearly two-thirds (62%) are described as overactive or usually unable to concentrate. They also present serious conduct problems: over half (54%) have violent or aggressive outbursts at least once a week, including a fifth for whom this is a daily occurrence. Over a third (34%) are said to lie or steal at least once a week, and this cluster also contains one of the highest proportions (17%) of children engaged in alcohol or drug abuse. Thirty-seven per cent are described as lacking a sense of danger.

CLUSTER 5: Children with severe communication disabilities as well as those of behaviour and intellectual functioning; minorities with a wide spread of other disabilities

n = 108 (11% of total);
population estimate = 600; mean age = 13 years

The types and combinations of disabilities experienced by the children in this cluster are far more varied than those in Clusters 1–4. Over half (54%) have scores on three scales; 31% on four or more. The disabilities found in this group range across all 11 scales.

All of these children have *communication* disabilities; 97% have *behavioural* disabilities; 80% have disabilities of *intellectual functioning*. This pattern of scores suggests that many of the children in this group will have mild, and some more severe, mental impairments. Just over a fifth (22%) are assigned the maximum severity score on the communication scale ('child finds it impossible to understand anything family/carers say'). Five per cent cannot speak and over a quarter (28%) use some means in addition to or instead of speech to communicate. It would seem likely that the intellectual functioning and communication disabilities in this group are linked with a variety of other areas of disability that include mental impairments, speech difficulties and hearing loss. A fifth have hearing disabilities, 5% being totally deaf. Although only 2% have scores on the seeing scale, just over a fifth (21%) have glasses or contact lenses, the second highest proportion of all the clusters. Thirteen per cent have a mild locomotion disability, but only one child uses a walking aid.

The distribution of severity scores on the behaviour scale is quite heavily skewed towards the severe end, with 18% of the cluster scoring the maximum. The behavioural problems presented by this group are very varied: 47% have outbursts of aggression or violent temper at least once a week; 42% engage in lying and stealing. In comparison with most of the other clusters, they also have fairly high scores on the items indicative of depressed and withdrawn behaviour. Nearly a third (32%) are said to be miserable, afraid or worried every day; 42% are unable to make friends or show little interest in other children. Nearly two-thirds (65%) are described as overactive or usually unable to concentrate, and just over a third (34%) are said to lack a sense of danger.

CLUSTER 6: Children who have severe intellectual functioning, communication and behavioural disabilities and who require a high level of personal care; significant minorities have locomotion, consciousness and continence disabilities

n = 65 (7% of total);
population estimate = 350; mean age = 11.6 years

The pattern of scores for this cluster suggests that nearly all of these children have severe mental impairments. Almost three-quarters (72%) were assigned the maximum severity score for their age on the *intellectual functioning* scale. Although nearly a fifth have no *communication* disability, over two-thirds have severe difficulties and over a quarter (28%) cannot speak. Fifty-six per cent use some means in addition to or instead of speech to communicate. Just over a quarter of the group have (mainly mild) visual disabilities and 16% hearing disabilities (4% are totally deaf).

This cluster is the first in which the children require a high level of assistance with *personal care* activities. They all need some help with washing and dressing, and just over half cannot feed themselves (the maximum severity point on the 'personal care' scale). A third of this cluster soil and 7% are doubly incontinent every day. A third of the group have fits.

This is also the first of the clusters to contain children with a significant level of motor disability. Forty-four per cent have a *locomotion* disability and use some form of aid, but only 3% use a wheelchair. However, very few have any problems with the control of their hands or arms.

All the children in this cluster have a severe *behavioural* disability, with just over a quarter (26%) being assigned the maximum severity score. The behavioural characteristics of this group are markedly different from the first five clusters. These children have high levels of behaviour that is indicative of overactivity and which puts them at risk. Eighty per cent are described as overactive; 40% are reported to stay awake for much of the night at least once a week, the highest proportions for any of the clusters. Seventy-seven per cent are said to lack a sense of danger, and over a quarter (26%) injure themselves deliberately at least once a week. A similar proportion wander off if not carefully watched. Although they have low rates of scoring on the items indicative of depression, this cluster has the highest proportion of children who are said to be unable to make friends (58%). It also contains the highest proportion of children who are described as doing 'peculiar or embarrassing things'. Nearly half (48%) have outbursts of aggression or violent temper at least once a week; for over a quarter (27%) this is a daily occurrence.

CLUSTER 7: Children who have very severe intellectual, communication, behavioural and continence disabilities and who require a high level of personal care; the majority also have a locomotion disability and a significant minority have a visual disability

n = 70 (7% of total);
population estimate = 400; mean age = 11.6 years

The children in this cluster have much higher levels of disability in the areas of *locomotion* and *continence* than the children in Cluster 6. Sixty per cent have locomotion disabilities, nearly half (48%) cannot walk and almost a third (32%) use wheelchairs. (Without assistance 8% are chairfast.) However, like Cluster 6, very few have any problems with hand or arm control. Almost all (99%) have continence disabilities, with over half (54%) being doubly incontinent every day.

The pattern of scores on the *intellectual functioning, communication* and *personal care* scales suggests that all these children have severe mental impairments. Ninety-two per cent obtained the maximum adverse score for their age on the intellectual functioning scale. Ninety-eight per cent scored on the top two points of the communication disability scale, with two-thirds being unable to speak. Eighty-four per cent use some means in addition to or instead of speech in order to communicate. For 13% it was impossible to ascertain whether they could understand anything. Over two-thirds (69%) scored the maximum on the personal care scale because (amongst other things) they are unable to feed themselves. Just under a quarter of the group have fits.

A third of these children have visual disabilities, although this includes 19% who have such severe communication disabilities that it was impossible to assess how well they could see. Four per cent have a hearing disability; the hearing of a further 14% could not be assessed because of problems of concentration or communication.

The children in this cluster have the highest mean severity score on the *behaviour* scale of any of the clusters, with 40% scoring the maximum. The pattern of behavioural characteristics in this group is very similar to that in Cluster 6 but even more severe in several areas. Fifty-nine per cent of the children are said to have outbursts of aggression or violent temper at least once a week; for 40% this is a daily event, the highest proportions for any cluster on both items.

The cluster also has the highest proportions scoring on all the items indicative of 'risk-to-self' behaviour: 83% of the children are described as lacking a sense of danger; nearly half (49%) are likely to wander off if not watched; and 39% deliberately injure themselves at least once a week. Like the children in Cluster 6, they are frequently unable to make friends (55%)

and prone to do peculiar or embarrassing things (39%). They also have high levels of overactivity: just over three-quarters (76%) are described as overactive and almost a third (31%) are awake for much of the night at least once a week.

CLUSTER 8: Children with multiple and severe disabilities

n=38 (4% of the total);
population estimate = 200; mean age = 11.3 years

This group has far higher levels of motor and visual disabilities than any of the previous clusters. Ninety-one per cent have *locomotion* disabilities. Without assistance 7% are bedfast and a quarter chairfast; 41% use a wheelchair. Just under half (48%) scored the maximum on the locomotion scale. This was the first cluster to have any significant disabilities of *dexterity*; all these children have a score on this scale, with 29% assigned the maximum severity score. Fifteen per cent have disabilities associated with reaching and stretching. All require a very high level of *personal care*, with 93% scoring the maximum on this scale. A quarter have a disability arising from problems with eating, drinking or digestion. Eighty per cent wet themselves daily and 63% are doubly incontinent every day. Just over half the group has fits and a little over a quarter a disfigurement.

The whole group has severe intellectual functioning and communication disabilities, although their physical disabilities mean that these areas of disability are hard to assess. Just over three-quarters were assigned the maximum severity score on the *intellectual functioning* scale, and 96% scored on the top two points of the *communication* disability scale. Seventy-five per cent cannot speak; for 40% it was impossible to ascertain whether they understood anything. Three-quarters of these children use some means other than speech to communicate, but a few have no means of communication.

Eighty-one per cent are classified as having a sight disability, although this figure includes 39% whose visual ability could not be assessed because of their communication difficulties. The visual disability of all those who were so assessed was considered to be severe. Nine per cent of the cluster are blind. As the hearing of a fifth of this group could not be assessed, only 4% are said to have definite hearing disabilities.

A fifth of the children in this cluster are too physically disabled for their behaviour to be assessed. However, the rest of the group have quite severe *behavioural* disabilities, with just over a quarter (26%) being assigned the maximum severity score. The overall pattern of behaviour was similar to that for Clusters 6 and 7, but with lower frequencies for each of the separate items of behaviour, especially those concerned with conduct.

Sixty per cent are said to lack a sense of danger and nearly a quarter (24%) deliberately injure themselves at least once a week. Over half (53%) are described as over active and more than a quarter (27%) are awake for much of the night at least once a week. Just over half (51%) are reported to be unable to make friends.

CLUSTER 9: Children with multiple and very severe disabilities

n = 37 (4% of total);
population estimate = 200; mean age = 11.2 years

The most important difference between the children in this cluster and those in Cluster 8 is that they have difficulty controlling their arms as well as their hands. Nearly all (98%) have very severe difficulty in this respect, with just over two-thirds scoring the maximum on the *reaching and stretching* disability scale. (This was the first cluster to have any significant disability in this area.) Ninety-one per cent have severe disabilities of manual dexterity, with over half (56%) scoring the maximum on this scale.

The children in this cluster also have far more severe *locomotion* disabilities than those in Cluster 8, with 86% being assigned the maximum score. Eighty-one per cent use a wheelchair. Without assistance 28% are chairfast and 18% bedfast. Even with assistance 16% remain chairfast. Ninety-five per cent of the cluster scored the maximum on the personal care disability scale, with the remainder on the next point down. Nearly a quarter (24%) have a disability arising from problems with *eating, drinking, or digestion*. Eighty-four per cent wet themselves every day and 60% are doubly incontinent every day. Two-thirds of the group have fits and 39%, the highest proportion for any of the clusters, have a disfigurement.

Eighty-three per cent obtained the maximum adverse score for their age on the *intellectual functioning* scale. However, this group has a lower level of communication disabilities than the other two multiple severe disability groups (Clusters 8 and 10). Eighteen per cent have no communication disability, but the remainder do have severe disabilities in this area with 75% scoring on the top two points of the scale. Two-thirds cannot speak, and for 23% it was impossible to ascertain whether they can understand anything. Just over half (51%) use some means of communication in addition to or instead of speech.

Fourteen per cent have a hearing disability, although this figure included 7% who could not be assessed because of communication difficulties; 3% are totally deaf. The children in this cluster are less likely to have visual disabilities than the children in the other two multiple severe disability groups. Even so, 61% have a sight disability, although this figure includes 24% whose sight could not be assessed; 7% are blind.

The profound nature of these children's disabilities means that very few of them could present many behavioural problems. Thirty per cent have no score on the behaviour scale, 18% because they are too physically disabled to be assessed. The scores for the remainder of the group are skewed towards the severe end of the distribution. Very few children present any conduct problems, the most frequent difficulties concern the lack of a sense of danger (42%), staying awake at night (37%) and the inability to make friends (35%).

CLUSTER 10: Children with multiple and extremely severe disabilities

n = 50 (5% of total);
population estimate = 300; mean age = 11.3 years

This group's mean severity scores for *communication, continence* and *consciousness* disabilities are far higher than for Cluster 9.

Ninety-three per cent scored the maximum on the *locomotion* scale. Without assistance 10% are bedfast and a further 67% chairfast. Even with assistance 16% are chairfast. Eighty-five per cent use a wheelchair (although it seems highly unlikely that they can propel it). Ninety-six per cent of these children were assigned scores on the top two points of the reaching and stretching scale. This figure includes 75% who have no control over the use of their arms and 13% whose ability in this area cannot be assessed. The children who have no control of their arms were not assessed on the dexterity scale but assigned the minimum score. This method of scoring seems rather misleading as, in practical terms, these children had no use of their hands and so could be said to have had a greater disability in this area than the children in Cluster 9, who received much higher scores on the dexterity scale.

All the children in this cluster scored the maximum on the *personal care* disability scale. They are all enuretic by day and night and 98% have some degree of encopresis. Ninety-one per cent are doubly incontinent every day. Almost a third, the highest proportion for any of the clusters, have a disability arising from problems of eating, drinking or digestion. Nearly three-quarters have fits; 9% scored the maximum on this scale, with the remainder of the scores being heavily skewed towards the severe end. Thirty-seven per cent have a disfigurement.

Three-quarters of the group were assigned the maximum adverse score for their age on the *intellectual functioning* scale. Ninety-three per cent obtained the maximum score on the communication disability scale. Eighty-two per cent are unable to speak, and for 63% it is not possible to ascertain whether they understand anything. Sixty per cent can use some means other than speech to communicate but the rest have no means of communicating.

The hearing of nearly a third (32%) of the group could not be assessed because of communication difficulties. Nine per cent have an ascertainable hearing disability but none is totally deaf. The sight of half of the group could not be assessed. A third have quite severe visual disabilities, including 11% who are blind.

The behaviour of just over half (51%) of the children in this cluster could not be assessed, and very few would have been able to engage in many of the activities that would have led them to receive a score on the behaviour disability scale. The pattern of behavioural disabilities among those children who could be assessed is very similar to Cluster 9 but, because of all the exclusions, the frequencies are much lower. Thirty per cent are described as lacking a sense of danger, just over a quarter (27%) have difficulties sleeping at night, and 22% are said to be unable to make friends, but this figure is unlikely to reflect the reality.

8. The similarities and differences between disabled children aged 5–15 in communal establishments and their peers in private households

The results of the two cluster analyses of children in communal establishments and private households highlight a number of similarities and differences. On average, the children in communal establishments were more severely disabled and also had higher prevalence rates of behavioural disabilities. However, they had similar combinations of disabilities. In both private households and communal establishments, the largest clusters were of children with 'only' behavioural disabilities. The second largest clusters in both surveys were of children with relatively severe communication and behavioural disabilities, frequently in association with disabilities of intellectual functioning. In both private households and communal establishments, there were smaller clusters of children with disabilities of 'continence' and 'consciousness'. However, in communal establishments these two clusters of children also frequently had behavioural disabilities. There were similar groupings of multiply and severely disabled children in both private households and communal establishments.

There were also a number of differences between the results of the two cluster analyses. Compared with the private households survey, there were relatively few children in communal establishments with only one mild disability. There were distinct groupings of children in private households with primarily 'hearing and communication' and 'hearing and behavioural' disabilities, which were, surprisingly, not evident in the communal establishments analysis. The 'personal care' cluster was also not replicated in the communal establishments survey, although there were problems of personal care. The most profoundly disabled children were typically found to be living in communal establishments (in hospitals) as would be expected.

9. Discussion

The multiple nature of the disabilities of the children raised considerable problems of classification. The complex pattern of the combination of their disabilities means that no simple system of classification is possible, nor will any be entirely satisfactory. We have suggested that the OPCS approach, by taking no account of the type or combination of types of disabilities nor of any number of disabilities beyond three, oversimplified a very complex picture and in so doing grouped together children who, especially for the purposes of service planning, may have had little in common.

The method of classification developed here took account of the number, type, severity and combination of up to 11 areas of disability. The resulting clusters not only provide far more detailed descriptions of the pattern of disability but also offer a considerable reduction in the heterogeneity of the categories in comparison with the OPCS groupings.

However, although this approach produced distinct and reasonably homogeneous categories, it could not take account of all the possible individual variations. There is always likely to be a conflict between the needs of *individual* planning, where classifications by type can be oversimplistic (and thereby too easily become a stigmatising label) and the need for *aggregate* planning to allow for a rational basis for the deployment of services at the local or national level. Certainly, the OPCS approach did focus upon the limitations on their activities experienced by individuals. However, when planning services, it is also necessary to have information which allows some account to be taken of the demands that a person's disabilities are likely to make upon the carers and the providers of services. This is especially true for children because, unlike adults, they are dependent upon adult care even when they do not have a disability.

The analysis clearly demonstrated the complex nature of the disability experienced by the children in private households and in communal establishments. The majority of children had more than one disability. There was no child, for instance, who was *only* deaf and very few who were *only* blind. The multiple nature of disability has numerous implications for service provision which we discuss elsewhere.

Not only did the cluster analysis prove to be effective in grouping together children with similar disabilities; it also grouped them by the number and severity of their disabilities and, in broad terms, by the severity and frequency of the individual disabilities. In the following chapters we will show that the clusters also have an explanatory value when used to analyse other social and service-related characteristics of the children in private households and in communal establishments.

The system of classification described in this chapter is reproducible and we believe that it has considerable potential for further development and application. Replication on other samples of children with disabilities would be one important way forward. Another valuable step would be to test the robustness of the classification by repeating the cluster analysis using the results from a similar sample of children but based upon *different measures* of the same areas of disability.

NOTES TO CHAPTER 2

[1] Full details are given in the OPCS report (Bone and Meltzer, 1989) and in a later statistical paper (Martin and Elliot, 1992).

[2] These were drawn from OPCS and DHSS staff; from professionals with appropriate experience; from disabled people and from carers (the last two groups being recruited through voluntary organisations).

[3] This is not to be confused with the final 10-point severity scale that these exercises produced.

[4] See Bone and Meltzer, 1989, p. 60. Ten per cent of the children screened in at the interview stage fell below the threshold and were excluded. The OPCS report does not give separately the proportions excluded from the private households and communal establishments surveys.

[5] However, it was found that the assessors had not simply summed the severity scores but had given additional weight to the more severe disabilities in any combinations. It was also discovered that, although they took account of the third most severe disability, they largely ignored the fourth and subsequent disabilities. With the co-efficient of the most severe disability fixed at one, the best model was: (1 × 'worst' disability) + (0.4 × second 'worst') + (0.3 × third 'worst').

[6] Following re-scaling, the possible range of overall severity scores was 0.5–21.4. This range was divided equally into the ten severity levels.

[7] A severity scale for disabilities of consciousness was developed in consultation with experts on epilepsy and aligned with the other *common* severity scales. In the case of problems of disfigurement and digestion, a 'threshold' (fixed) score of 0.5 was added when these occurred. This was done because the surveys collected insufficient information in these areas to allow scales to be constructed.

3 The children and their families

1. The children

Age[1]

OPCS provided a good deal of information about the ages of children under 16 with disabilities living in private households and in communal establishments (Meltzer *et al.*, 1989). However, the age distribution was sharply different in the two settings. Whereas a fifth (21%) of the children living at home were 13, 14 or 15 years old, this proportion rose to two-thirds (65%) of the residential sample. At the other end of the scale, 55% of the children in private households were under ten years old and a fifth under five (21%). Only 12% of those in the residential survey were between five and nine years old. There was, therefore, a significant difference between the ages of the children in private households and those in communal establishments, as Table 3.1 shows.

Table 3.1 Comparison of the ages of children with disabilities living in private households (1985) and communal establishments (1988)

Ages	Children in private households (%)	Children in communal establishments (%)
0–4	21	–
5–9	34	12
10–12	24	23
13–15	21	65
Total	**100**	**100**
Base	*1200*	*1000*

Notes:
a As we have seen, OPCS assumed that virtually no disabled children under five lived in communal establishments and therefore omitted them from that survey.
b Throughout this chapter, all the figures are weighted to give the totals of 1200 or 1000 (as used by OPCS) except those that refer to the clusters as a variable.

As one would expect, disabled children are more likely to move into residential establishments of one kind or another as they get older. Had 16- and 17-year-olds been included in the children's surveys, this pattern would doubtless have been even more pronounced.

For the 5–15-year-old children in private households the average age did not vary very much between the 11 clusters (see Chapter 2). However, for children under five in private households the average age in each of the seven clusters did vary from cluster to cluster (see Chapter 14). Likewise, as we shall see in Chapter 10, there were significant differences[2] in the ages of children in certain of the clusters that emerged from the communal establishments survey data. For example, 95% of the children in Cluster 1 (behavioural disabilities only) were between the ages of 10 and 15, whereas in Clusters 8, 9 and 10 (characterised by multiple severe disabilities) the proportion fell to 72%.

In addition to the OPCS data concerning the ages of the children in their surveys, the 1991 census provided information about the ages of disabled children. For the first time questions were asked about any 'limiting long-term illness' (LLTI) suffered by a member of the household.[3] Although limiting long-term illness and disability are different concepts, there is a considerable degree of overlap between them (Pearce and Thomas, 1990; Charlton et al., 1994), particularly amongst younger adults and children (Forrest and Gordon, 1993). It seemed useful, therefore, to compare the OPCS data about ages with that collected by the census. This could be done by drawing upon the Individual Sample of Anonymised Records (SAR), a 2% sample (just over 1.1 million individuals) taken from the 1991 census, thus enabling us to produce tables that have not hitherto been published.

Using this source we were able to set out the prevalence rates of limiting long-term illness amongst children of different ages and compare them with the prevalence rates of disability in children obtained from the OPCS survey (Table 3.2).

The 1991 census Sample of Anonymised Records estimated that in Britain there were 271,000 children under 16 with a LLTI – compared with the OPCS estimate of 355,000 disabled children.[4] However, far more children under four were estimated to have a LLTI than a disability. The difference in the rates for young babies (under one-year-old) is particularly marked, three times as many of them being considered to have a LLTI than a disability (9000 compared with 3000). These differences highlight the difficulty in trying to measure disability in young children 'objectively'. It seems likely that, in the 1991 census, parents not only reported limitations in the *current* daily activities which were caused by the ill health of babies under one but, in addition, predicted the likely effects that their baby's health problems would have on limiting the child's activities as they grew older.

Table 3.2 Estimated numbers of children with a disability/LLTI in private households in Britain, analysed by age

Age (OPCS groupings)	1985 OPCS disability survey (000s)	1991 census sample of anonymised records (000s)
0–1	3	9
1–2	13	15
2–3	13	15
3–4	19	19
4–5	26	15
5–6	28	18
6–7	23	19
7–8	25	17
8–9	23	18
9–10	24	18
10–11	27	17
11–12	27	18
12–13	28	21
13–14	29	18
14–15	25	18
15–16	22	18
Total	**355**	**273**

However, as Table 3.2 makes clear, for all ages, from four onwards, the OPCS survey estimates of the number of children with disabilities in Britain were higher than the census figures for LLTI, especially for those between the ages of 4 and 6, 10 and 11 and 13 and 14.

Gender

There was no difference in the ages of the children in the private households survey with respect to gender, although there was a greater prevalence of disability amongst boys at all ages. As Meltzer *et al.* (1989, p. 2) pointed out in reporting on the OPCS survey, there were some 'three boys for every two girls in each [age] band'. There was a similar distribution in the survey of children in communal establishments.

However, there were a few differences between the boys and girls living in private households with respect to the clusters. In the 5–15 age group, girls significantly outnumbered boys in Clusters 4, 5 and 11, that is, amongst those suffering from fits, those with hearing and communication problems and those with the most severe multiple disabilities. By contrast, there were more boys than expected in Clusters 6 and 8, namely, in the 'behaviour and communication' and 'hearing and behaviour' categories. Clearly, we should not assume that, because disabled boys generally outnumbered disabled girls, that difference applied to all types, combinations and severities of disability.

Ethnicity

Six per cent of the children with disabilities living in private households were from minority ethnic or mixed backgrounds (the figure was 8% amongst those who lived in communal establishments; this is discussed further in Chapter 10). When compared with data from the Labour Force Survey (LFS) of about the same period,[5] it is apparent (Table 3.3) that the ethnic minorities were, in general, under-represented amongst children with disabilities. However, since it is unlikely that the incidence of disability in children from such backgrounds is lower than that for other children, this may indicate that the OPCS survey failed to identify children with disabilities in some minority ethnic groups who were living in private households. If that was so, it sounds a note of caution with respect to the accurate enumeration of certain children 'in need' in the community.

Table 3.3 The ethnic backgrounds of children with disabilities (comparing OPCS surveys and Labour Force Survey)

Ethnic background (OPCS categories)	Disabled children aged 0–15 in private households (OPCS) (%)	Disabled children aged 5–15 in communal establishments (OPCS) (%)	All children aged 0–15 enumerated in the 1987/89 Labour Force Survey (averaged) (%)
White	93.8	92.7	90.8
West Indian/Guyanese	0.7	1.9	1.0
Indian	1.4	0.5	2.1
Pakistani	1.8	0.4	1.8
Bangladeshi	0.3	0.2	0.5
African	0.3	0.8	0.3
Arab	0.1	0.7	0.2
Mixed origins	1.3	2.8	1.4
Other		0.1	1.7
Not stated	0.5	–	
Total	**100.0**	**100.0**	**100.0**
Base	*1200*	*1000*	*33,000*

Table 3.3 compares children in private households and in communal establishments with respect to their ethnic backgrounds. Proportionately more disabled West Indian, African and Arab children, as well as those of mixed backgrounds, were cared for residentially than were living at home, whereas proportionately more Asian children with disabilities were found to be living in private households. However, overall there still appeared to be an under-representation of children with disabilities from minority ethnic backgrounds in both of the OPCS surveys. This conclusion finds

support in the results from the 1991 census on the ethnic background of children under 16 with a limiting long-term illness. Table 3.4 shows the ethnic background of boys and girls with a LLTI compared with the ethnic backgrounds of all children as recorded in that census.

Table 3.4 The ethnic backgrounds of children with LLTI compared with the ethnic backgrounds of all children, 1991 census

Ethnic group (1991 census categories)	Children with a LLTI resident in households (1991 census)		All children resident in households (1991 census)	
	Boys (n = 144,405) (%)	Girls (n = 109,208) (%)	Boys (n = 5,646,659) (%)	Girls (n = 5,377,064) (%)
White	88.8	88.5	91.0	90.9
Black – Caribbean	1.5	1.6	1.0	1.0
Black – African	1.1	1.4	0.6	0.6
Black – other	1.3	1.3	0.8	0.8
Indian	2.0	1.9	2.2	2.3
Pakistani	2.5	2.4	1.9	1.8
Bangladeshi	0.8	0.8	0.7	0.7
Chinese	0.2	0.2	0.3	0.3
Other Asian	0.4	0.4	0.4	0.4
Other	1.4	1.5	1.1	1.2
Total	**100.0**	**100.0**	**100.0**	**100.0**
Children born in Ireland (included in 'White' above)	0.4	0.5	0.3	0.3

Source: OPCS (1993a) and 1991 Census, *Local Base Statistics*, Table 6.

Table 3.4 shows that there were fewer white, Indian and Chinese boys and girls with a limiting long-term illness resident in private households than would have been expected from the ethnic distribution of all children. Conversely, there were more boys and girls with a LLTI with black, Pakistani, Bangladeshi and other ethnic backgrounds than would have been predicted from the overall population distribution of these groups. There were also somewhat higher prevalence rates of LLTI amongst children born in Ireland than would have been expected. Since recent research shows that there are few genetic differences between ethnic groups (Cavalli-Sforza *et al.*, 1996), the differences in these prevalence rates are likely to reflect socio-economic and cultural variations. The 1991 census results showed that white, Indian and Chinese families were on average 'better off' than black, Pakistani, Bangladeshi and 'other' families (see Robinson, 1997; Cheng, 1997 and Peach, 1997 for discussion).

Thus the OPCS surveys probably under-enumerated disabled children from minority ethnic backgrounds, both in comparison with the Labour Force Survey figures of about the same time and in comparison with the 1991 census data on limiting long-term illness. Indeed, the latter actually indicated that proportionately *more* children from minority ethnic groups suffered from a LLTI than would have been predicted from their distribution in the child population.

The lack of knowledge about the complex interrelationship between poverty, ethnicity and childhood disability is problematic. Disabled children and adults often suffer from discrimination and a lack of support (Barnes, 1991). Unfortunately, research has demonstrated that disabled children from minority ethnic groups can sometimes be doubly discriminated against because of both their disability and their ethnicity (Amin and Oppenheim, 1992; Beresford, 1996; Chambra *et al.*, 1998, 1999). Even when support is available to disabled children and their families it can be culturally insensitive. In a recent study which included deaf children from minority ethnic groups, Ahmad *et al.* (1998, p. 18) found that 'whilst valuing a positive deaf identity, for many parents deaf culture was simply an extension of the white culture'. The Social Services Inspectorate (1994) has recommended that: 'Social Services Departments should ensure that a more systematic approach is taken to the planning and provision of culturally sensitive services. This should include consultation and ethnic monitoring.'

Before leaving the discussion of the children's ethnic backgrounds, it should be noted that, in the results of the cluster analysis, we found no substantial differences in this respect amongst either the children under five or amongst those between the ages of 5 and 15 living in private households. This was also true of those looked after in communal establishments.

The care arrangements

Almost nine out of ten children with disabilities were looked after by their parents at home. However, Table 3.5 shows that other forms of care and other carers also played a part. Thus, if parents were not looking after their disabled children, the most likely alternative was placement at a boarding school, from which nearly all the children returned home at vacations or more frequently.

At this point it is important to note that, overall, 4% of all the children in the OPCS surveys were in the care of local authorities, some 2.5% were in foster homes and 1.5% in communal establishments. However, one of the most startling results of our further analysis was the discovery that 86%

Table 3.5 The care arrangements for children with disabilities (private households and communal establishments combined)

	%
Private households survey (1985)	
With parents	91.2
With other relatives	0.6
In foster homes	2.4
Attending boarding schools (as termly or weekly boarders)	4.4
Communal establishments survey (1988)	
In communal establishments	1.5
Total	**100.0**

of the disabled children living in communal establishments were 'in care'. Likewise, it was somewhat surprising to find that the children in foster care were significantly older and more severely disabled than other disabled children living in private households. We shall look at these and other issues connected with the group of children who were in public care in Chapters 9 and 10. For the moment, however, it is sufficient to bear in mind that, although children in care constituted only a small proportion of all disabled children, they were extremely numerous in the communal establishments.

Boarding away but counted as living at home

Although the education of the children is dealt with in Chapter 8, it is useful to report on the extent to which those living in private households were also away at boarding schools for some of the time. Of the children between the ages of 2 and 15 (the band for which questions about education were asked) 4.3% were boarders. Of these, 34% came home every weekend, 16% at least once a month but not every weekend, 22% only during school holidays, and a further 28% less frequently.[6] Thus, of those away at boarding school, about half were back home quite often and half only at school holidays or less often.

Of the children attending boarding schools, 40% were 14 or 15 years old and 37% were aged 11–13. Only 2% were under eight years old. Thus, boarding schooling for children with disabilities was used principally for the older age groups.

With respect to the cluster analysis, 60% of the children at boarding schools (but classed as living at home) fell into either the 'behaviour' category (Cluster 2) or into that in which 'communication and behavioural' problems predominated (Cluster 5). By contrast, only 13% of the three clusters of multiple and severe disabilities (9, 10 and 11) were away at school, partly, of course, because it would have been impractical for some of them to attend. Thus it appears that, as we shall see also for those in the communal establishments, it was problems of behaviour, or problems of behaviour together with other disabilities, that were liable to lead to residential – or in this case semi-residential – care.

2. The families of the children in private households

Most of the information that OPCS collected about the families dealt with those whose disabled children either lived with them at home or returned home from boarding schools on a regular basis. As few data were gathered about the families of those children resident in communal establishments, this section concerns only the families of the children living in private households.

One of our purposes in looking afresh at the OPCS findings was to explore the patterns of childhood disability and the provision of services in relation to certain socio-economic characteristics of the families in which the children lived.[7] Principally, this involved a more detailed and extensive analysis of the data in terms of family and household composition, social class, family income and poverty. What follows is a review of the nature and relevance of these variables.

Family and household composition

OPCS used a four-fold division of family type in presenting much of its material. This is a useful but somewhat crude classification because, as can be seen in Table 3.6, 78% of the cases fell into a single category (the child and two parents).

Table 3.6 The percentage of children living in different types of family

Family type	%
Foster children	2.2
Child and two parents	78.5
Child and one parent	18.6
Child and relative	0.7
Base = 1200	100.0

Although we refer to these family 'types' from time to time we prefer to use the data about *household* composition. As can be seen from the first column of Table 3.7, this gives a somewhat different and more varied distribution.

For purposes of comparison, we have added, in the second column, data derived from the 1% Household Sample of Anonymised Records taken from the 1991 census.[8]

Table 3.7 The percentage of children living in different types of households

Household type	Disabled children (1985 OPCS disability survey) n = 1200 (%)	Children with LLTI (SAR 1991 census) n = 2478 (%)
One adult and one child	3.1	6.9
One adult and two or more children	11.6	14.9
Two adults and one child	9.7	12.1
Two adults and two children	30.9	27.5
Two adults and three children	20.9	15.3
Two adults and four or more children	7.6	8.0
Three adults and one child	5.3	4.4
Three adults and three or more children	6.6	6.7
Four or more adults and children	4.2	4.1

Whereas, according to the OPCS survey, 19% of children with disabilities lived in a family with one parent (Table 3.6), only 15% of them lived in a household with one adult (Table 3.7). This difference arises because 20% of the children lived in households that contained more people than just their parents (or step-parents) and/or other children. Some of these 'other' people will have been grown-up brothers or sisters; some will have been grandparents or other relatives; some will have been unrelated adults. Sadly, although the OPCS data might have permitted these differences to be distinguished, the problems of doing so were prohibitive.

It would also have been of considerable interest had the OPCS data been able to show whether there was more than one disabled child (or, indeed, disabled adult) in the household, but this information was not collected. However, a similar survey of disabled children in Northern Ireland in 1989 and 1990 (Smith *et al.*, 1992) showed that in 'benefit units' with disabled children, 7.2% contained two or more disabled children (see also Zarb and Maher, 1997). More recently, Lawton (1998a, 1998b) has analysed the records of the Family Fund Trust, a government-supported body established in 1973 to provide grants and information to families with severely disabled children[9] in the UK (see also Cooke *et al.*, 1983; Lawton and Quine, 1990; Cowen, 1996). Lawton examined the details of over 100,000 families with one or more disabled children under the age of 19. More than 10,000, about eleven in every hundred, had two or more children with a disability. A similar analysis of data derived from a 1995 national survey of over 1000 families, also known to the Family Fund Trust, found that 39 of them had two or more disabled children. These two pieces of research indicate, therefore, that between 4% and 11% of families with disabled children contained two or more such children. However, these results should be treated with some caution: it seems probable that families with more than one disabled child might be more likely to have made an application to the Family Fund Trust than those with only one.

Another source of information about the number of families looking after more than one disabled child is to be found in the Household Sample of Anonymised Records (SAR). Table 3.8 shows the number of children under the age of 16 with a limiting long-term illness in the 2153 households that contained at least one such child.

Table 3.8 Number of households with resident children with LLTI in the 1% Household Sample of Anonymised Records, 1991 census

Number of children with a LLTI in the household	Number of households	Percentage of households
1	1876	87.1
2	222	10.3
3	45	2.1
4	7	0.3
5	2	0.1
6	1	–
Total	**2153**	**100.0**

This gives an indication of the number of households that needed to provide care for more than one child with a LLTI. Thus, although most households (87%) containing a child with a LLTI had just one child so affected, there were 10% with two and 2.5% with three or more.

Thus, whether we take Lawton's figures or those derived from the census as a reflection of the number of families (or households) looking after more than one disabled child, the message is similar: there is a sizeable minority of parents who face the extraordinarily taxing task of caring for two or more disabled children.

Social class and disability

There is a widely held belief that disability in childhood is a 'misfortune' that is just as likely to befall the rich as the poor. Indeed, this view is often strengthened by the fact that many of the voluntary organisations that care for and campaign on behalf of children with disabilities are run and supported by people from the middle classes or by those who are reasonably well off. The prevalence of childhood disability is not perceived to have a social class gradient in the same way as diseases such as childhood tuberculosis.

This perception is hard to understand given the crucial effects that maternal health and nutrition are known to have on the prevalence of congenital abnormalities. Numerous studies have shown that women of child-bearing age are much more likely to be in poor health if they are in Social Classes IV or V than if they are in Social Classes I or II (Townsend and Davidson, 1988; Whitehead, 1988). The same social class gradient in women's health is observed if they are classified by their partner's social class. Given this known variation, it would not be surprising to find that childhood disability followed the same gradient. However, there are a number of factors that might mask this effect. In particular, the risk of congenital abnormality in children is also known to increase with maternal age. Since middle-class couples tend to have children at an older age than working-class couples, this 'life-stage' effect may obscure social class differences.

Table 3.9 shows the percentage of children with disabilities in the OPCS survey analysed by the social class of the head of household.[10] This distribution can be compared with that of all the children recorded in the 1991 census. OPCS found that 4.5% of children with disabilities lived in households whose head fell into Social Class I, whereas the 1991 census reported that 7.3% of all children lived in such households. In short, there were far fewer children with disabilities in Social Class I households than would have been expected. By contrast, there were 1.7 times as many children with disabilities in Social Class V households than would have been predicted from the census distribution.

Table 3.9 Percentage of children with disabilities in the OPCS private households survey compared with the percentage of children in the 1991 census, both analysed by social class of head of household

Social class of head of household	Disabled children (1985 OPCS private households survey) n = 1200	All children in households (1991 census 10% sample) n = 856,520	Average number of children per household (1991 census, 10% sample)	Ratio of the % of disabled children to the % of all children
	(%)	(%)	Number	Ratio
I	4.5	7.3	0.71	0.6
II	18.4	31.3	0.66	0.6
III Non-manual	12.3	11.5	0.55	1.1
III Manual	36.3	30.9	0.76	1.2
IV	20.1	14.2	0.68	1.4
V	8.2	4.7	0.65	1.7
Total	100.0	100.0		

These results must be interpreted with some caution since there was a six-year gap between the OPCS disability survey and the 1991 census. There were also slight differences in the definition of 'head of household' in the two surveys. For these reasons, we undertook a second analysis of the OPCS data in order to compare the distribution of children with disabilities according to the socio-economic group into which the head of household fell with the distribution of all children as recorded in the 1985 General Household Survey and divided up in the same way.

Table 3.10 Percentage of children in private households with disabilities in the 1985 OPCS disability survey compared with the percentage of children in the 1985 General Household Survey (GHS), both analysed by socio-economic group of head of household

Socio-economic group	Disabled children (1985 OPCS disability survey) n = 1200 (%)	All children in households (1985 GHS) n = 6454 (%)	Average number of children per household (1985 GHS) n = 10,653 (Number)	Ratio of % of disabled children to % of all children (Ratio)
Professionals	4.5	7.2	0.82	0.63
Employers and managers	15.5	20.1	0.68	0.77
Intermediate non-manual	7.6	8.9	0.52	0.85
Junior non-manual	7.9	8.2	0.45	0.96
Skilled manual	37.6	35.9	0.72	1.04
Semi-skilled manual	19.2	15.9	0.52	1.21
Unskilled manual	7.7	3.8	0.40	2.03
Total	**100.0**	**100.0**		

Table 3.10 shows that there was a clear gradient in the prevalence of childhood disability with respect to the socio-economic group of the head of the household. The children of unskilled manual workers were more than twice as likely to have a disability than would be expected. Expressed in another way, in 1985 a child was more than three times as likely to have a disability if the father was an unskilled manual worker than if he was a professional, despite the fact that professional fathers have, on average, twice as many children as unskilled manual workers.

The 2% Individual Sample of Anonymised Records (SAR) from the 1991 census (Dale and Marsh, 1993) can be used as a further check on the association between parental social class and the likelihood of disability in childhood. Table 3.11 shows the prevalence rates of limiting long-term illness in children, broken down by the social class of the family head. Once again, there is a clear gradient of increasing prevalence of childhood LLTI as one moves from Social Class I to Social Class V. In short, there were 1.44 times as many children with a limiting long-term illness in families whose head came into Social Class V than would have been expected.

Table 3.11 Prevalence rates of limiting long-term illness in children, analysed by social class of family head (data taken from the 2% Sample of Anonymised Records of the 1991 census)

Social class of family head	Children with a LLTI 1991 census (SAR) n = 3867 (%)	Children without a LLTI 1991 census (SAR) n = 190,269 (%)	Ratio of the % of children with a LLTI to the % of children without a LLTI
I	4.2	6.7	0.63
II	22.9	29.0	0.79
III Non-manual	12.6	12.8	0.98
III Manual	29.4	29.0	1.01
IV	21.3	15.3	1.39
V	7.2	5.0	1.44
Armed forces	1.1	1.3	0.85
Inadequately described	0.4	0.5	0.80
Not stated	0.9	0.6	1.50
Total	**100.0**	**100.0**	

Of course, it is not possible to determine from this kind of 'moment of time' data whether it is 'poor' parental socio-economic status that causes childhood disability or whether it is childhood disability that creates family poverty. However, considerable debate was created about the nature of these possible relationships (Illsley, 1985; Wadsworth, 1986) around the time of the publication of the Black Report (Townsend and Davidson, 1988).

Research using longitudinal, case control and retrospective recall studies has shown that there is a strong association between adult poverty and adult disability, a lesser association between childhood poverty and disability in later life and only a relatively weak association between childhood disablement and adult poverty (Power *et al.*, 1990, 1991; Elford *et al.*, 1991; Ben-Shlomo and Davey Smith, 1991; Kuh *et al.*, 1994; Rahkonen *et al.*, 1997). In brief and crudely put, it appears that poverty is much more likely to make you 'sick' than being 'ill' is likely to make you poor.

The sets of data used to analyse the prevalence of disability in childhood by social class and by the socio-economic groups into which families are classified are large, comprehensive and reliable. There is little doubt, therefore, that 'working-class' children have a higher risk of suffering from a disability than children from the 'middle' and 'upper' classes. This rarely appears to be taken into account in the formulation of policy and in the allocation of resources for the provision of services for children with disabilities.

We should make one further point before leaving this discussion of social class and disability. The use of the social class or the socio-economic group of the man in the household to determine that of the family or household as a whole may be inappropriate for many of those in which there are children with disabilities. However, the OPCS survey recorded the social class and socio-economic group of both the respondent and their partner. When this information was extracted, considerable differences emerged, as can be seen from Table 3.12. This should be borne in mind because throughout this report we have defined the 'head of household' as the respondent or partner with the higher social class, irrespective of their gender. We have also used this procedure in our classifications by socio-economic grouping.

Table 3.12 The social class of the respondent and of their partner in the OPCS survey of disabled children in private households

Social class	Respondent n = 1154 (%)	Partner n = 931 (%)
I	1	5
II	15	21
III Non-manual	30	10
III Manual	11	40
IV	33	16
V	11	5
Inadequately described	–	1
Total	**100**	**100**

Poverty and disabled children

OPCS did not set out to try to measure poverty in families with disabled children. Their main focus was on the additional costs of disability and, to a lesser extent, on family income. However, they did ask a limited number of the questions that had been used by Mack and Lansley (1985) in the *Poor Britain* survey of 1983. This study pioneered what has been termed the 'consensual' or 'perceived deprivation' approach to measuring poverty. The methodology has since been adopted widely by other studies, both in Britain and abroad (Veit-Wilson, 1987; Gordon and Pantazis, 1997). It sets out to establish whether there are some people whose standard of living is below the minimum acceptable to the society in which they live. Thus, it defines 'poverty' from the standpoint of the public's perception of minimum need. As Mack and Lansley (1985, p. 45) explained, the question of 'how poor is too poor?' could be tackled 'by identifying the minimum acceptable way of life for Britain in the 1980s. Those who have no choice but to fall below this minimum level can be said to be "in poverty". This concept is developed', they went on to explain, 'in terms of those who have an enforced lack of *socially perceived* necessities. This means that the "necessities" of life are identified by public opinion and not by, on the one hand, the views of experts or, on the other hand, the norms of behaviour *per se*.'

This approach is a variation of the 'scientific' or 'relative' measurement of poverty that was developed by Townsend (1979) and is now widely accepted. For example, in December 1984 the European Economic Community (1985, 1991) adopted the following definition of poverty: 'the poor shall be taken to mean persons, families and groups of persons whose resources (material, cultural and social) are so limited as to exclude them from the minimum acceptable way of life in the Member State in which they live'. Since the United Kingdom was a signatory to this formulation, it is currently the nearest we have to a 'working definition' of poverty.

However, the authors of the *Poor Britain* report added more detailed elements to the definition. They argued that poverty existed when the deprivation of necessities had a *multiple* impact on an individual's or family's way of life. They offered an example to illustrate this refinement: if a family just about manages but, in order to do so, goes without an annual holiday, they would be considered to be deprived by current standards; however, if this were their *only* deprivation they would not be judged to be in poverty. Several criteria were chosen for the purpose of actually determining the point at which multiple deprivation could be regarded as causing poverty. These were that the poverty line should be drawn where the overwhelming majority of those who lacked necessities[11] had low incomes in the bottom half of the income range and that overall spending reflected financial difficulty rather than high spending on other goods. Furthermore, after an examination of extensive evidence, Mack and Lansley (1985) decided that it was not until families suffered the enforced lack of three 'necessities' or more that they should be classed as 'in poverty'.[12] Applying this threshold (and their other criteria) they considered that 14% of British households could be regarded as living in poverty in 1983.

As we have noted, in its disability surveys OPCS asked a number of questions that identified the lack of the kinds of 'necessities' that Mack and Lansley had included in their analysis. As a result, we could use this information in order to obtain a reasonably comparable figure for the level of poverty amongst households with a disabled child. However, at this point it is important to record that the result of applying the Mack and Lansley formula to the OPCS material was to find that 55% of the households in which there was a disabled child were likely to have been living in poverty or at its margins in 1985. This is an extraordinarily high level. Indeed, according to this analysis, it seemed that households with disabled children were four times more likely than the generality of British households to be 'poor'. More specifically, they were more likely to have been living in poverty than lone-parent households, unemployed households, households with heads in Social Class V, ethnic minority households or households with large families. In 1985 families with disabled children were, arguably, the 'poorest of the poor' (Gordon and Heslop, 1998).

Somewhat more flesh may be put on these bare bones if, as in Table 3.13, one sees the kinds of 'necessary' items that different types of households were unable to afford. Since another study of poverty undertaken in 1990 (*Breadline Britain*) used much the same approach as Mack and Lansley, (Gordon and Pantazis, 1997) we have included its results in the final column alongside those derived from the OPCS surveys of both disabled children and disabled adults living in private households. When, in later chapters, we use the terms 'deprivation index' or the 'poor' and the 'not poor', we refer to our analysis based upon the Mack and Lansley approach.

Table 3.13 shows that both households with disabled children and households with disabled adults and non-disabled children were much more likely than those with no children but with a disabled adult to lack necessities because they could not afford them. In turn, households with disabled adults lacked more necessities due to financial constraints than the average British household. The much higher levels of deprivation experienced by families with children, where either the adults or the children were disabled, is very marked. For example, 35% of households with disabled children and 32% of those with children and disabled adults could not afford two pairs of all-weather shoes in 1985; this compared with only 9% of all British households in 1983 and 4% in 1990.

Supporting evidence for the considerable extent of poverty experienced by disabled people is provided by the work of Berthoud *et al.* (1993) who, using a completely different methodology, estimated that 45% of all disabled adults were living in poverty. However, it must be noted that some of the respondents, who were defined as objectively living in poverty in that study, expressed themselves as 'fairly satisfied' with their standard of living. Likewise, drawing upon data in the OPCS disability surveys and the *Breadline Britain* survey, Table 3.14 shows that 61% of the OPCS respondents in households with disabled children were either 'very' or 'fairly satisfied' with their standard of living, compared with 75% of all British households (the final column).

Given the extent of poverty in households with disabled children, this difference seems comparatively modest. It should warn us against assuming that those who would be considered to be living in poverty by others may not regard themselves in this way or, if they do, may not be willing to admit as much, especially to an unknown interviewer.

Table 3.13 Households unable to afford a selection of consumer durables and certain other items considered to be necessities by the majority of the British public, 1983–1990

Survey	'Poor Britain' survey, 1983	OPCS disability survey, 1985	OPCS disability survey, 1985	OPCS disability survey, 1985	'Breadline Britain' survey, 1990
Target group	All households	All disabled adults	Disabled adults with children	Adults with disabled children	All households
	n = 1174	n = 8945	n = 954	n = 1200	n = 1831
	Percentage of households lacking item because they can't afford it				
Warm winter coat	7	8	21	19	4
Two pairs of all-weather shoes	9	15	32	35	4
Presents for friends and family once a year	5	13	15	14	5
Celebrations on special occasions, e.g. Christmas	4	13	13	9	4
New, not second-hand, clothes	6	17	30	33	4
Meat or fish every other day	8	7	13	10	3
Roast joint once a week	7	12	15	14	1
Cooked meal every day	3	3	5	4	1
Toys for children	2	–	12	8	1
Money for school trips	9	–	17	10	4
Telephone[a]	11	14	13	23	7
Washing machine	6	9	9	6	4
Fridge	2	2	2	2	2
Video[b]	–	21	37	33	11

Notes:
a The telephone was not considered to be a necessity by the majority of people in 1983 but it was by a small majority in 1990.
b Only 13% of the 'general public' in 1990 thought that a video was a necessity.

Table 3.14 Satisfaction with standard of living by household type

Satisfaction	All disabled adults, OPCS survey, 1985 (%)	Disabled adults with children, OPCS survey, 1985 (%)	Adults with disabled children, OPCS survey, 1985 (%)	All adults, 'Poor Britain' survey, 1983 (%)
Very satisfied	21	11	12	17
Fairly satisfied	50	42	49	58
Neither	14	17	14	8
Fairly dissatisfied	9	17	12	10
Very dissatisfied	6	13	13	7
Total	100	100	100	100

Income and disability

There has now been considerable research which shows that families with a disabled child have lower incomes than equivalent families without a disabled child (Bradshaw, 1975; Disability Alliance, 1975; Loach, 1976; Baldwin, 1977; Piachaud *et al.*, 1981; Baldwin, 1985; Smyth and Robus, 1989; Walker *et al.*, 1992; Beresford, 1995; Kaganet *et al.*, 1998). However, all but one of these studies have been based on selected samples of families with disabled children. The exception was that of Piachaud and his colleagues which was particularly important because it presented evidence from an analysis of nationally representative data from the general household surveys of the 1970s. More recent information from these surveys is now available and has been analysed by Gordon and Heslop (1998). This work shows that the household incomes of families with disabled children were considerably below those of equivalent families without disabled children during the 1990s. For example, in 1993, households containing two adults and four or more children, one of whom had a limiting long-term illness, received on average £164 a week less in gross income than those not containing a child with such an illness. This is a difference of £8528 a year, without taking into account the extra costs of the child's disability.

As pointed out in the introduction, the results of the OPCS surveys with respect to the additional costs that disability incurred and the financial circumstances of families with disabled members were the most controversial and contested (Abberley, 1996). There are clearly extra financial costs that disabled people and their families face because of their disability, such as the expense of special equipment, extra heating or clothing, individual transport, help with cleaning or cooking and personal care services (see, for example, Baldwin, 1977; Howard, 1994; Dobson and Middleton, 1998). Attempts to gauge these extra costs are fraught with difficulty, and the results are not only dependent on the type, nature and severity of the disabilities but also on cultural factors and the availability and cost of social, educational and health services (Horn, 1981; Chetwynd, 1985; Graham, 1987).

As a result of questions asked about the extra costs of disability in the OPCS disability surveys, it was estimated that, on average, these amounted to £6.10 a week for disabled adults (Martin and White, 1988). However, two smaller-scale studies carried out by the Disablement Income Group (DIG) found the additional extra costs of disablement for adults to be up to seven times greater than this (DIG, 1988, 1990). A re-analysis of the OPCS data by Berthoud *et al.* (1993), taking into account the severity of the disability as well as income and standard of living, concluded that the extra costs of disability for adults amounted to over three times the OPCS estimate – that is, an average of £19.70 per week at 1985 prices. In the case of disabled children, OPCS reported that the extra costs were £7.65 a week, again at 1985 prices. Unfortunately, Berthoud and his colleagues did not re-analyse the OPCS data on families with a disabled child in the way that they had done for those with a disabled adult, so there is no alternative figure against which to compare the OPCS estimate.

Other studies that have looked at the extra costs of childhood disability have tended to be small scale and limited to particular medical conditions, or focused on the type of extra expenses incurred and not on their exact level. Using expenditure diaries and information from parents, Baldwin (1985) found that families with a disabled child spent some £16 a week more (at 1985 prices) on items that they bought regularly (such as food, clothing or transport) than other families on average incomes – more than twice the figure arrived at by OPCS. In addition, she found that extra expense was incurred in the purchase of aids and appliances or special equipment, as well as for larger commitments such as housing adaptations. It was also noteworthy that still other additional costs were associated with hospital in- and out-patient attendances. In a more recent study of children with a motor impairment in Scotland, Gough *et al.* (1993) found that 63% of the families reported a need for additional special expenditure against a background of reduced parental employment and reduced earnings.

Budget standards research has shown that it would cost on average £125,000 to bring up a child with a severe disability from birth to 17 years of age at 1997 prices. This is three times more than the cost of a child without a disability if the goods and services regarded as essential were all being purchased (Dobson and Middleton, 1998). Benefits for severely disabled children would need to be increased by 20–50%, depending on the child's age and type of impairment, to meet the costs of the minimum essential budgets.

Throughout much of their private households survey reports, OPCS used the families' net income (that is, after the deduction of taxes, national insurance contributions, housing costs etc.) in making their analyses. This was then 'equivalised' using the McClements' Scale favoured by the Department of Social Security. The need to equivalise income is based on the self-evident idea that the larger the household the more income will be needed in order to maintain the same standard of living. It is also clear that economies of scale exist within a household; for example, it does not cost a family of four twice as much as a family of two to maintain a comparable standard of living. Even so, it is not self-evident how *much* extra the larger households need in order to maintain the same standard of living as smaller households.

However, the McClements' Equivalisation Scale has been criticised on methodological grounds and also because it makes less allowance for the additional costs of children than any of the other widely used equivalisation scales (Muellbauer, 1979, 1980; Whiteford, 1985). Over and above these problems, the McClements' Scale, designed as it was with non-disabled children in mind, can hardly be appropriately applied to families with disabled children given the recognised additional costs. For this reason, throughout this report, we have used the raw net family income figures (which are unequivalised) and converted them into income per person; that is, the net income divided by the number of people in the family. We have termed this the 'effective family income'.

The socio-economic distribution of disabled children aged 5–15

In the previous chapter, we showed how disabled children aged 5–15 could be grouped into 11 categories (clusters) based on the combination, number, type and severity of their disabilities. We now examine whether there are any systematic differences in the prevalence of these clusters of disability in relation to the socio-economic circumstances of the children's families. Tables 3.15 to 3.17 show the percentage of children in each disability cluster according to the social class of the head of their household (3.15), by the income quintile into which that household falls (3.16) and by whether or not it was in 'poverty' as defined by the formula explained earlier (3.17). The percentage distribution of all disabled children aged 5–15 is shown in the final row of each table (for example, 23% of all disabled children lived in households with a head in Social Class I or II; 20% in households in the highest income quintile; 45% in households that were 'not poor').

Table 3.15 Percentage of children aged 5–15 in private households in each disability cluster, analysed by social class of head of household

Cluster	Description	I+II (%)	III Non-manual (%)	III Manual (%)	IV+V (%)
1	Mild disabilities	22	13	36	29
2	Behaviour	19	14	37	30
3	Incontinence	14	13	40	33
4	Fits	37	16	29	18
5	Hearing and communication	29	13	38	20
6	Communication and behaviour	23	10	41	26
7	Personal care	40	13	38	9
8	Hearing and behaviour	19	11	46	24
9	Multiple disabilities	24	8	38	30
10	Multiple and severe	18	18	32	32
11	Multiple and very severe	31	13	26	30
Total		**23**	**13**	**37**	**27**

Table 3.16 Percentage of children aged 5–15 in private households in each disability cluster, analysed by income quintile of household

Cluster	Description	Income quintiles				
		Highest (%)	Second (%)	Third (%)	Fourth (%)	Lowest (%)
1	Mild disabilities	27	21	12	21	19
2	Behaviour	18	18	17	22	24
3	Incontinence	12	16	22	28	23
4	Fits	20	34	12	10	25
5	Hearing and communication	16	21	26	22	15
6	Communication and behaviour	20	17	23	19	21
7	Personal care	35	25	20	13	8
8	Hearing and behaviour	19	19	23	19	20
9	Multiple disabilities	28	15	29	19	8
10	Multiple and severe	24	32	20	16	8
11	Multiple and very severe	39	36	11	7	8
Total		**20**	**20**	**20**	**20**	**20**

Table 3.17 Percentage of children aged 5–15 in private households in each disability cluster, analysed by poverty status of household

Cluster	Description	Not poor (%)	Poor (%)
1	Mild disabilities	51	49
2	Behaviour	43	57
3	Incontinence	41	59
4	Fits	44	56
5	Hearing and communication	44	56
6	Communication and behaviour	53	47
7	Personal care	71	29
8	Hearing and behaviour	41	59
9	Multiple disabilities	42	58
10	Multiple and severe	42	58
11	Multiple and very severe	61	39
Total		**45**	**55**

As can be seen, several of the clusters show socio-economic differences from the generality. In households whose heads belonged to Social Classes I and II, in households with incomes in the top two quintiles and in 'not poor' households, there were more disabled children than would be expected in the 'personal care' cluster (7) and 'multiple and very severe' cluster (11). Similarly, children living in households in the 'best' socio-economic circumstances appear slightly more likely than would be expected to be in the 'fits' cluster (4) and the 'mild disabilities' cluster (1). Conversely, in households with heads in Social Classes IV and V, in households where the income is in the bottom two quintiles and in households classified as 'poor', there were more children than would have been anticipated in the 'behaviour' cluster (2) and the 'incontinence' cluster (3).

However, it should be noted that social class, income and poverty are different measures of socio-economic circumstances and, as would be expected, the size of the differences in the distribution of childhood disability varies in different ways with each indicator. Although there is a considerable degree of overlap between social class, poverty and income, they provide different kinds of information on disabled children's circumstances and living conditions. For example, it seems possible that the families of the most severely disabled children living at home (Cluster 11) and of the 'personal care' group (Cluster 7) are 'relatively' well off because the benefits system helps to provide a supplement to their incomes.

3. Discussion and implications

Several general and useful conclusions may be drawn from our review of children with disabilities living in private households and of their families, many of which still seem to be relevant today.

Unlike the findings in the communal establishments survey (where older children predominated) the ages of the disabled children in private households were fairly evenly spread. *Services, therefore, need to be adapted to a wide range of ages as well as to a variety of disabilities.*

Although boys outnumbered girls by three to two, there were few other differences in the profile. However, in the 5–15 age group living in private households there did appear to be some differences between boys and girls according to the type, combination and severity of the disabilities, although the evidence was not sufficiently strong to draw firm conclusions. Nevertheless, *gender differences according to the disabilities suffered by children may warrant more careful study than would at first sight seem to be justified.*

There were few differences between the children with respect to their ethnic backgrounds. However, there is good evidence from the Labour Force Survey and from the 1991 census to suggest that *OPCS did not identify as many children with disabilities from some minority ethnic backgrounds living in private households as might have been expected.* This finding has a particular cautionary relevance for those who are compiling 'needs registers' and, especially, registers of the disabled as a basis for the planning and provision of services.

A small proportion (about 4%) of the children classified as living in private households attended boarding schools. Of these, about half came home quite frequently, half only at school holidays or less often. When we look at respite care (Chapter 6) we shall have to take the contribution of the boarding schools into account but, on the face of it, *boarding away did not appear to be widespread amongst children with disabilities.* However, both *older children and children with significant behaviour disabilities (often the same group) were more likely than others to be attending boarding school.*

It is clear that there are sharp differences in the prevalence of childhood disability according to the social class of the household or family. '*Working-class' children have a higher risk of suffering from a disability than children from the 'middle' and 'upper' classes. This needs to be taken into account when allocating resources* for the provision of services for children with disabilities, not least because it seems likely that OPCS underestimated the additional financial costs associated with childhood disability.

Almost 55% of the families with children with disabilities were living in or on the margins of poverty in 1985 – according to a definition of poverty that would be accepted by a large majority of people. Families with children with disabilities could be regarded as 'the poorest of the poor'; they had a greater likelihood of living in poverty than any other social group. This is important to recognise because it implies that major legislation was failing in its purported aims – and may still be doing so. Financial supplements for the families of disabled children appear to have been insufficient to put them on a par with the rest of the population, let alone to cover the extra costs of disability. The Children Act 1989 has placed a duty on local authorities to examine the barriers and difficulties that confront disabled children and to provide services to minimise these impediments. It is likely that, in many areas, more could still be done.

Similarly, the Disability Discrimination Act 1995, which deals (to some extent) with discrimination in the provision of goods, facilities and services to disabled people, does not directly address discrimination against disabled children and their parents. In the short term, as the families of disabled children in Beresford's (1995) study explained, the greatest need is for more financial assistance through higher weekly disability benefits so that child care and development needs can be adequately met. Furthermore, the evidence about the circumstances of the families of disabled children that we have reviewed lends support to the contention that what is really needed in the longer term is a more comprehensive, legally enforceable anti-discrimination policy that is relevant to all disabled children and their families (Gordon and Heslop, 1998).

Finally, some socio-economic differences were to be found with respect to the clusters of disabled children living in private households. In particular, the households of *the children in the 'personal care' cluster (7) and the 'multiple and very severe' cluster (11) were more often to be found in Social Classes I and II and amongst the better off, whilst those of children in the 'behaviour' cluster (2) and the 'incontinence' cluster (3) were more likely to be located at the opposite end of the spectrum.* However, at least with respect to income, this may be a reflection of the differential effect of the disability benefits system.

NOTES TO CHAPTER 3

[1] We have used the data on children's ages at the time of interview rather than the standardised ages employed in the OPCS reports. Hence, there may be some small discrepancies between their figures and ours.

[2] Throughout this report where we refer to significant results, we imply statistical significance at less than the 5% level.

[3] Question 12 in the census asked if any member of the household had a 'long-standing illness, health problem or handicap' which limited their work or daily activities.

[4] The 1991 Individual SARs is a 2% sample from the 1991 census. The number of children with a limiting long-term illness has been estimated by first multiplying the raw SAR count

by 50 and then by the relevant age-related design factor in order to allow for clustering and undercounts in the SAR and in the census (see Simpson *et al.*, 1993, Table 5).

[5] OPCS, 1991. *Labour Force Survey 1988 and 1989*. Figures used in this section are derived from Table 5.30, p. 25.

[6] It will be recalled that, if a child was in a boarding school and never went home, OPCS placed them in the communal establishments survey.

[7] Baldwin and Carlisle (1994) provide a valuable review of the literature on social support for disabled children and their families.

[8] This is a 1% sample of all households in Britain, drawn from the 1991 census (and not to be confused with the previously mentioned 2% Individual Sample of Anonymised Records). The Household SAR contains full census details of over 500,000 individuals living in 215,789 households on census night 1991.

[9] A disabled child may have a physical impairment, a sensory impairment, a mental impairment, or complex and multiple impairments.

[10] The 'head of household' is defined as the man where there is a couple or the woman if she is a lone parent.

[11] A lack of necessities refers to circumstances where households did not have a 'necessity' because they could not afford it; not because they did not want it.

[12] Further confirmation of the appropriateness of this definition of a 'poverty line' was provided by Desai and Shah (1985) and Desai (1986).

4 | Domiciliary services provided

for the 5–15 age group living in private households

1. The pattern of provision

Only 32% of the parents or carers of the 5–15-year-olds said that, in the previous year, they had received a domiciliary service from any of the 25 sources on the OPCS card shown to them when they were interviewed. The list of possibilities is reproduced in Figure 4.1.

Several interesting results emerged when we explored the pattern of provision. Whether or not families had received a domiciliary service was

Figure 4.1
The domiciliary services listed on the OPCS card (OPCS titles and order)

District nurse
Nursing auxiliary
Psychiatric nurse
Mental handicap nurse
Health visitor
Other nurse
Physiotherapist
Occupational therapist
Chiropodist
Visiting teacher
Local authority home help
Meals on wheels
Laundry service
Incontinence service
Night sitting service
Mobility officer
Local authority social worker
Voluntary worker
Visiting service
Private domestic help
Private nurse
Probation officer
Speech therapist
Educational psychologist

unrelated to a number of major social variables. For instance, there were no significant differences with respect to household composition (although lone-parent families comprised 15% of the sample); nor were there any significant variations according to ethnic background, social class or income (although the poorest fifth was somewhat less likely to have had a service than the rest). In addition, when we applied the 'poverty index' derived from the *Poor Britain* survey (Mack and Lansley, 1985) and the *Breadline Britain* study (Gordon and Pantazis, 1997) we found there were no significant differences in relation to this compound variable.

These findings raise a number of issues. First (the nature and extent of a child's disability apart), one might have expected lone-parent households to have received rather more help than those in which there were two adults. Likewise, one might also have expected a distribution that favoured families having to care for several children.

Secondly, since at least some of the services listed by OPCS were (or could have been) provided privately, one might have anticipated that the better-off parents would have purchased more services than those who were poorer: they did not.

Thirdly, if a family was living in a general state of poverty, it would not have been unreasonable to have presumed that – whatever the disability – they might require and obtain more help than those who were living in less disadvantageous circumstances. Again, there was no evidence to suggest that such factors influenced whether or not a family received a domiciliary service.

However, there was a significant difference in respect to whether or not a domiciliary service had been provided to one 'family type'. It was nearly four times as likely that foster carers would have received some such service than any other family. This might well be expected, given that the foster home placements had been made by social services departments and, at the very least, should have been supervised by a visiting social worker. Furthermore, as we shall see in Chapter 9, foster carers looked after some of the more severely disabled children. Bearing that in mind, however, it is somewhat surprising to find that 19% of the foster carers said that they had had no domiciliary service in the previous 12 months, or since the child had been placed with them if that were more recent.[1]

There was one other matter which we investigated in relation to the receipt or non-receipt of a domiciliary service that did show some variation: the distribution of results by standard regions of the country. Although most of the regions clustered around the national average of families receiving some domiciliary service (32%), there were notable differences at the extremes: in particular, families in Scotland received less help (23%), whilst those in the East Midlands received the most (43%).

This finding supports that of Plank (1982), who surveyed the services available to 'mentally handicapped' children and their families. The OPCS data are set out in Table 4.1.

Table 4.1 Whether or not any domiciliary service had been provided in the previous year, analysed by standard regions

Region	Service provided (in ascending order) (%)
Scotland	23
North England	26
West Midlands	26
South-west England	26
Yorkshire and Humberside	32
North-west England	32
South-east England	32
GLC area	34
Wales	40
East Anglia	40
East Midlands	43
Britain	**32**

Of course, as in other results, this pattern may well have changed in the succeeding years, and a regional analysis takes no account of variations within regions. Nevertheless, the fact that certain regional differences did exist should alert us to the possibility of continuing geographical variations in the level of service provided.

When we turned to examine the receipt or absence of a domiciliary service in relation to the cluster analysis, we discovered pronounced differences, as Table 4.2 makes clear.

Table 4.2 Whether or not any domiciliary service had been received in the previous year, analysed by clusters

Cluster	Description	Service provided (%)
1	Mild disabilities	17
2	Behaviour	27
3	Incontinence	32
4	Fits	13
5	Hearing and communication	24
6	Communication and behaviour	31
7	Personal care	27
8	Hearing and behaviour	30
9	Multiple disabilities	63
10	Multiple and severe	54
11	Multiple and very severe	68
All	**n = 989**	**32**

Significantly more of the families with children who fell into the three most severely and multiply disabled groups (Clusters 9, 10 and 11) obtained help than any of the others. By contrast, significantly fewer of those with children whose disabilities were characterised by fits (Cluster 4) and by the presence of low levels of relatively mild disabilities (Cluster 1) received a service. In general, therefore, one might conclude (as indeed OPCS did) that services were distributed in a way that reflected the severity of disability.

However, such a conclusion should be tempered by three provisos. First, it is important to re-emphasise that barely a third of all the families reported having received a service in the preceding year and that, even in the cluster comprising children with both multiple and extremely severe disabilities (Cluster 11), almost a third said that they had had no domiciliary service whatsoever.

Secondly, although the three clusters of multiple and severe disabilities certainly posed enormous problems it would be unwise to conclude that other clusters (such as 'behaviour') did not. All that can be said is that the problems are likely to be different and that they will make different demands upon the carers. The severity of the disability may not be the same as the severity of the problems of care.

The third proviso is that OPCS set its threshold for a child's inclusion in the study at a relatively high level of disability. Thus, in general, the degree of severity was greater than that reflected in previous studies.

It is obviously important to know in more detail how specific domiciliary services were distributed. However, because, overall, only 32% of the families received any kind of service, the proportions assisted by a particular service were low. Indeed, OPCS noted that 'so few' had used any one domiciliary service that they omitted these details from their tabulations (Meltzer *et al.*, 1989). Nevertheless, we felt that we should pursue the analysis down to this level, not least in order to demonstrate unequivocally the sparsity of most of the services in question at the time of the survey and thereby establish a bench-mark for assessing subsequent developments.

The two most commonly received services were those provided by health visitors (to 14% of the families) and by social workers (to 11%). The only other service received on any scale was that of a visiting teacher (to 4% of the children). Thereafter, as can be seen from Table 4.3, the proportions of families or children having any of the other services were minuscule.

It may be somewhat surprising perhaps to find the health visitor service standing at the head of this rather sad list, given that in this chapter we are only reporting on the data obtained for the 5–15-year-olds. However, it must be borne in mind that, during the 1970s, the role of the health visitor

Table 4.3 Type of domiciliary service provided in the previous year, analysed by the proportion of families receiving it (*n* = 989)

Service (OPCS terminology)	Received service (%)
District nurse	1.2
Nursing auxiliary	0.2
Psychiatric nurse	0.3
Mental handicap nurse	2.1
Health visitor	14.2
Other nurse	1.3
Physiotherapist	1.3
Occupational therapist	0.6
Chiropodist	0.3
Visiting teacher	4.2
Local authority home help	0.1
Laundry service	0.2
Incontinence service	2.5
Night sitting service	0.3
Mobility officer	0.2
Local authority social worker	11.3
Voluntary worker	0.4
Visiting service	0.1
Private domestic help	0.5
Probation officer	0.1
Speech therapist	0.2
Educational psychologist	0.7

a Totals more than the 32% receiving services because some families had more than one service.

in providing a service to disabled people was promoted by both the Snowden (1976) and the Warnock (1978) committees. The latter, which recommended the designation of a 'named person' for each disabled child, considered that health visitors were ideally placed to provide the support that this envisaged. As can be seen from Table 4.4, all clusters received some health visitor service, although there was a concentration on the three multiple and severe categories (Clusters 9, 10 and 11).

Similarly, although all but one of the clusters received some social worker visits, there was, again, a heavy emphasis on the three clusters with the severest disabilities, and noticeably thin provision elsewhere. This may have reflected the findings of earlier studies which suggested that – exceptional cases apart – regular supportive contact between social workers and families with a disabled child was accorded a low priority by social services departments (Butler *et al.*, 1977; Shearer, 1978; Armstrong and Race, 1979; Ayer and Alaszewski, 1984). It may also have mirrored the concern that had been expressed about the ability of social workers with generic caseloads to provide the specialised information and advice needed by disabled children and their families (Glendinning, 1983). The current position could well be different, especially as a result of the Children Act

Table 4.4 The three main domiciliary services received, analysed by clusters

Cluster	Description	Percentage of families receiving visits from:		
		Health visitor	Social worker	Home teacher
1	Mild disabilities	8.9	5.2	2.2
2	Behaviour	11.4	9.0	3.1
3	Incontinence	17.1	7.9	1.3
4	Fits	12.2	–	–
5	Hearing and communication	11.8	1.5	8.8
6	Communication and behaviour	12.1	11.3	5.7
7	Personal care	19.2	5.8	3.8
8	Hearing and behaviour	10.3	13.2	2.9
9	Multiple disabilities	29.9	31.2	7.8
10	Multiple and severe	22.0	22.0	8.0
11	Multiple and very severe	21.4	42.9	7.1
All	*n* = **989**	**14.2**	**11.3**	**4.2**

1989 which heralded the creation of registers of children with disabilities in each local authority area as well as the establishment of children's services plans, both of which developments should have drawn more attention to the needs associated with disabilities in childhood.

In fact, later studies (such as Beresford, 1995; Aldgate and Tunstill, 1995) do suggest that more is now being done. For example, Beresford reported that 32% of school-age disabled children in her study had been seen by a health visitor in the previous year and almost a half (46%) by a social worker. In Aldgate and Tunstill's broader study of the way in which Section 17 of the Children Act was being implemented (the section requiring local authorities to provide services for children identified as being in need), almost all (79) of the 82 local authorities included claimed to be providing advice and counselling to 'children with disabilities and parents'. Indeed, the authors concluded that 'the special emphasis placed on disabled children under the Act seems to have enhanced provision of services and budgets for them'. However, much still turns upon the definition and identification of a 'disabled child', an issue to which we return in our final chapter.

The very low levels of services (other than health visiting and social work) that were provided for certain of the clusters seem extraordinary. For example, none of the children whose problems were largely associated with hearing and communication (Cluster 5) had had any domiciliary help from a speech therapist, and none of the families looking after children in the three clusters of multiple and severe disabilities had had a local authority home help; indeed, as Table 4.3 shows this service was virtually absent from the scene. Likewise, a laundry service hardly appeared to exist, and none of the families with children in the cluster where incontinence was a dominant problem (Cluster 3) had received such help. This situation paralleled that revealed earlier by Wilkin (1979): although 42% of the disabled children in that study were frequently incontinent, only one family had ever been offered a laundry service. However, the survey undertaken by Aldgate and Tunstill (1995) suggests that there has been a marked improvement in the availability of this particular service. Half of the 82 authorities claimed to be providing a laundry service, either directly or through other agencies; but the extent to which it was received by the families of disabled children was not recorded.

Unfortunately, the OPCS survey collected only limited information about how often a service was received, or how much of it a family or child enjoyed. We do not know, therefore, how intensive a service was for the recipients or exactly what it entailed. There may have been just one instance of provision in the previous year, or many. Other more recent research about this is inconclusive. For instance, Gough *et al.* (1993), in a Scottish survey, reported limited contact with community health and social care professionals, whereas Sloper and Turner (1992) found that there were relatively frequent contacts with a large number of professionals.

Notwithstanding these gaps in the OPCS data, certain general conclusions can be drawn from the surveys. However, it is first salutary to consider what the carers said they needed.

2. The services that carers said they needed

As well as gathering data on the domiciliary services that parents and carers said they had received, OPCS asked them what they considered they needed but were not getting. Although they were again shown a card listing the different possibilities, their answers will probably have been influenced both by what they knew about the services potentially available and by their general level of expectation about receiving 'outside' help. It must also be remembered that there was no differentiation between the parents' own needs and those of their children. The data in Table 4.5 should be viewed with these considerations in mind.

Given the prompting that the card provided, it was somewhat surprising that only 18% of the carers of these 5–15-year-olds said that they, or their children, needed extra domiciliary services (although the rate was somewhat higher (23%) amongst families from minority ethnic backgrounds). Those who wanted additional help divided fairly evenly between families who had received such a service in the previous year (they wanted more or a different kind) and those who had not. However, as in

Table 4.5, we have combined these two groups in the discussion that follows.

In the light of the generally poor media image of social work, it is noteworthy that the most commonly expressed unmet need was for extra social work contact (21%). This echoes the findings of Glendinning's (1983) survey, which revealed that many parents considered that a routine, regular visit from a social worker would help 'enormously' in that assistance, information and advice might be offered, rather than this always having to be sought and requested. The need for extra social work contact was followed by requests for more assistance from a visiting teacher and from an incontinence service (17% in each case). It should be noted that these three services are the ones that parents from minority ethnic backgrounds also highlighted. The need for a laundry service was mentioned only slightly less frequently (by 15% of the parents).

The only other services that were much in demand were those of health visitors and 'other' nurses (7% and 6%, respectively). Given the various types of nurses specified in the OPCS list, it would have been interesting to know exactly what 'other' kind of nursing help respondents had in mind.

Table 4.5 Opinion of parents regarding the provision of domiciliary services

Service	Percentage of parents requesting more of various services[a]
District nurse	0.6
Nursing auxiliary	0.6
Psychiatric nurse	2.8
Mental handicap nurse	0.6
Health visitor	7.3
Other nurse	6.2
Physiotherapist	5.1
Occupational therapist	1.2
Chiropodist	0.6
Visiting teacher	17.0
Local authority home help	2.8
Laundry service	15.4
Incontinence service	17.1
Night sitting service	1.7
Mobility officer	1.1
Local authority social worker	21.1
Voluntary worker	2.3
Visiting service	1.2
Private domestic service	4.0
Private nurse	1.2
Speech therapist	0.6
Other	6.9

a The total adds to more than 100% because of multiple responses.

A number of points need to be made in considering the implications of these findings. At least two of the domiciliary services that were already most commonly provided were at the top of the list of requests: social work and home teaching. Whatever the precise reasons for some one in six parents wanting home teaching (or additional home teaching) for their child, the issue deserves more attention than the OPCS data allowed. However, a clue to what 'home teaching' may involve is given in Beresford's (1995) study: that over half of the parents of disabled children thought that their child had unmet needs in terms of developing skills for future independence and extending their learning abilities. Over two-fifths (43%) of the parents also reported that they themselves needed help in learning how best to help their child. As one parent put it: 'she [the home teacher] taught me how to teach, how to break tasks down' (Byrne *et al.*, 1988, p. 108). What some parents may have had in mind was a combination of home- and school-based teaching (see Chapter 8).

Amongst those parents whose children *were* incontinent (32% of the total), the demand for greater help from an incontinence service was almost certainly more extensive than the 17% shown in Table 4.5. The parents of those who were not incontinent would obviously not have needed this service.

The issue of a laundry service is more complicated. On the face of it, all parents dealing with problems of incontinence are likely to have extra requirements for washing clothes and bed-linen. However, the general wear and tear associated with disabled living would suggest that the need goes beyond this. Indeed, we know that 40% of the respondents said that they spent more on washing as a result of their child's disability – but only 3% said that they spent more on sending clothes or bed-linen to the laundry. As one might expect, the additional costs of washing (leaving aside the labour and time) were significantly greater amongst the three multiple and severe disability clusters (67%, 80% and 89% of parents reporting such extra expenditure in, respectively, Clusters 9, 10 and 11) and in the 'incontinence' cluster (88%). However, higher washing costs were claimed by substantial proportions in all but one of the clusters (around 30%), the exception being the group where hearing and communication problems predominated (Cluster 5).

To a significant degree, 'poor' families (applying the poverty index) said that they spent extra on washing more often than families who were 'not poor'. This may well have reflected the lack of washing and drying appliances in the home or that these additional costs were relatively more burdensome for those trying to manage on low incomes. There was, however, also the fact that the 'poor', significantly more often than the 'not poor', claimed that they needed extra help with laundry but could not afford it.

Thus, especially for families dealing with incontinence and for those who are 'poor', there would appear to be a strong case for the expansion or creation of a laundry service on some kind of subsidised or non-profit basis. Amongst the many needs that families looking after children with disabilities have, this at least ought to be one that could be efficiently and effectively met at a comparatively low cost – certainly by comparison with other more labour-intensive and professional services.

Returning to the discussion of the general pattern of expressed need for additional domiciliary services, it is noteworthy that there was no significant difference in the levels of requests for more domiciliary services with respect to income, ethnic background, social class or the children's ages (although, as we shall see later, substantially more parents of children under five did want extra help). The only more detailed variation was with regard to the stated need for more help from a visiting teacher: there was greater demand from Social Classes I and II and from those in the highest of the quintiles into which we divided household income.

Table 4.6 Expressed unmet need for domiciliary services, analysed by clusters

Cluster	Description	Percentage of parents requesting more services
1	Mild disabilities	12.7
2	Behaviour	16.9
3	Incontinence	30.3
4	Fits	4.9
5	Hearing and communication	4.4
6	Communication and behaviour	17.7
7	Personal care	15.4
8	Hearing and behaviour	11.8
9	Multiple disabilities	35.1
10	Multiple and severe	20.0
11	Multiple and very severe	35.7
All	*n* = 989	**17.7**

When we came to look at the pattern of reported unmet need for domiciliary services by clusters (Table 4.6), we found significant differences. The three categories in which the greatest need for additional services was expressed were Cluster 11 (36%), Cluster 9 (35%) and Cluster 3 (30%). This last cluster, it will be recalled, is the one in which enuresis stands out as a major problem. At the other end of the scale, little desire for extra services was expressed by parents with children in Clusters 4 and 5 (where, respectively, 'fits' and 'hearing and communication' were the main manifestations of disability).

We have already touched upon the question of the specific services with which the parents of children in each of the clusters wished to be provided, but we should draw these details together for the four main services that were most in demand. The reported need for social work help was greatest in Clusters 9 and 10 (two of the multiple and severe categories); that for home teaching in Clusters 6, 7 and 9 (communication and behaviour, personal care and the first of the multiple and severe groups, respectively); that for an incontinence service was associated largely with the enuresis cluster but also, to a lesser extent, with the three multiple and severe clusters. But the demand for a laundry service was spread fairly evenly over all the clusters with the exception, somewhat puzzlingly, of the one characterised by the need for personal care (Cluster 7).

However, these broad conclusions should be treated with some caution. Although, overall, 18% of the parents said that they wanted extra services, the proportions in any *one* of the clusters reporting the need for any *one* of the particular services was nearly always substantially lower – the only exceptions being the request for more social work help from parents of children in Cluster 10 (17% seeking more) and the request for more help from an incontinence service from those in Cluster 3 (22%).

Thus, overall, only 18% of the parents or carers of children in the 5–15 age group felt themselves to be lacking the kinds of domiciliary services that appeared on the OPCS list – which did, it should be borne in mind, include a category 'other', thus enabling respondents to add any service that had not been specified. The apparently low level of expressed need for help at home might suggest a number of conclusions. First, it could reflect a comparatively modest expectation of organised service or, secondly, that other informal sources of assistance played a more important part. A third possibility is that, having had some experience of the services or certain prejudices about them, parents were disinclined to use what they regarded as too unreliable, too unacceptable or simply not good enough. Finally, of course, some of the main services might have been available elsewhere; in particular in hospitals and clinics, and this is something that we explore in Chapter 5. However, it should be noted that several years after the OPCS survey both Sloper and Turner (1992) and Beresford (1995) reported high levels of unmet need for supportive services amongst disabled children and their families.

3. Discussion and implications

Only one in three of the families had received a domiciliary service in the previous year. Sadly, the data did not allow us to determine what quantity or quality was provided. However, whether or not there had been a service was unrelated to most of the major social variables that we were able to extract from the material: there were no significant differences with respect to household structure, social class, ethnic background, income or poverty. There were, however, significant differences when it came to the various clusters. In particular, it was much more likely that a service had been received by families in the three clusters where the disabilities were both multiple and severe. The general conclusion that we drew from these results was that *it was factors associated with the nature of the child's disabilities (especially their perceived severity) that encouraged the provision of domiciliary services rather than the social circumstances of the family.* On the face of it, this appears to be appropriate; but the problems of caring are, in reality, the consequence of a combination of these two groups of factors. Likewise, *the severity of a child's disability is not necessarily the same as the severity of the difficulties of providing day-to-day care.*

There were certain regional differences in the receipt or non-receipt of domiciliary services that suggest that *the question of territorial distribution warrants further investigation and consideration* – in particular, at the extremes.

The two most commonly received services were those provided by health visitors and social workers. With the exception of home teaching, which was available to 1 in 25 of the children, no other service was received by more than about 1 in 50 of the families. These are very low proportions, and the fact that the provision of such tangible assistance as a home help, a laundry service, or a night sitting service was virtually non-existent indicates that *a great deal of ground will have to be made up if anything approaching adequate support for the carers of children with disabilities is to be achieved.*

The sparsity of provision apart, it is of interest to find that *health visitors, social workers and, to a lesser extent, home teachers, appeared to supply the majority of whatever services there were.* In particular, in light of some of the rather critical conclusions about the role of health visitors that the Audit Commission (1994) drew in its report on services for children, it would be important to know just what kind of service they were (and are) providing, especially since the findings in this chapter apply only to the 5–15 age group.

Both health visitors and social workers were more likely to have seen families with children in the three clusters of multiple and severe disabilities, although the former appeared to have spread their visiting more evenly over all the clusters. It is somewhat surprising that social workers did not have contact with more of the families in the clusters where disabilities of behaviour predominated or were significant (for example, Clusters 2, 6 and 8).

Not only were we surprised at the low level of domiciliary service being received but also at *the relatively low level of expressed demand on the part of parents or carers for more service*. Given that a measure of prompting was introduced by the cards shown to them, unawareness of what might be available did not seem to be the only reason for the modest degree of demand. Other explanations may lie in a generally low level of expectation of outside help, in beliefs about the unhelpful and unacceptable nature of the services, in an unwillingness to have service providers working in the home, or in a fear of deviating from an established and known routine. Whatever the reasons, the results suggest that many families – either by choice or necessity – had to find a way of caring that did not include the help of the conventional domiciliary services. At what cost we do not know.

However, it is important to re-emphasise that *the four services most in demand were: social work (asked for by by 1 in 5); home teaching (sought by about 1 in 6); incontinence services (by a similar proportion); and a laundry service (requested by about 1 in 7)*. No other service came close to these four in terms of what parents said that they needed. Health visiting and 'other' nursing help ranked next but were only mentioned by some 1 in 15 of the respondents.

Given the increased responsibilities of social services departments for the assessment, planning and orchestration of services for children with disabilities and their families since the time of the survey, the demand for more social work help may be beginning to be satisfied. But it *would be important to establish just what kind of social work parents and carers had in mind and what the main problems were with which they hoped to be helped.*

The request for more home teaching warrants fuller exploration, particularly in the light of moves to achieve the further integration of disabled children into the main school system. It is of note that the demand was somewhat greater amongst Social Classes I and II and the better-off; but it was also greater amongst parents with children in the cluster characterised by communication and behavioural disabilities.

Two services that clearly deserved to be expanded were those providing advice and assistance with incontinence and help with laundry. Given the complexity of many of the problems associated with disability these would appear to be straightforward and tangible services that could be developed comparatively inexpensively and (especially in the case of laundry) on a contract basis. It is obviously necessary to check the current coverage of these services but, on the evidence of the OPCS data, there was a clear unmet need for such help.

NOTES TO CHAPTER 4

[1] No information was collected by OPCS about the length of time that children had spent with their present foster carers.

<table>
<tr><td>5</td><td>

Hospitals, clinics and the general practitioner

</td></tr>
</table>

Services provided for the 5–15 age group living in private households

Unfortunately, the OPCS survey grouped hospital and clinic-based services together. Although some clinics will have been attached to hospitals, others would not have been. The data did not permit this distinction to be made. In this chapter, therefore, we deal with out-patient and clinic attendances together. It should also be noted that the attendances in question were those that were directly connected with a child's disabilities; attendances for other reasons were not included. However, it must be borne in mind that disabled children may be more prone to trauma and illness as a result of their medical condition, and that even normal childhood illnesses may make their care more problematic. Indeed, we consider briefly the children's admissions to hospitals as in-patients, although the information OPCS collected on this matter was not restricted to contacts associated with the disabling conditions.

What all the services discussed below have in common is that they were provided *outside* the home. They need to be viewed, therefore, in the light of the pattern of domiciliary services described in Chapter 4.

1. The rates of contact with hospitals and clinics

Overall, 57% of the 5–15-year-olds had attended a hospital out-patient department or a clinic in the previous year and, in general, the younger they were, the more likely this was to happen. Between the ages of five and nine, the rate of attendance was 61%, whereas, between the ages of 10 and 15, it fell to 54%.[1] This is a pattern recognised elsewhere in the literature (for example, by Suelze and Keenan, 1981; Hirst and Baldwin, 1994; Chamberlain *et al.*, 1993). The rates of contact with hospital and clinic services showed some interesting differences in relation to certain major social variables. There was, for instance, some indication that the higher social classes used these services more than those in the skilled manual, semi-skilled or unskilled categories, as Table 5.1 shows.

Table 5.1 Whether visits had been made to a hospital out-patient department or clinic in the previous year, analysed by the Registrar-General's classification of social class

Social class	Percentage making a visit
I and II	63
III Non-manual	63
III Manual	54
IV and V	51
All (*n* = 440)	**57**

Similarly, as Table 5.2 indicates, there was a sharp diminution in the receipt of hospital-based services amongst families with the lower incomes.

Table 5.2 Whether visits had been made to a hospital out-patient department or clinic in the previous year analysed by effective family income, divided into quintiles

Income quintiles	Percentage making a visit
Highest	61
Second	62
Third	63
Fourth	52
Lowest	47
All (*n* = 562)	**57**

We found no significant difference in the rate of hospital or clinic attendance in relation to ethnicity (except that there was some indication – although the number was small – that children from African–Caribbean backgrounds were rather less likely to have made a hospital or clinic visit than others). These various results gain a greater significance when it is recalled that there was no difference with respect to class, ethnicity or income in the case of the receipt of the domiciliary services.

On the other hand, given the existence of certain regional variations in the receipt of domiciliary services, it was somewhat surprising to find little difference on this count when it came to contact with hospitals or clinics. The only noticeable divergence was in the former Greater London Council (GLC) area, where 70% of the children had attended for services in the past year in comparison with the overall rate of 57%. This would suggest, perhaps, that the availability of hospital and clinic-based services was an important factor in determining the level of their use; that is, assuming that these services were generally more plentiful in the metropolis than elsewhere. Or it could be that certain relevant specialisms were concentrated in the London area.

As well as seeing whether or not children had visited a hospital or clinic, it is important to know the services that were received. These data are set out in Table 5.3, which lists the professions or services that were displayed on the OPCS card used in the interviews as well as the proportions of the children making visits who saw each specialist.

Table 5.3 Services received on visits to hospital out-patient departments or clinics in the previous year (*n* = 562)

Professions/services (OPCS listing)	Percentage receiving this service[a]
Doctor	95.7
Radiographer	11.6
Physiotherapist	9.2
Occupational therapist	2.5
Speech therapist	11.0
Hearing therapist	16.7
Optician	13.1
Chiropodist	0.4
Dietician	1.4
Psychologist	13.7
Psychotherapist	2.0
Osteopath	0.4
Homeopath	0.5
Artificial limbs	2.5
Health visitor	2.1
Hospital social worker	1.4
Nurse	11.2
Technicians	3.0
Dentists	3.4
Other	4.8

a Proportions add to more than 100% because of multiple contacts.

It is clear that the most commonly seen professional was a 'doctor' (the OPCS data did not identify specialisms). The next most frequently provided service was that of a hearing therapist (17% of those visiting) followed by that of a psychologist (14%), an optician (13%), a radiographer (12%), a speech therapist and a nurse (11% in each case). However, this general picture hides one or two rather interesting items of detail. For example, it was notable that where the services of a hearing specialist were most common, contact with a doctor was significantly less likely, perhaps suggesting clinic rather than hospital visits. Likewise, no occupational therapy was received by any of our first five clusters, and hospital social workers were only involved with Clusters 1, 2 and 6 (mild disabilities, behaviour alone and behaviour and communication).

Taken in conjunction with the data on the provision of domiciliary services (discussed in Chapter 4) these results offer no strong evidence that a low level of service in one sector was compensated by a high level in the other: certainly, that was so for physiotherapy, occupational therapy and speech therapy. Even so, what is plain is that services (although not necessarily the same services) are more likely to be provided in hospitals or clinics than on a domiciliary basis – crudely expressed, by a factor of three.

However, there were some significant regional differences in the kinds of services that children received when they went to a hospital or clinic. For example, the rate of contact with a doctor was much lower in south-east and south-west England (71% and 73%, respectively) than the overall rate of 96%. Physiotherapy and speech therapy were significantly more often received in East Anglia and the GLC area than elsewhere. There was a low rate of contact with hearing therapists in the West Midlands but a high rate in Scotland. The services of an optician were most commonly used in East Anglia, least often in the West Midlands. Help from a psychologist was more often received in Wales, north-west England and the GLC area, and visits to a psychotherapist only occurred in 5 of the 11 standard regions and were concentrated in East Anglia and the GLC area.

Much more detailed analysis of regional variations is warranted than was possible with the available data, but what we do have makes the prima facie case that there is an issue to be explored. Furthermore, although we did not find any compensatory effect between the hospital and domiciliary care services sectors, there was some evidence that regions (East Anglia, for example) may have been in a relatively favourable position in regard to both hospital-based and domiciliary service provision.

There were also some significant differences, by social class and by income, with respect to *which* services were seen by those who attended a hospital out-patient department or a clinic. For instance, children in the 'non-manual' division of Social Class III stood out from those in the other categories in having been more often the recipients of physiotherapy, hearing therapy and the services of an optician. In Social Classes I and II, the only service that was especially prominent was that of a psychologist. Children in Social Classes IV and V, on the other hand, were more likely than other children to have attended for speech therapy.

The pattern with respect to family income also revealed some interesting variations. When they went to a hospital or a clinic, children whose families fell into the lowest of the income quintiles saw a doctor less often than the others (84% compared with 96% overall). Similarly, they had less contact with a radiographer (5% as against 12%) or a physiotherapist (3% versus 9%). However, they were more likely to have seen a hospital social worker than the rest (5% compared with 1%). There were no such differences with respect to any of the other four income quintiles.

It is hazardous to draw conclusions about the pattern with respect to ethnic background because the numbers were small; however, children from ethnic minorities did seem to see a doctor less than other children and a nurse rather more often.

Although the data are limited, there is certainly some evidence to suggest that children in the poorest 20% of families received a different pattern of services from the other 80%. The social class material is somewhat more confused, but the greater likelihood of children from Social Classes I and II seeing a psychologist and those in Classes IV and V a speech therapist may warrant closer attention.

When we looked at whether or not a child had made a hospital or clinic visit in the previous year with respect to the clusters, we found significant differences, as Table 5.4 shows.

Table 5.4 Whether a child had visited a hospital out-patient department or a clinic in the previous year, analysed by clusters

Cluster	Description	Percentage making a visit
1	Mild disabilities	47.8
2	Behaviour	47.6
3	Incontinence	47.4
4	Fits	61.0
5	Hearing and communication	66.2
6	Communication and behaviour	47.5
7	Personal care	71.1
8	Hearing and behaviour	61.2
9	Multiple disabilities	77.9
10	Multiple and severe	82.0
11	Multiple and very severe	85.7
All	*n* = 989	**56.8**

Children in the three 'multiple and severe' clusters were the most likely to have made a hospital or clinic visit in the previous year, but the proportion was also high in the 'personal care' group (Cluster 7) and, to a lesser extent, in the hearing and communication category (Cluster 5). However, it should be noted that at least half – or thereabouts – of the children in *all* the clusters had made visits that were connected to their disabilities.

Those in the various clusters who did attend hospitals or clinics saw rather different people, as might be expected. We have endeavoured to simplify these somewhat complicated data in Table 5.5.

Generally speaking, this pattern is what might be expected given the dominant characteristics of the clusters. It must be emphasised, however, that many children were in contact with a number of services, doubtless reflecting the complexity of their conditions and the multiplicity of their

Table 5.5 Pattern of contacts of children visiting a hospital out-patient department or a clinic in the previous year, shown by clusters

Cluster	Description	Significantly more contact (than other clusters) with
1	Mild disabilities	Radiographer/Optician
2	Behaviour	Psychologist/Social worker
3	Incontinence	–
4	Fits	–
5	Hearing and communication	Hearing therapist
6	Communication and behaviour	Speech therapist
7	Personal care	Physiotherapist
8	Hearing and behaviour	Hearing therapist
9	Multiple disabilities	Physiotherapist/Speech therapist/Nurse
10	Multiple and severe	Speech therapist/Optician
11	Multiple and very severe	Physiotherapist/Optician/Dentist

disabilities. Table 5.6 lists the number of different hospital- or clinic-based services that children in the various clusters had received in the previous year. Of course, this does not mean that every child in the respective clusters used this number of services; rather that this was the number of services associated with each of the clusters.

Table 5.6 Number of different hospital out-patient department or clinic services that children had received in the previous year, analysed by clusters

Cluster	Description	Number of different services seen out of the 20 listed
1	Mild disabilities	15
2	Behaviour	18
3	Incontinence	10
4	Fits	12
5	Hearing and communication	11
6	Communication and behaviour	18
7	Personal care	14
8	Hearing and behaviour	12
9	Multiple disabilities	18
10	Multiple and severe	15
11	Multiple and very severe	11

So far, we have discussed and analysed the data in terms of whether or not a child made a visit to a hospital or clinic in the previous year. Fortunately, OPCS also collected information about the number of such visits, so that we have a rough indication of the intensity of the contacts. We consider this aspect next.

2. The frequency of visits to hospitals and clinics

Although the OPCS survey asked no questions about the frequency of visits by domiciliary services, it did include questions about the frequency of visits to hospital out-patient departments or clinics. It is, therefore, possible to provide some idea of the *amount* of service that the children and families had received. The average number of visits made in the previous year by those who attended a hospital or clinic was 10.6. Amongst those who went to these centres, therefore, there was a considerable degree of contact, although it should be pointed out that the standard deviation was 25.9, suggesting a rather wide spread in the frequency of such visits.

There was no significant difference between the average number of hospital out-patient or clinic visits with respect to the family's poverty index, although the standard deviation was greater amongst the 'poor' than the 'not poor' (30.8 as against 20.2). Nor were there significant differences in the mean number of visits with respect to ethnicity. However, the regional differences proved to vary significantly; the mean number of visits in north-west England being a little over four times greater than that in Yorkshire and Humberside, as Table 5.7 shows.

Table 5.7 Mean number of visits to hospital out-patient departments or clinics in the previous year, analysed by standard regions ($n = 563$)

Standard regions	Mean number of visits
Yorkshire and Humberside	3.9
Wales	6.6
South-east England	7.8
South-west England	8.0
West Midlands	10.0
East Anglia	10.2
North England	11.0
East Midlands	13.0
Scotland	13.6
GLC area	15.2
North-west England	16.1
Britain	**10.6**

The amount of variation is interesting, given that there were few differences between the regions with respect to the proportion of children who visited hospitals or clinics in the year. The distribution is also notable inasmuch as it (again) does not suggest any 'substitution' effect by comparison with the regional rates of provision of domiciliary services, except perhaps in the case of Scotland.

The analysis of the mean number of visits to hospitals or clinics in relation to the clusters provided results that might have been expected, as Table 5.8 indicates. However, attention should be paid to the standard deviations associated with these means because they give a good sense of the extent to which, as we have said, a relatively small number of children making very few or very many visits may be affecting the mean. Nonetheless, the general conclusion is plain: those in the 'severest' clusters made the most visits.

Table 5.8 Mean number of visits to hospital out-patient departments and clinics in the previous year, analysed by clusters (n=563)

Cluster	Description	Mean number of visits	Standard deviation
1	Mild disabilities	5.6	7.1
2	Behaviour	8.5	18.0
3	Incontinence	8.8	19.1
4	Fits	4.8	5.5
5	Hearing and communication	7.3	20.0
6	Communication and behaviour	9.3	18.2
7	Personal care	13.8	23.5
8	Hearing and behaviour	7.2	17.2
9	Multiple disabilities	13.2	23.5
10	Multiple and severe	25.4	65.0
11	Multiple and very severe	21.6	37.6
All	**n = 563**	**10.6**	**25.9**

Whereas OPCS gathered information about the number of hospital or clinic contacts, they did not (as they had done for the domiciliary services) ask parents what services in these centres they felt that they or their children needed but were not getting. Nor did they ask whether the location of services was important to parents (or children) and whether they had any preferences.

3. In-patient stays in hospitals

As we did not undertake any further analysis relating to the children's stays in hospital as in-patients, we report briefly on the OPCS findings. Of the 5–15 age group, 18% had been in hospital at least once in the previous year (although not necessarily in connection with a disability). By comparison, the rate for this same age group in the general population at the time was 6%. There was, therefore, a much greater likelihood that children with disabilities would need to go into hospital than other children. However, typically, there was just one such visit in the preceding year for most of those who were admitted, and this was usually for less than a week. As we shall see, amongst the under-5s, the proportion who had stayed in hospital in the past year was much greater than for the 5–15-year-olds (41% compared with 18%) (Meltzer *et al.*, 1989).

4. Contact with general practitioners

The general practitioner (GP) would normally be the doctor of first contact in most cases of illness or injury. In addition, the GP is responsible for screening, immunisations and other preventive medicine, as well as being a 'gate-keeper' to other services (such as incontinence or mobility aids and the skills of more specialised medical and paramedical professionals). That being so, one might expect disabled children to have at least some contact with a GP over the span of a year. In fact, only 77% of the 5–15-year-olds in the private households included in the OPCS survey had had such contact in the previous 12 months. A similar result was found by the Northern Ireland survey of disabled children in 1989: only 80% of children had contact with their GP in the previous 12 months (Duffy, 1995b). The older the child the less likely they were to have been seen (indeed, it is noteworthy that the rate of consultation for the under-5s was 92%).

The overall rate of contact reported by OPCS may seem low but, as they pointed out, 'disability does not necessarily imply illness and so children with some types of disability may be no more likely to see their GP than non-disabled children'. However, they went on to add that 'a visit provides the opportunity for the parent of a disabled child to mention any problems in connection with the disability and for the GP to assess whether the patient is in contact with the relevant services' (Meltzer *et al.*, 1989). Opportunities of this kind may have become more frequent since the research was conducted; Beresford (1995), for example, found that the rate of GP contacts for the 0–14-year-old disabled children in her study was 91%.

One reason for rates of GP contact being rather lower than might have been expected has been advanced by Glendinning (1983). She found that a number of parents of disabled children tended to bypass their GP and consult hospital or school medical staff directly. This, it was suggested, depended on the 'rarity of the child's condition; the frequency and urgency with which she or he needs medical attention; the proximity and accessibility of specialist hospital services; and the GP's ability to respond to both the medical and non-medical needs of the disabled child'; and, one might add, to those of their parents.

Nine times out of ten the children who were seen by their GPs were taken to the surgery, although there was a tendency for home visits to be made more often to those who were most severely disabled. The relative infrequency of home visits may also have dissuaded some parents from using GP services; certainly, the costs of surgery visits in terms of time, transport, domestic re-arrangements and waiting may have introduced an element of deterrence.

Over and above whether or not the child had seen a GP in the previous year was the question of how often such contacts had occurred. The average number was 4.5,[2] although there were significant variations in relation to the poverty index, by certain minority ethnic groupings, by the standard regions and by the clusters.[3]

The poor, as defined by the deprivation index, consulted their GP about their children significantly more often than those who were not poor (an average of 5.6 times a year compared with 3.4). This is an important finding when taken together with the fact that children from the poorer families attended hospitals and clinics somewhat less often than others. This could suggest that the better off gravitate to these centres, whereas the poor rely more on their GPs, perhaps because they are felt to be more approachable or because the costs of a visit are lower than those incurred in a journey to hospital. One possible implication may be, therefore, that access to specialist advice is more restricted – for whatever reason – for the poor than for those who are not. Or, of course, disabled children from poorer families may more often suffer from illness or injuries of a general kind, something that would be expected from what we know about the distribution of illness amongst the whole child population.

Although, as we have said, conclusions about the distributions with respect to ethnicity must be treated cautiously because of the rather small numbers, it was significant that, whereas there was little difference between white children and those of African-Caribbean backgrounds, Asian children averaged many more visits to their GP than either of the other groups. The respective annual means were, respectively, 5.0, 4.4 and 16.5, although the standard deviation amongst the Asian children was large (29.28).

We also looked at the mean number of GP consultations by the standard regions and again found significant differences. Once more, the most contacts were in East Anglia and the least were in Scotland; and there was a high consultation rate in the former GLC area. However, one has to bear in mind the big differences that existed in some of the standard deviations. These data are shown in Table 5.9.

The analysis of the number of GP consultations with respect to the clusters also showed significant differences, although not as great as might have been expected. Table 5.10 sets out the data, again with a cautionary column showing the standard deviations.

Table 5.9 Mean number of contacts children had with a GP in the previous year, analysed by standard regions

Region	Mean number of visits	Standard deviation
Scotland	3.1	4.0
North England	3.5	4.4
West Midlands	3.7	4.6
South-east England	3.8	7.5
North-west England	3.9	6.5
East Midlands	4.1	4.6
South-west England	4.4	5.4
Wales	5.4	8.3
Yorkshire and Humberside	5.7	11.1
GLC area	6.7	16.0
East Anglia	8.0	21.0
All (n = 987)	**4.5**	**9.3**

Table 5.10 Mean number of times the children had seen a GP in the previous year, analysed by clusters

Cluster	Description	Mean number of contacts	Standard deviation
1	Mild disabilities	3.7	8.94
2	Behaviour	4.9	9.18
3	Incontinence	4.2	5.00
4	Fits	3.1	3.15
5	Hearing and communication	3.7	4.16
6	Communication and behaviour	3.0	3.92
7	Personal care	6.0	14.15
8	Hearing and behaviour	5.1	6.06
9	Multiple disabilities	5.1	11.88
10	Multiple and severe	7.7	16.35
11	Multiple and very severe	6.8	18.83
All (n = 987)		**4.5**	**9.27**

Clearly, contacts with a GP were more frequent for the two most severely and multiply disabled groups (Clusters 10 and 11), but also for the cluster where personal care was the dominant problem. By contrast, it is interesting to note that, using their scale of severity, OPCS did not find any relationship between severity and the mean number of GP contacts (Meltzer *et al.*, 1989, p. 27). This would tend to suggest that it is more the *number* of disabilities that made the difference rather than severity alone. It will be recalled that one of the purposes of the cluster analysis was to take account of all the disabilities a child suffered rather than the maximum of three that the OPCS approach allowed.

Looking at the contacts with hospitals (mainly with doctors as we have seen) and contacts with GPs together, there were, as OPCS pointed out, 12% of these 5–15-year-olds who had had no contact with a hospital, a clinic or a GP in the previous 12 months; that is, one in eight had had no contact with a medical service (although that does not include any of the 'medical' domiciliary services discussed in Chapter 4).[4]

Nevertheless, doctors remained important in the range of services that parents and children received, and GPs in particular would have been likely to have occupied a crucial position as 'gate-keepers' to hospital and domiciliary services. However, we do not know from the OPCS data what proportion of the consultations were specifically concerned with a child's disability and what proportion were concerned with general illness. Certainly, in the 'community' setting GPs ranked alongside health visitors and social workers as the most commonly used services.

5. Discussion and implications

Nearly twice as many children had contact with a hospital or clinic service than were provided for by a domiciliary service (57% compared with 32%). Furthermore, *the frequency of visits to hospital out-patient departments or clinics was high*: an average over the preceding year of 10.6 visits amongst those who attended. For the most multiply and severely disabled children (Clusters 10 and 11) the mean number of visits rose significantly – to 25.4 and 21.6, respectively. Given the current emphasis upon community-based services, *one must ask how many of these centre-based services could have been provided at home* and for how many this would have been a more desirable, less expensive or more convenient arrangement, not least from the viewpoints of the children and their families.

When the children visited a hospital or clinic, *it was a 'doctor' who was most commonly seen* (by 96%) followed a long way behind by hearing therapists (17%), psychologists (14%), opticians (13%), radiographers (12%), nurses and speech therapists (11% in each case). The predominance of visits to a doctor may well have reflected a good deal of regular appointments for check-ups.

When we investigated whether there might have been some 'substitution' effect between the hospital and the domiciliary sectors, we found no compelling evidence that this existed. Generally, a low level of receipt of a particular service in one context was not off-set by a higher level in the other. This was still the case when we analysed the data at a regional level. These results prompt questions about the relationship between hospital and clinic services for children with disabilities and those provided for them and their families on a domiciliary, educational or general practitioner basis. How well are these various services integrated and do the prevailing divisions best serve the needs of the child and the family? Furthermore, one must ask what burdens are placed upon both parents and children as a result of the need to travel to and from hospital or clinic facilities, and what kind of waiting times confront them?

The contact and the frequency of contact that children in the various clusters had with the hospital and clinic services follow a pattern that might be expected. However, the differences were considerable; for example, with respect to whether or not a contact had occurred; the frequency of those contacts; who the child saw and what combinations of specialisms were involved. By and large, however, *these differences seemed to reflect fairly faithfully the nature of the characteristic problems of each of the clusters.* Even so, as with the domiciliary services, one must ask whether the apparently appropriate distribution of hospital and clinic services is, *in fact*, appropriate. That is, should such a large share go to those children who are most multiply and severely disabled (as it seemed to be doing at the time of the OPCS survey)? Could more of those children whose needs appear to be less overwhelming also be effectively helped by some of the services in question?

In general, as with the receipt of domiciliary services, one of the outstanding questions was: what mechanisms were at work that seemed to vary the hospital and clinic services for disabled children according to area, class, income or the deprivation of the child's family? Are such variations (and possibly others) becoming more or less common and what, in any case, is their impact upon the present and future well-being of the child and their family?

A little under a quarter of these 5–15-year-olds had not seen a GP in the preceding year. Far more had not been seen at home by a health visitor or social worker. Of course, independently, the parents may have had contact with such services; but one is still left with the question: what professional assistance was being provided in the *co-ordination* of community-based provisions. The more general issue of responsibility for overall co-ordination was addressed by OPCS in their interviews. They asked: *'Is there one particular doctor, hospital department or other person in the health and social services who takes overall responsibility for your child's health (disability) problems?'* There was a positive response in 56% of the cases, but with significant differences between the clusters. The highest rate (71%) of 'professional co-ordination' was found in the 'multiple and extremely severe' category (Cluster 11) and in that characterised by 'personal care' (Cluster 7). The next highest rate (68%) was in Cluster 10 (multiple and very severe disabilities). By contrast, the lowest rate (41%) was found in the cluster typified by problems of behaviour and communication (Cluster 6), followed by the group (Cluster 8) where hearing and behaviour were the principal issues (48%).

[1] The rate was somewhat higher for the under-5s, at 64%.

[2] This included those who had made no visits in the previous year.

[3] It should also be noted that, throughout Britain, the average number of GP consultations per person in the same year for the same age group was 3.0 (OPCS, 1990, Table 4.30, p. 116).

[4] Again, the rate for the under-5s is different: only 4% had had no contact with any doctor in the previous year.

6 | Respite care

for the 5–15 age group living in private households

Some of the most valuable help that families looking after disabled children can be given is the opportunity to take 'time off'. Service providers in many countries have found that the provision of adequate amounts of respite care is one of the most acceptable and cost-effective ways of offering support to the families of disabled people (Orlik *et al.*, 1991). Until the 1980s such assistance was located mainly in hospitals or hostels. However, a number of projects dedicated to family-based respite care were introduced during the late 1970s, after the National Health Service Act 1977 had made it explicit that local authorities could provide free care away from the child's home without receiving them into care. Indeed, such schemes mushroomed, a peak being reached in 1984, the year before the OPCS survey. More recently, some respite care has become available within the disabled person's own home. However, OPCS only asked questions about the short-term care of children away from home and about holidays arranged apart from their parents.

1. Short-term care away from home

Overall, amongst these 5–15-year-olds, only 5% had had a period of short-term care away from their families in the previous 12 months – that is, omitting residential schooling, holidays and any episodes as a hospital in-patient. Obviously, short-term respite care is not appropriate in all cases but, even so, the proportion receiving it seemed to us to be very low. Comparable figures are difficult to obtain because of the different samples employed in different studies, and due to the fact that studies have generally been mounted in places where respite projects existed. Thus, for example, Robinson (1986) reported that 35% of the children attending special schools in Avon had used the local respite service; but by the nature of her sample only a proportion of the whole disabled child population in the area was included. Similarly, Robinson and Stalker (1989) based their estimates of the take-up of respite care on the rate for people with severe learning difficulties in three local authority areas. Among young people aged up to 20, they reported rates of 31% in Sheffield, 36% in Croydon and 43% in Somerset.

Despite the low rate of respite care revealed in the OPCS survey (and, as we shall see, it was equally low amongst the under-5s) it was notable that the average number of times that it was provided (for those for whom it was available) was fairly high: a mean of 5.2 occasions during the preceding year. This suggests a generous concentration on certain children and families rather than a more widely but thinly spread provision.

Amongst other things, we thought that it would be important to analyse the data with respect to the structure of the households in which the children lived, on the assumption that the demands of caring are likely to be heaviest where there is only one parent or where there are several other children to be looked after. However, the pattern that emerged did not indicate that considerations of this kind were affecting the provision of respite care, as Table 6.1 shows.

Table 6.1 Whether a child had a period(s) of short-term care away from the family in the previous year, analysed by household structure

Household type	Percentage having help with short-term care
One adult, one child	6
One adult, two+ children	4
Two adults, one child	9
Two adults, two children	4
Two adults, three children	3
Two adults, four+ children	2
Three adults, one child	6
Three adults, two+ children	8
Four adults and children	1
All (n = 987)	5

As can be seen, the group of families most likely to have had short-term care consisted of two adults and one child (9%). The families least likely to have benefited from the service were those with several children – especially when there were three or four. Lone parents did not appear to be especially favoured. Although the numbers are small and are not quite significant, these findings seem to fly in the face of results from other studies. For example, in a review of respite services in Great Britain, Cotterill *et al.* (1997), drawing on research by Robinson (1988) and

Salisbury (1990), point out that the users of respite services tend, more often than the non-users, to have larger families and to be single parents.

When we looked at a somewhat different aspect of family composition – namely whether a child was cared for by parents, relatives or in a foster home – we found significant differences, even though, again, the numbers were small. Of the fostered children, 19% had had short-term care and, of those living with relatives, 16%. By contrast, the rate was only 4% for those looked after by their parents. Clearly, although some factors associated with certain aspects of family structure did not appear to affect whether or not short-term care was received, other considerations relating to out-of-family placements seem to have exercised an influence. We suspect that what was important in these cases was the status of the child. Furthermore, it was almost certain that all the children in foster homes were in care and that a number of those living with their relatives were also the responsibility of a local authority. Whether respite care was seen as necessary in order to sustain these placements, or whether it was the regular availability of a social worker who informed and encouraged, is a matter for speculation.

Although the major social variables that we have considered in earlier chapters were not significantly associated with the provision of respite care, the distributions were all tipped towards the higher income groups, the higher social classes and those who were classified as not suffering poverty. For example, whereas 6% of the two highest income quintiles had had short-term care, this fell to 3% for the two lowest. The same difference existed between the 'not poor' and the 'poor'. These may not seem to be big variations (and the numbers are small) but they were all in the opposite direction to what might have been predicted if factors likely to have been connected with a family's need (other than the disability itself) had played a part in the allocation. Other studies of family-based respite care have suggested that the association between low income and non-use may be due to a shortage of volunteers from low-income backgrounds to link with people from low-income families who are waiting for a service (Bose, 1989; Salisbury, 1990).

With respect to the use of respite care by families from minority ethnic groups, the OPCS data broadly reflected the findings of other studies, such as those of Robinson and Stalker (1989) and Orlik *et al.* (1991), both of which highlighted the under-representation of disabled children from such groups amongst those using respite care. Furthermore, these studies also indicated that when a respite service was provided it tended to be residential rather than family-based, a distinction not made in the OPCS survey. However, although the evidence OPCS did gather showed a slanting of respite care towards what it referred to as 'white' families, it was not conclusive because of the relatively small number of children from minority ethnic groups. Nonetheless, it is worth noting, for example, that no child from an Asian family had received such a service in the previous year.

It is important to distinguish between the receipt or non-receipt of services like respite care and the frequency with which they were provided. For example, our analysis of the OPCS data showed that although 'poor' children were less likely to have been provided with respite care than those from 'not poor' families, those who *did* have short-term care away from home were likely to have done so more often than the 'not poor' recipients – an average number of 5.6 occasions in the preceding year compared with 3.4. Likewise, we found that, amongst those actually having had short-term care away, it was received more times in the year by Social Classes III (manual), IV and V than by Social Classes I and II, as Table 6.2 shows.

Table 6.2 Mean number of times short-term care was received in the previous year, analysed by the Registrar-General's classification of social class

Social class	Mean number of episodes of short-term care (amongst those receiving the service)
I and II	4.7
III Non-manual	5.0
III Manual	7.1
IV and V	6.5
All (*n* = 35)	**5.6**

Thus, once short-term care *was* provided (albeit to very few of the families), it seemed that somewhat more attention may have been paid to social needs in determining the *number* of occasions on which it was offered.

We also carried out our routine analysis in relation to the standard regions. There was some variation: most notably nobody reported having had short-term care during the year in East Anglia (again the region that appeared to have a distinctive pattern) and only 1% had done so in the north of England. Most other regions clustered around the 5% level, except south-west England where it reached 8%. The average number of times that a child received respite care showed similar differences: from a mean of 2.2 in the north of England to 7.4 times in south-west England.

The dominance of 'disability' factors over 'social' factors in determining the receipt of short-term care was vividly demonstrated when we analysed the data by clusters. As Table 6.3 makes clear, the service was heavily concentrated amongst the children in the top three clusters of multiple and severe disability (9, 10 and 11). Furthermore, those in Cluster 11 (the most severe of these three) who received this particular help did so significantly more often than the others – virtually once a month on average. Halpern (1985) and Marc and MacDonald (1988) also found that the most severely disabled children were those most likely to have used respite services.

Table 6.3 Whether a child had a period of short-term care away from home in the previous year, analysed by clusters

Cluster	Description	Percentage receiving short-term care	Mean number of times short-term care received
1	Mild disabilities	4	1.0
2	Behaviour	9	3.2
3	Incontinence	2	2.0
4	Fits	2	3.0
5	Hearing and communication	–	–
6	Communication and behaviour	9	3.0
7	Personal care	–	–
8	Hearing and behaviour	7	1.7
9	Multiple disabilities	31	5.2
10	Multiple and severe	15	3.1
11	Multiple and very severe	20	11.4
All ($n = 987$)		**5**	**5.2**

One of the surprising features of this table would seem to be the absence of short-term care for the group where the problems of personal care predominated (Cluster 7). It might have been expected that such children and their parents would have been strong candidates for a service of this kind. However, in a similar vein, Robinson and Stalker (1989) found evidence that the heaviest users of respite services were children with severe learning difficulties, whilst those with primarily physical disabilities received less such care.

Thus, from the OPCS survey material it appears that short-term respite care was thin on the ground, thinner in some parts of the country than in others and likely to be provided according to the nature and severity of the child's disability rather than in relation to any of the other conventional indicators of social need. However, these results may have been influenced by the amount of informal and family support that was being received as well as by what parents and carers actually knew about short-term care, and hence by whether or not they were in a position to ask for it. Fortunately, OPCS included questions about this, so we had some data with which to work.

2. Whether or not parents had heard of short-term care

Overall, 46% of the parents said that they had heard about short-term care. However, it was evident from our analysis that there were significant social differences between those who were and those who were not aware of what was available: 63% of Social Classes I and II were knowledgeable, compared with only 35% in Social Classes IV and V. Likewise, 59% of the highest income quintile knew that short-term care existed but only 37% of those in the lowest quintile. Similarly, 54% of the 'not poor' were aware of what could be available but only 39% of the 'poor'. Only 18% of Asian parents had heard of respite care, although the rates amongst those from other minority ethnic groups were no different from the majority. There was little difference with respect to family or household structure.

There was, therefore, evidence to show a link between parents' social circumstances and their awareness of the possibility of short-term care, a finding mirrored in the work of Stalker and Robinson (1991), which drew attention in particular to the lack of information about respite services amongst minority ethnic families. Furthermore, they reported that the parents of older disabled children were more likely to lack information than those of younger children.

However, there was no conclusive evidence to suggest that knowledge necessarily led to demand – as we have seen nearly half of all parents knew about the possibilities but only 1% had asked for help (as distinct from being offered it). Other studies of the non-users of respite care services suggest that parents are disinclined to seek such assistance when they already have sufficient informal support (Malin, 1982; Stalker and Robinson, 1991; Salisbury, 1990), are anxious about its quality, or have strong feelings about their own responsibilities for caring (Robinson, 1988; Baxter *et al.*, 1990; Poonia and Ward, 1990; Robinson and Stalker, 1992). The explanation that parents do not seek respite care because of disparaging comments that they may have heard about what is offered seems unlikely, given that OPCS found that, overwhelmingly, those who had used short-term care were pleased with it (Meltzer *et al.*, 1989).

There were significant differences with regard to whether parents within the different clusters had heard about short-term care. Those with children falling into the most multiply and severely disabled clusters (9, 10 and 11) and the 'personal care' category (Cluster 7), were the most likely to have known what might be available (58%, 53%, 100% and 62%, respectively). At the other end of the scale, the 'hearing and behaviour' and 'incontinence' clusters (8 and 3) were the least likely to have been aware that short-term care existed (38% and 39%, respectively). To some extent, the awareness of respite care on the part of parents of children in the different clusters reflects their opportunity for learning about it. For instance, in a study of short-term care in Avon almost half of the parents who had heard about the family support scheme had done so via the special school that their child attended and another fifth through their social worker (Robinson, 1986) – avenues of information often available only to those looking after certain categories of disabled children. Again, the question of the availability of sources of information is likely to be a reflection of the prior distribution of a variety of contacts, be they self-help groups, GPs, social workers, schools or health visitors.

Of course, awareness of respite care and the form that it has taken have changed since the time of the survey. However, our results do suggest that the relationship between knowing about a service and asking for it (let alone receiving it) is complicated. Whatever the nature of the complexity, it would be surprising if it has been much altered in the intervening years. For example, Beresford (1995) reported in her study that although one in four of the parents of disabled children under 14 had used short-term care (mostly in the form of respite care centres and 'family link' schemes), a third of the remainder said that they did not know such services existed and a similar proportion had chosen not to use it,[1] suggesting that 'inadequacies in the quality of the care provided discouraged them' (Beresford, 1995, p. 31), a conclusion that was also reached by Hubert (1991).[2]

3. Holidays

As well as organised respite care, children with disabilities may be offered holidays. Overall, these were more common than short-term care – 10% of the children having been away during the year. The NCH Action for Children study of disabled children and their families reported that the time of most need mentioned by parents was school holidays, with the demand being for more holiday camps and play schemes (Bennett, 1994). The parents in Robinson and Stalker's survey (1990) saw the provision of a holiday as being primarily in the child's interests, in contrast to the provision of other forms of respite care, the main purpose of which was generally seen as allowing the parents themselves 'time off'. This may explain, to some extent, the higher take-up of holiday provision found in the OPCS research.

There was, however, a significantly uneven distribution between the clusters, with a third (32%) of the multiply and severely disabled group (Cluster 10) and a quarter of those in the multiply and very severely disabled group (Cluster 11) having had a holiday. None of those in Cluster 4 ('fits') and only 2% in Cluster 7 ('personal care') had had a holiday break, and levels were also low (4%) amongst those with moderate levels of several disabilities together with locomotion problems (Cluster 1) and amongst those in Cluster 2, characterised by problems of behaviour (5%). There was, therefore, no evidence that holidays and short-term respite care were alternative forms of help. The tendency was for the groups that got the one to get the other as well – although not necessarily the same children. Take, for example, children in foster care: we have seen that they were the most likely to have received respite care, but they were also some two and a half times more likely than the other children to have had a holiday (28% of them). By contrast, the least likely to have had a holiday were children from one-parent families (7%).

Again, with the exception of the children who were fostered, the availability of holidays would seem mainly to be determined by 'disability factors' rather than by any 'social factors' generally associated with need. This is, however, somewhat at odds with the findings of Robinson and Stalker (1991) who examined a holiday centre in Cornwall. Here, they found the children to be primarily from Social Classes I, II and III on the Registrar-General's scale and to have lower levels of physical dependency and fewer long-term health problems than any other group of disabled children studied.

4. A note on special boarding schools

Before drawing this chapter to a close, it should be pointed out that the special boarding schools which some of the children attended on a regular basis could be regarded as a form of short-term care away from home, although they are usually considered to fall under the auspices of 'education'. It will be recalled that just over 4% of the children in the survey were boarders. About a third of these came home at weekends, the others less often; indeed, 28% came home less often than the regular school holidays.

Thus, if we include this group of boarders in the picture of short-term care, it might not be unreasonable to claim that some 8% or 9% of the parents or carers had had some form of 'formal' respite care during the year in question. However, it should be noted that, in terms of the clusters, the group away at special schools was significantly different from the group receiving short-term care. Amongst the former, there was a preponderance of children with disabilities of behaviour or with problems of behaviour associated with other disabilities. Amongst the latter, it was, as we have seen, the multiple and severe disability clusters that were the main beneficiaries.

5. Discussion and implications

At the time of the 1985 OPCS survey, *short-term respite care was rarely used. Only 5% of the families had benefited from it.* This was a much lower rate than those reported in other studies of about the same period and later. One of the explanations may be the different composition of the populations covered, in particular the fact that OPCS included a large group of children with emotional and behavioural disabilities. Another explanation may be found in the 'local' rather than national nature of these other studies.

Those who might have been assumed to have been in greatest need of respite care – notably one-parent families and families with several children to care for – did not get more than other families. Indeed, the least likely to be assisted were parents with three or four children. Apart from foster carers and relatives caring for disabled children, the most likely to have obtained respite care were two parents with only one child. We also found that *the distribution of short-term care was slanted in favour of Social Classes I and II, the top two income quintiles and those we classified as 'not poor'.* Although not all these differences were statistically significant, their uniform 'direction' does, once more, draw attention to the question of the determinants of the distribution of services to disabled children and their families.

There were some regional differences, but *most areas clustered around the 5% level of provision.* At the two ends of the scale, however, nobody in East Anglia reported having had short-term care whereas the proportion of those receiving it in south-west England was 8%.

We found significant variations with respect to the different clusters. *The three multiple and severe disability groups (Clusters 9, 10 and 11) received short-term care more often than all the other clusters.* The mean rate of provision for these three clusters combined was 19%. Indeed, they accounted for two-thirds of all the families who received help, although they comprised only 13% of the sample. *Likewise, these three clusters received, on average, more episodes of short-term care in the year than all others;* in Cluster 11, for example, this virtually amounted to a period of respite every month. Thus, we concluded that, *at the very limited level of provision of short-term care at the time of the survey, it was the nature of the child's disabilities that chiefly determined whether or not it was received. Factors that might have been assumed to indicate parallel social needs* – family structure, income or deprivation – *did not appear to play a part.* Indeed, *the pattern was the opposite to what one might have expected* on all these counts.

These findings raise important questions about the processes whereby short-term respite care was (or is) allocated and about prevailing policies and practices. It may well have been the best use of these resources to concentrate them on the most severely disabled children but, as we have pointed out, the severity of disability is not necessarily the same as the severity of the caring task. This is mediated by a variety of other factors, not least by those of a social or economic nature. However, the employment of the 'disability criterion' (if such it was) may well have been the simplest and apparently fairest basis for distributing a service that was in short supply. There have certainly been changes in the succeeding years, but we suspect that the broad policy issues that these data raise have not disappeared.

There is one proviso that we should make to the general tenor of our conclusions in the previous paragraph: namely, that *when we looked at how much short-term care was given to those who received it, we found that social factors as well as disability factors did seem to come into play*. For example, the 'poor' who were provided with short-term care received it, on average, on more occasions in the year than the 'not poor'. This would tend to indicate (as does some of the other evidence concerning the clusters) that policies of concentration or selectivity were operating at two stages: first, at the point of *access* and, secondly, in the determination of the *quantity* of service. The results of decisions at these two stages (however they are arrived at) may or may not reinforce each other; it is obviously important to recognise this and to assess what the most appropriate relationship may be.

It is generally assumed that, whether or not people know about a service is a crucial factor in determining whether or not they ask for it, and also whether or not they receive it. *Overall, 47% of the parents had heard of short-term care but only 1% had requested it, as opposed to it being offered*. There was, therefore, no evidence of a direct link between 'knowing' and 'receiving'. However, there were significant differences by class, income, poverty and ethnic background as to who had heard about short-term care and who had not. For example, 63% of Social Classes I and II were so informed, but only 35% of Social Classes IV and V and only 18% of Asian parents had such knowledge. Furthermore, those with children in Clusters 9, 10 and 11 (the multiple and severe categories) were significantly more likely to have been aware of the service than the others. The exception was Cluster 7 (personal care), where, despite considerable parental knowledge, no child had received short-term care.

Since only 1% of all parents had asked for this service (although nearly half knew about it) *those who did receive it must have been offered it or guided towards it. If that was so, it lends additional weight to the conclusion that the actions of social workers, health visitors or other professionals with whom the families were in contact were important factors in the provision of short-term respite care.* Certainly, that would seem to hold true for the foster carers, in particular.

We thought that the provision of holidays for the children might have been distributed rather differently from that of short-term care. In the event, although *more children – 10% as against 5% – had had a holiday than had had respite care in the previous year, it was, broadly speaking, the same kinds of children and families who received both* – although not necessarily the same children and families. For instance, 28% of foster children had a holiday but only 7% of those living in lone-parent households.

Finally, we should note that about *4% of the children were away for substantial parts of the year at boarding special schools – a form of respite for parents that needs to be borne in mind. Even taking that into account, however, the overwhelming impression from all these data is of a very thinly provided service that was concentrated on certain groups of children who were mainly distinguished by the severity and complexity of their disabilities.*

NOTES TO CHAPTER 6

[1] The other third, presumably, knew about the service and had wanted it but had not been provided with it.

[2] For a further discussion of some of these issues, see Russell, 1995 and Geall *et al.*, 1991.

7 Equipment, appliances and adaptations provided

for the 5–15 age group living in private households

OPCS undertook a detailed analysis of both the use of special equipment by disabled children and adaptations to their homes. It also gathered the views of the parents or carers as to what further help of this nature was required. However, in most cases, only those parents of children with the relevant disability were asked about the equipment that was specific to these disabilities. Since certain aids and gadgets and special furniture could be useful to children with several kinds of disability, all were questioned about these matters, as they were about adaptations to their home.

The approach that OPCS adopted in this part of the survey was essentially the same as that followed with respect to the provision of health and other services; that is, parents were shown cards listing the possible equipment and adaptations that might be needed and asked what was used and what else they would like for their children.

OPCS divided its analysis into: wheelchairs; mobility equipment (such as walking aids and certain surgical appliances); aids to hearing (including aids to communication, such as pointer boards and typewriters); incontinence aids (for example, pads, pants, catheters, bags for urine and rubber sheets); small aids and gadgets (in particular, those that assisted with problems of dexterity, reaching and stretching); and, finally, adaptations in or to the home (such as special furniture, ramps, handrails and stair lifts).[1] We have followed these divisions in this chapter but have also covered the possession of telephones, since they are a valuable facility in organising support and in simplifying the daily routine for carers.

Overall, a third of the children of five years of age or more in the sample used some form of special equipment (excluding glasses). As can be seen from Table 7.1, the most common items were various aids to incontinence. No other equipment or adaptation was as widely used. There was no significant difference in the rate of use of equipment or in the provision of adaptations between boys and girls. However, the proportion did decline somewhat amongst the older children, although there was an increase in the use of some particular equipment, such as wheelchairs.

Table 7.1 Proportion of children with disabilities using different types of equipment or with adaptations to their homes

Type of aid or adaptation	%
Wheelchairs	5
Mobility aids	5
Walking aids (including surgical aids)	9
Aids to hearing	6
Incontinence aids	18
Small aids and gadgets	3
Aids to vision (excluding glasses)	1
Adaptations to the home or special furniture	6
All (*n* = 947)	**33[a]**

a Proportions do not add to 33% because of double counting.

1. Mobility equipment

OPCS divided mobility equipment into wheelchairs, mobility aids (such as special bicycles or pushchairs) and walking aids (walking frames, sticks, crutches, surgical footwear, callipers or splints), and we used the same three categories. It should be borne in mind that the questions about mobility equipment were only put to those families in which a child suffered from a locomotion disability that was above the OPCS defined threshold.

Wheelchairs

Thirty per cent of the children aged 5–15 suffered from a disability of locomotion. Of these, 18% had a wheelchair, although it was reported that a few did not use them. Only 8% of the wheelchairs were powered (and three-quarters of this small number were owned by families in the top income quintile). Just over a quarter were self-propelled and some two-thirds had to be pushed. About a fifth of the children only used their wheelchairs indoors. No parent said that their child needed a wheelchair and did not have one.

There was a heavy concentration of wheelchair ownership in four of the clusters: the three most severe and multiply disabled groups and Cluster 7 (personal care). In all, these four clusters accounted for 88% of the wheelchairs; Cluster 11 alone for 35%.

In looking at wheelchair ownership in relation to the socio-economic variables, it was necessary to bear in mind the relatively small number of children involved. However, it was notable that no child whose family fell into the lowest income category had a wheelchair, although this group was represented in the above-mentioned four clusters.

Mobility aids

Eighteen per cent of the children with disabilities of locomotion used mobility aids. However, 10% of the parents considered that their children needed such aids but did not have them, or needed something in addition to what they already possessed.

The mobility aids used were mainly special pushchairs (79% of those who had a mobility aid), followed by special bicycles (26%). Special prams (2%), trolleys (2%) or other similar aids (2%) completed the list. Somewhat in contrast, the aids that parents wanted, but which their children were lacking, were primarily special bicycles (79% of the expressed need) followed by special pushchairs (18%). It should be noted that the demand for special bicycles was not restricted to children in the more severely disabled clusters.

There was no significant difference between the use of mobility aids according to social class or by reference to the poverty index, although there was with respect to income. However, it was only amongst the families in the lowest quintile of effective income that this significant difference occurred. For example, whereas in the top four income quintiles 20% of the children with locomotion disabilities had mobility aids, this fell to 5% amongst the poorest fifth.

There were also some significant differences when we examined parental wishes for additional aids: for instance, Social Classes IV and V had a much lower level of expressed demand than any of the others (4% compared with 13%). In light of this, it was somewhat unexpected to find that the rate of demand for mobility aids amongst the 'poor' group of parents was approaching double that found amongst the 'not poor'. There were no such sharp divisions, one way or the other, in terms of income (although those in the highest income quintile were rather more satisfied with what their children already had than those in the other four-fifths).

What seems to emerge, therefore, is an association between the lowest levels of family income and a lower than might have been expected use of mobility aids amongst children with disabilities of locomotion. On the other hand, it was social class and poverty that seemed to affect the level of parents' desire for aids that their children did not have, albeit in opposite directions. As elsewhere in this report, such findings warn us against the interchangeable use of the concepts of class, income and poverty – at least in this field of analysis.

We also analysed the data on mobility aids by household composition.

Whereas the rate of use in two-parent families with one child was 32% of those with locomotion disabilities, it was significantly less in all other types of families, with the lowest level of 11% prevailing amongst children who were the only child in lone-parent households. There were, however, no significant differences in the demand for mobility aids according to family type.

Finally, there were (as might have been expected) pronounced differences between the clusters in the possession of mobility aids by children with disabilities of locomotion. The highest rates of use were amongst those with the severest conditions in Clusters 9, 10 and 11 (33%, 21% and 54%, respectively) and in Cluster 7 ('personal care', 21%). However, even though there was a good deal of provision amongst the three clusters of severest disability, a substantial level of unmet need was still expressed. For example, although over half of the relevant children in Cluster 11 had some mobility aid, a quarter of their parents considered that something extra was needed. However, this level fell to some 1 in 6 of those with children in Clusters 9 and 10 and to 1 in 20 of those with children in Cluster 7.

Given that the OPCS data concerning mobility aids were derived only from parents of children with locomotive disabilities the overall rate of use appears to have been rather low, a conclusion supported by the number of parents reporting an unmet need, especially amongst children with multiple and severe conditions.

Glendinning (1983) suggested that it was the identification and referral of children who needed mobility aids that created the particular area of difficulty, with various professionals failing to pick up problems, and parents, ignorant of the equipment available, unable to ask for it. The association which we revealed from the OPCS data of a lower than expected use of mobility aids by children from families with the lowest level of incomes may reflect the fact that these families, as we have seen, tended to have less contact with hospitals and clinics than others, thus potentially restricting the specialist advice that might have been given.

Walking aids

The equipment included in the walking aids category covered walking frames, sticks, crutches, callipers, splints, surgical footwear, elastic supports, artificial limbs and 'other' unspecified aids. Of those children with a locomotion disability, 27% used such aids and 5% of the parents considered that they were needed but were either unavailable or inadequate. The most common aid was surgical footwear (59% of the users), followed by walking frames, callipers and splints (all around 20%).

The type of walking aid that parents wanted, but which their child did not have, followed much the same pattern, with half seeking to have improved surgical footwear.

There was no significant difference in the use of walking aids with respect to social class, the poverty index or family type but, yet again, the use was significantly lower in the bottom income quintile than in any of the other income groups (8% by comparison with 26%). However, there was no significant difference in the demand for such equipment with respect to any of these family characteristic variables.

The distribution of the use of walking aids amongst the clusters was largely as might have been expected and mirrored that of mobility aids. However, the demand from parents for such equipment was largely confined to Cluster 11, where one in ten wanted something extra or better.

2. Hearing and speech aids

As with some of the other types of equipment, questions about aids to hearing and speech were only asked when the child suffered from the relevant disability at a level of severity above the determined threshold. This applied to a third of the OPCS sample of 5–15-year-olds. However, only 16% of this group was said to be using aids. Parents claimed that another 13% were in need of them, or in need of something different or better than they had.

As might be expected, we found the highest rates of use of these aids amongst the two clusters that were characterised by the presence of hearing problems – Cluster 5 (hearing and communication) and Cluster 8 (hearing and behaviour). Indeed, children in these two groups accounted for 60% of the users. Even so, it was somewhat surprising to learn that only 26% of those in the two clusters with hearing disabilities above the defined threshold of severity used any kind of aid.

The most commonly used pieces of equipment were hearing aids – 91% of those who used some aid – followed by a phonic ear (26%). There was a negligible use of anything else (no more than 7% in any category of aid). However, what parents wanted for their children revealed a rather different pattern. Although 28% of the requests were for hearing aids (mostly for better kinds), 27% were for telephone adapters and a further 23% for TV adapters. Flashing lights for different purposes (on telephones, doors or alarm clocks, for example) together comprised 30% of the aids that parents wanted for their children.

These results are only capable of being interpreted if one knows how many of the children had residual hearing that would be enhanced by a hearing aid. Deaf (as opposed to deafened) children are likely to have learnt sign language. Unfortunately, the OPCS data did not allow these distinctions to be made.[2]

There were no significant differences in the use of aids amongst children considered to have hearing disabilities with respect to social class or family type. There were, however, differences when it came to income and the poverty index. Those children in families in the top fifth of the income groups stood out as having the highest level of use, and the rate of use amongst children in 'poor' families was only half that amongst the 'not poor'. Despite these findings, demand for hearing or speech aids was significantly greater in the top income group than in any of the other four. Little difference emerged with respect to other socio-economic variables.

On the face of it, therefore, given the number of children who were considered to suffer from hearing disabilities, there appeared to be a rather low level of use of aids to hearing and speech. Although few parents had purchased aids privately, the effective income of the family did appear to have influenced the rate of use and the rate of demand for additional items: more children with a hearing disability in the richest fifth of the families used aids, and their parents were the most likely to wish for additional or better equipment.

3. Visual aids

Only 1% of all the children aged 5–15 had a visual disability but, of those who did, 18% used aids other than glasses. Of the parents of these children, 16% said that more was needed. Both the use and the demand for these aids were concentrated in Cluster 1 (the mixture of mild disabilities).

4. Incontinence aids

Overall, 37% of the children between 5 and 15 in the OPCS survey were classified as having the disability of incontinence. Of these, 61% used some form of aid to deal with the problem. Rubber sheets and other protection for bedding were the most commonly employed equipment (85% of users), followed by pads (33%), special pants (15%) and bed alarms (10%). Altogether, 30% of the parents of the children with a defined incontinence disability wanted something extra, although it should be noted that a further 6% (whose children were not so classified) also mentioned that they, too, would benefit from such help. Taking both of these groups of parents together the most commonly sought aids were bed alarms (by 54%

of those seeking additional help), rubber sheets (28%) and special pants (27%). None of this would seem to be difficult or costly to supply, although it should be noted that most parents had themselves purchased protective bed coverings whereas other aids had been supplied free by various agencies.

When we looked at the distribution of incontinence problems above the OPCS defined threshold in relation to the clusters, we found virtually all the children in Clusters 3 (incontinence)[3] and 11 (multiple and very severe disabilities) to be affected. There were, however, fairly high levels in the two other 'multiple and severe' clusters: 48% in Cluster 9 and 38% in Cluster 10. There was also a sizeable minority (27%) in Cluster 1 (mild disabilities) and smaller proportions (13%, 10% and 9%, respectively) in Clusters 8 (hearing and behaviour), 7 (personal care) and 2 (behaviour). Thus, incontinence was a fairly common problem in most (but not all) clusters. The demand for additional equipment was low in Cluster 11 (multiple and very severe disabilities) but high in Cluster 2 (behaviour), where half the parents of those classed as incontinent felt that more was needed. Although the proportion of children who had the disability of incontinence was low, or fairly low, in Clusters 4, 5, 6 and 7 (fits, hearing and communication, communication and behaviour, personal care), their parents expressed relatively high levels of demand for what they did not have. This may suggest that the need for incontinence aids was more easily overlooked by agencies when other problems dominated the picture.

When we examined the rate of use of aids amongst the children considered to have the disability of incontinence, we discovered no significant differences with respect to family type, social class and income or with reference to the poverty index. However, there were significant differences in the demand for extra equipment in relation to all but the first of these variables. The level of expressed 'unmet' need was high amongst 'poorer' and semi-skilled and unskilled families but low amongst the better-off and professional classes. Table 7.2 sets out the details.

These figures might suggest that richer families were able to deal with the problem of incontinence in ways other than by obtaining equipment or more equipment – for example, by spending on laundry. As we saw in Chapter 4, OPCS actually gathered data on whether families spent 'extra' on laundry services, as well as on whether parents felt that they needed more laundry services but could not afford them. Although these questions were asked of *all* parents (not simply of those whose children were deemed to be incontinent) the results are of some interest and warrant reiteration here. Overall, 10% of parents said that they needed extra laundry services but could not afford them. However, this 'unmet need' was particularly pronounced amongst one-parent families with two or more children (24%)

Table 7.2 Children suffering from the disability of incontinence whose parents considered that additional aids were needed

	Percentage wanting additional aids
Social class	
I and II	25
III Non-manual	30
III Manual	28
IV and V	63
All (n = 354)	**36**
Income quintiles	
Highest	24
Second	21
Third	34
Fourth	49
Lowest	51
All (n = 354)	**36**
Poverty index	
'Not poor'	20
'Poor'	46
All (n = 354)	**36**

and two-parent families with four or more children (18%). Likewise, whereas only 3% of the parents in Social Classes I and II felt that they needed more laundry services but could not afford them, this figure rose to 6% in Social Classes IV and V combined. As might have been expected, a similar pattern prevailed with respect to income. Whereas 4% of those in the highest quintile of income wanted more laundry services but could not afford them, the proportion rose to 16% in the two lowest income quintiles. The comparable figures for the 'not poor' and the 'poor' were, respectively 2% and 18%.

This analysis suggests that there was a considerable unmet need for various services and aids to help parents cope with problems associated with their children's incontinence and that, generally speaking, this unmet need was most acute amongst poorer families. Of course, the roots of these differences may have lain in the parents' knowledge of the services available and their ability to obtain them; or it may be that those who controlled the distribution of the free aids were more responsive to some groups than to others. Again, children who were not using aids may have been on a training programme that would have been delayed if, for example, they wore pads. Whatever the explanation, it is plain that the level, availability and distribution of help with incontinence demanded careful attention in the late 1980s and may still do so today.

A recent qualitative study of 35 children and young adults with chronic faecal incontinence found that 'families felt that there was little real appreciation of the very distressing nature of this disability. Their need for support often went unrecognised.' Also: 'Families required more information, both about the full implications of the original impairment and about practical methods of managing faecal incontinence' (Cavet, 1998). There seems to be no compelling evidence that there has been any improvement in the provision of adequate services for children with incontinence disabilities during the 1980s and 1990s.

5. Small aids and gadgets

Altogether only 3% of all the children in the survey aged 5–15 used small aids or gadgets but, unlike most of the other aids, these were usually privately purchased (in 75% of the cases). Questions about these aids were asked of all parents, although OPCS analysed the results separately for children with dexterity disabilities and those with problems of stretching and reaching. The proportion of users of small aids or gadgets in these two groups was, respectively, 20% and 14%. Some 20% of the parents of these children considered that a small aid or gadget that they did not have (or which could be improved) was needed.

The most common type of equipment used was special cutlery (34% of those who used small aids or gadgets) followed by unspecified 'other' relevant aids (26%), electric toothbrushes (25%) and special crockery (22%). Apart from 'call help' (11%), other aids in this category (such as special door handles, tap turners, pick-up aids or dressing aids) were hardly used at all. The aids that parents considered their children needed but did not have were mainly electric toothbrushes, special cutlery and special utensils.

As one might expect, most of the use of these aids and, to a lesser extent, the demand for them, was found in the three most severe disability clusters (71% of the users, and 50% of those for whom more was desired). However, the number involved was too small to analyse the results further.

6. Adaptations

Questions about adaptations were asked of all parents. The replies indicated that only 8% of homes were specially adapted to take account of the disabilities of the 5–15-year-olds in the survey. By contrast, 19% of the dwellings were said to have disadvantages with respect to the child's disabilities, and 14% of the parents considered that one or more of the possible adaptations listed on the interview card were needed but had not been made. OPCS presented the data separately for children with locomotion and personal care disabilities, and for both these groups the level of adaptations rose to 20%, with about a third of the parents of children in each group saying that further work was needed.

Table 7.3 sets out the adaptations that had been provided for all the groups and also those that parents felt were still needed.

Table 7.3 Special adaptations made to the homes of children in the survey (all disabilities) and those that parents wished to be made

Types of adaptations	Installed (%)	Missing but wanted (%)
Outside ramps	15	8
Inside ramps	–	1
Outside handrails	9	5
Inside handrails	20	11
Modified doors	11	7
Stair lift	5	7
Improved access	8	1
Modifications to bathroom/toilet	16	31
Shower	33	33
Safety devices	28	8
'Other' types	27	14
All (*n* = 947)	**8**	**14**

Clearly, a relatively small number of homes had several adaptations and likewise, more than one parent often considered that adaptation would be advantageous. The most common of those being used were special showers, safety devices and inside handrails, but the rather large proportion of 'other' adaptations suggests that the range of possibilities is considerable. Chiefly what was thought to be needed were showers and modifications to bathrooms and toilets – in principle not difficult or hugely expensive adaptations. However, the complexity of the 'adaptations system', with its maze of legislation, organisations and sources of finance may in part explain the relatively high levels of unmet need (Heywood, 1994).

Most adaptations (58%) had been made for children in the three 'multiple and severe' clusters but, clearly, there was some need for these modifications in other clusters as well. This is borne out by the fact that, although most demand for such improvements came from parents of children in the three severest of the clusters, there was a similar level of demand (13%) from the parents of children in Cluster 2 (behaviour).

Adaptations were more likely to have been made in the homes of the better-off parents, as Table 7.4 shows. However, there were less pronounced differences in the pattern of expressed 'unmet need', although those in the top income group were the most 'satisfied'. In this respect, it was noteworthy that whereas a fifth of the top income group who wanted extra adaptations wanted a stair lift, no parents in the lowest fifth mentioned this. They most often wanted a shower.

Table 7.4 Adaptations made to the home and those that were wanted, analysed by effective family income

Income quintiles	Installed (%)	Wanted (%)
Highest	11	10
Second	10	16
Third	7	16
Fourth	3	17
Lowest	5	13
All (*n* = 947)	**8**	**14**

Although there was no significant difference between the homes of 'poor' and 'not poor' families (according to the deprivation index) with respect to adaptations having been made, there was a difference when it came to their wanting adaptations that they did not have: 19% of the 'poor' parents had a demand, but only 9% of the 'not poor'.

Thus, again, one sees a pattern of provision and a pattern of expressed need that appear to be influenced by the families' incomes as well as by the type and severity of the child's disability. Of course, fewer of the adaptations than other aids are likely to have been available free, and this might well explain some of the effect of income levels. Indeed, of those parents who had had adaptations made, just over half had paid for them entirely out of their own pockets. Alongside the question of a family's financial resources, however, the type of tenure and the policies and practices of local housing authorities may also have been important factors in determining whether or not adaptations were made, points emphasised in Beresford's study some ten years later (1995).

Similarly, Heywood and Smart (1996) found that parents of disabled children were often unable to pay their assessed contributions to the discretionary Disabled Facilities Grant (DFG), which was introduced in 1990 to provide funds for adaptations. Although, social services departments have obligations to disabled children under Section 17 of the Children Act 1989, Heywood and Smart (1996) found that only 18% of local authorities were using this source of funding to help with adaptation costs.

Recently, Oldman and Beresford (1998) have found that three out of four families with disabled children reported that their housing was unsuitable, and four out of ten reported that their housing was poor overall. Families felt that unsuitable housing made the task of caring harder and contributed to their high stress levels. However, where successful adaptations had been made, the task of caring had become very much easier and the child gained greater independence. The poor housing conditions and difficulties with obtaining necessary adaptations that disabled children and their families experienced in the 1980s (Cooke and Lawton, 1985) have persisted during the 1990s (Oldman and Beresford, 1998).

7. Special furniture or other similar equipment

According to the OPCS survey, 'special furniture' included special beds or bedding, aids to toileting or bathing, aids to sitting and hoists. Overall, 9% of these 5–15-year-olds used such equipment. The most common were special beds or cots (36% of those using this form of equipment), followed by non-slip mats (32%), bath seats (16%), special chairs (15%) and special incontinence aids other than those already discussed (12%).

The furniture aids that parents wanted for their children but did not have were much the same as those already in use: 53% of the requests were for special beds or cots, 20% for non-slip mats and 11% for special chairs. Overall, however, the rate of additional demand was low. Only 5% of the parents thought that they lacked special furniture, despite being shown an extensive list on the prompt cards during the interview. However, it should be borne in mind that this question was asked of all parents, some of whose children would certainly not have required any of these forms of aid. For example, amongst the parents of children with personal care disabilities (as defined by OPCS), the demand for special furniture rose to 16%.

As might have been expected, the use of special furniture was heavily concentrated in the three multiple and severe clusters (9, 10 and 11) and in the 'personal care' cluster (7). The rate of use in Cluster 11 was 71%, in Cluster 10 it was 24%, in Cluster 9 it fell to 19% and in Cluster 7 to 17%. In no other cluster was it more than 7%. The demand for 'special furniture' followed a similar pattern, but it should be noted that in the multiple and very severe cluster 32% of the parents sought more help – clearly, in many cases, in addition to what they had already received. In none of the other clusters was the demand as great.

When we analysed the results on the basis of the socio-economic variables, we found a significantly higher rate of use of special furniture amongst two-parent families with one child than in any of the other household types. Whereas the rate of use amongst this group was 22%, it fell, for example, to 5% amongst lone-parent families. There were, it will be recalled, several other services and aids that were used significantly more by two-parent/one-child families than by other families. (It is, of course, useful to bear in mind that such households only comprised 16% of those in the sample, a similar proportion to that of lone parents.)

There was no significant difference in the use of special furniture in relation to social class or the deprivation index, but there was in relation to income, as Table 7.5 demonstrates.

Table 7.5 Child's use of special furniture, analysed by effective family income

Income quintiles	Used (%)
Highest	13
Second	18
Third	16
Fourth	7
Lowest	4
All	**10**

With respect to the demand for additional special furniture, there was no significant difference with regard to income, the poverty index or family type, although there was when we looked at social class. Whereas only 1% of Social Classes I and II considered that extra help was needed, this proportion rose to 10% amongst Social Classes IV and V.

Once more we see that the use of this form of aid was substantially less in the lower income groups and, given that some 18% of the parents whose children used such equipment said that they had bought it themselves, this may not seem surprising. However, as with several of the other aids and services, it did not follow that there was a greater demand amongst the parents who might appear to have been disadvantaged because of their low income.

8. The Family Fund

The Family Fund is run by the Joseph Rowntree Foundation and financed by the government. It helps families who care for severely disabled children by giving them a lump sum grant for specific items or by furnishing information (Bradshaw, 1980; Bradshaw and Lawton, 1985; Lawton and Quine, 1990; Lawton, 1992; Cowen, 1996).

Ten per cent of the families in the OPCS survey had received help from this source in the year preceding the survey; 2% had applied unsuccessfully. The parents who had been assisted were principally those with children in the three multiple and severe clusters. Altogether, Clusters 9, 10 and 11 accounted for two-thirds of this group, with a scattering in all the other clusters. However, when asked, only a quarter of the parents said that they had heard of the Family Fund, although this rate was substantially higher in the three multiple and severe disability clusters – up to 89% in Cluster 11, for example.

9. Telephones

Whereas, at the time of the survey, some 85% of all households in Britain had a telephone, the rate amongst the families of the 5–15-year-olds in the disability survey was only 76%. Rates were similar to the national level amongst the families looking after children in the three multiple and severe clusters and in that characterised as 'personal care' (Cluster 7). Even so, the absence of a telephone is likely to have been an additional and special disadvantage for parents of children with disabilities when it comes to organising day-to-day care, gaining access to services, obtaining information, or tapping and maintaining informal helping networks. Furthermore, in an emergency a telephone could be considered a lifeline. For example, one family in Glendinning's study (1983, p. 152) who had applied for help in having a telephone installed reported: 'They said I'm not handicapped, but I am really, if you've got a child who is having a fit and you've got to leave them to go and fetch somebody.'

Baldwin (1985) found that the telephone bills of families with disabled children were £3.60 per quarter higher than those of other families with children, thereby supporting the claims of parents that they made heavier use of their telephones in order to keep in touch with services and to reduce isolation. Thus, although the tenth most frequent type of help given to families by the Family Fund between 1983 and 1992 was for the installation of a telephone (Lawton, 1992), telephone bills may still make this form of communication prohibitively expensive for some families. Amongst the families in the OPCS survey who did not possess a telephone, 85% said it was because they could not afford it. The highest rate (96%) of those saying this were families with four or more children.

As one might expect, there were significant differences between the rates of telephone ownership amongst the families in the OPCS survey in relation to all of the socio-economic variables. For example, whereas the rates of ownership amongst Social Classes I and II, amongst those families in the highest income quintile and amongst those classified as 'not poor' were, respectively, ,96%, 95% and 94%, these percentages fell to 53%, 48% and 55% amongst Social Classes IV and V, amongst those with the lowest fifth of incomes and amongst the 'poor'. These are all significant differences.

Therefore, the evidence indicates that, at the time of the survey, not only was there an overall lower rate of telephone ownership amongst families with disabled children than in the rest of the community, but also this lack was heavily concentrated amongst the poor, however precisely one chooses to identify that group. Yet the value of a telephone to families coping with disability – for all the obvious reasons – is indisputable. The cost of installation is one issue; the cost of use is another. Both would seem to warrant greater subsidisation, albeit perhaps according to income.

10. Discussion and implications

Several conclusions of a general nature can be drawn from the results examined in this chapter. However, it has to be borne in mind that much of the special equipment and many of the domestic adaptations will only be required by children with particular disabilities or when these disabilities reach a certain level of severity. This was recognised in the OPCS survey, as parents were only asked about their children's use of specific aids if the child suffered from a disability that might reasonably be assisted by those aids. However, as we pointed out at the beginning of this chapter, questions about some equipment and all special furniture and adaptations were put to every parent, irrespective of their child's type of disability. As a result, the data needed to be analysed carefully and conclusions suitably qualified. We have endeavoured to reflect this in what follows.

Overall, *a third of the children in the survey used some form of special equipment or had their homes adapted to take account of their disability*. In a substantial minority of cases more than one kind of aid was provided. *The most commonly used equipment was that required because of the child's incontinence*; almost a fifth of the sample was helped in this way. The next most frequently used appliances (by one in ten of the children) were various types of aid to walking.

Generally speaking, *the rate of use of relevant aids was rather low* when compared with the disability in question. For example, only a fifth of the children with locomotion disabilities used a mobility aid and just over a quarter used a walking aid. Only a fifth of them had had any adaptations made to their homes. The fact that three-fifths of those who had a problem of incontinence used some form of protective equipment looks, at first sight, to be quite a high proportion; however, given the simplicity and inexpensiveness of most of the equipment, the rate actually seems rather low.

In the light of the whole range of these and other findings, one might have predicted a fairly high level of demand from parents who, for one reason or another, had been unable to obtain what they considered their children needed. In fact, the pattern was uneven and the rates rather low.

Demand was certainly greater amongst parents in the three 'multiple and severe' clusters as well as in the cluster we characterised as 'personal care'. Nonetheless, there were calls for additional aids and adaptations that, on the face of it, did not seem to be relevant to the cluster in question. For example, a fifth of the parents in the 'incontinence' cluster said that their children needed mobility aids that they did not have. This kind of evidence should warn us that *the need for aids to assist with what are perceived as secondary disabilities may be overlooked if attention is fixed on what is considered to be the primary problem.*

Why did children not have the aids (or the kind of aids) that their parents thought they needed? There are several possible answers. *First,* there may have been an unawareness of what was available. It should be remembered that the parents' responses were partly elicited by being shown a card listing the possibilities. For some, this may have been the first time that they had heard about or considered certain items. *Secondly,* parents may have asked for assistance but been refused. It will be recalled, for instance, that this happened to a small proportion of applicants to the Family Fund. *Thirdly,* because of the nature of the question, it is difficult to know how many children utilised aids that their parents considered inadequate or difficult to use. It may have been that what they felt their children needed were improved versions of what they already had. *Fourthly,* where items had to be privately purchased (or were thought to have to be privately purchased), parents may have been unable to acquire them because they were too poor. However, since much equipment could be provided free of charge, this is not a sufficient explanation. *There were obviously other barriers between wanting and obtaining;* for instance, as Beardshaw (1988) highlighted, the supply of aids and equipment is split between a number of agencies in a way that creates confusion for both service users and providers.

It was also surprising that many children who, apparently, would have benefited from aids neither had them nor had parents who thought that they were lacking. One possible explanation is that an acknowledgement of a child's disability (especially amongst the younger ones) was not the same as a recognition of its severity. There may have been a degree of denial involved, and this would be challenged by the admission that certain aids were necessary, especially those that might be felt to stigmatise a child by their public use. This is a matter of conjecture on the basis of these data, but it may well be an issue that warrants further investigation.

There were significant differences in the distribution of certain aids and adaptations in relation to some of our socio-economic variables. However, the most discriminative was the effective income of the family.[4] For example, whereas 20% of the children with locomotion disabilities in families in the first four income quintiles had mobility aids, this fell to 5% for those in the lowest fifth. A similar pattern existed with respect to walking aids, where the figures were, respectively, 26% and 8%. In the case of adaptations, 11% of the children in families in the top two-fifths of the income bands were provided with such facilities; only 4% of those whose families fell into the lowest two bands. Likewise, in the top three-fifths of the family income bands, 16% of the children had the benefit of special furniture but only 5% in the lowest two. The picture with regard to aids to hearing was different but still significant: 20% of the children in families in the top fifth of incomes used such equipment; only 13% in the second and third; 10% in the fourth; and a bare 8% in the fifth. It must be stressed that these figures, with the exception of adaptations and special furniture, refer to children who suffered from the relevant disability.

The one exception to the significant differences in the use of aids by children in better-off or worse-off families was found with respect to equipment to cope with incontinence. This was fairly evenly distributed across the income bands.

There is, therefore, compelling evidence that, at the time of the OPCS survey, the level of family income influenced the children's use of disability aids. In particular, those whose families were located in the lowest fifth of the income bands appeared to have been especially disadvantaged. Nonetheless, the reasons for this are not immediately obvious, since much of the equipment in question was usually available free of charge. However, differential rates of contact with hospitals, clinics, schools or other services may be a relevant factor.

The pattern of use with respect to the other socio-economic variables was less clear-cut, but the differences that did exist suggested certain conclusions. One was that, *with respect to mobility aids and special furniture, children with two parents and no siblings were significantly better provided for* (most evidently in the case of special furniture) in comparison with lone-parent families. *This echoes some of the findings that we discussed in the chapters dealing with the provision of other services and should sharpen the question about the relationship between family (or household) composition and the various forms of assistance that disabled children and their families receive – and why.*

We had thought that the *poverty index* would point to discrimination between the families when it came to considering which ones did or did not have aids and adaptations for their children. *This only proved to be so in the case of aids to hearing, the children of the 'not poor' families having a rate of use that was double that of the 'poor' families*. Since this variable was reduced to a simple dichotomy in our analyses, it would have been likely to identify only the most pronounced differences. If that was so, then *it suggests that particular attention should be paid to the aids needed by children with a hearing (or speech) disability who live in circumstances of relative deprivation.*

The analysis of the parents' wishes for the aids and adaptations that their children did not have produced an interesting, although somewhat complicated, picture with respect to the socio-economic variables. Surprisingly, *those in the lowest income quintile wanted significantly more help only with respect to incontinence aids*. Similarly, parents in Social Classes IV and V and in our 'poor' category also expressed a significantly greater demand than other groups for these same items. Apart from this, only in the case of mobility aids and adaptations did 'poor' parents register unmet needs significantly more often than those who were 'not poor'.

The conclusion that might be drawn from these results is that, *although family income is an important determinant (amongst the socio-economic variables) of a child's use of aids and adaptations, this was not the case when it came to what parents said their children needed but did not have*. The poverty (deprivation) index and, to a lesser extent, social class appeared to be somewhat more discriminative in this respect – the 'poor' families saying more was needed; Social Classes IV and V combined expressing more need than the other categories. Thus, as we argued earlier, *the factors that play a part in determining levels of use of aids and adaptations may not be the same (or have the same weight) as those that influence the expression of unmet need*. What is plain is that, *in addition to the types and severity of a child's disabilities, the families' social circumstances affected what aids and adaptations they had and what additional help of this kind their parents considered they needed.*

Finally, *a child's access to aids and adaptations may (as with other services) be determined by his or her parents' knowledge of what is available and by the ease with which they can communicate with possible sources of assistance*. For example, we saw that knowledge of the Family Fund was uneven; that, overall, families with disabled children had a lower rate of telephone ownership than the country as a whole; and that this was even more pronounced amongst those in the lower income bands. Families need not only the means but also the opportunities to make contact with those who provide information, give support or recommend them for the appropriate services.

[1] Vision aids, other than glasses, were included, but the number of children using them was negligible. For that reason, OPCS published few details.

[2] However, OPCS did classify the children according to the level of their hearing disability (Meltzer *et al.*, 1989, p. 43). It found a sharp increase in the proportion of those using hearing aids at the higher levels of severity, although the uppermost of these was characterised by the child having 'difficulty hearing someone talking in a loud voice in a quiet room'.

[3] A few children in the 'incontinence' cluster would not have suffered a sufficiently severe level of this disability to meet the OPCS threshold.

[4] It will be recalled that effective income was a measure of income per head. It may be that cruder measures of income would have given somewhat different results – either way. 'Effective income' does, of course, take family size into account; therefore, some 'poor' small families (say, one parent and one child) will not necessarily have been placed in the lowest income quintile.

8 Education

of the 5–15 age group living in private households

1. The changes brought about by the Education Act 1981

One of the stated aims of the OPCS children's surveys was to monitor the implementation of the Education Act 1981 (Bone and Meltzer, 1989). This introduced a new system of comprehensive assessments and also required that all children who were identified as having special educational needs[1] should be provided with a formal written statement, giving details of their needs and the provision that should be made to meet them. The new system came into effect on 1 April 1983; therefore, by the time of the survey of children in private households it had been in place for two years. As Meltzer *et al.* (1989) point out, however, considerable confusion still existed among parents about the new procedures; indeed, they reported that only 22% of the parents interviewed had heard about the new system. Furthermore, 'the survey was carried out at a time when transitional arrangements were in operation with regard to children already receiving special education and this may have caused parents some confusion. For example, children who had been receiving special education prior to 1 April 1983 . . . were deemed to be the subject of statements under the Act without going through any formal assessment process' (Meltzer *et al.*, 1989, p. 51).

Thus, the OPCS private households survey was undertaken at a time of major change in the special education system, and parental confusion inevitably limited the extent to which the impact of the 1981 Act could be assessed. Certainly, many of the children surveyed would have been covered by the transitional arrangements. However, the information produced does give an idea of the priority being assigned to different groups in the assessment and statementing procedures.

Table 8.1 shows the proportion of children in each cluster who had been assessed for special educational needs and who had received a written statement. Overall, only a third had undergone assessment, with just under a fifth (19%) either having received or expecting to receive a written statement. As could be predicted, the proportion assessed and the proportion with a statement both broadly increase across the clusters in the direction of increasing severity. The majority of children in the multiple disability clusters (Clusters 9–11) had been assessed. The priority given to the most severely disabled children is even more pronounced when the proportions who received a written statement are examined.

However, there are some notable exceptions to the broad pattern. Children who experienced fits (Cluster 4) had by far the lowest priority for assessment, only 7% of them having been assessed. Two of the clusters in which the children were characterised by high levels of behavioural difficulties (Clusters 2 and 6) also stand out from the general trend, having higher proportions who were assessed and statemented than might have been expected from the nature of the trend.

Table 8.1 Proportion of children (5–15) who had been assessed for special educational needs, had been statemented and were receiving the help specified in the statement, analysed by clusters

Cluster	Description	Assessed for special needs	Had received/ expected to receive written statement		Statemented and receiving the help specified	
		(%)	(%)	Base	(%)	Base
1	Mild disabilities	14	5	134	100	6
2	Behaviour	29	13	254	94	32
3	Incontinence	20	8	76	79	5
4	Fits	7	7	41	0	1
5	Hearing and communication	24	12	67	100	8
6	Communication and behaviour	38	24	141	85	33
7	Personal care	35	19	52	67	9
8	Hearing and behaviour	35	22	68	100	11
9	Multiple disabilities	59	44	77	87	31
10	Multiple and severe	77	45	49	95	19
11	Multiple and very severe	72	54	28	71	14
All		**33**	**19**	**987**	**88**	**168**

The great majority of children with statements were said by their parents to be receiving the help that was specified in them. The small base numbers prevent any detailed analysis by cluster, but the lower than average level of provision of what was considered to be necessary for those in the most severe of the clusters (Cluster 11) is notable. Of course, these children would have had the most complicated needs to meet.

OPCS found that the probability both of the children being assessed and of their having a formal written statement increased with age. However, when they examined this in combination with the severity of the children's disabilities, they found that this only held true for children with less severe disabilities. Amongst those children whose disabilities were more severe, the likelihood of assessment and statementing were broadly similar across the age range (Meltzer *et al.*, 1989).

2. The extent of learning disabilities among 5–15-year-olds in private households

Learning difficulties, as measured by a severity score on the scale of 'intellectual functioning', was one of the areas of disability covered by the OPCS survey. Of the children aged 5–15 years in private households, 28% were found to experience this disability. As can been seen from Table 8.2, small minorities of children in the first five clusters and in Cluster 7 have mild to moderate learning disabilities. However, in Cluster 6, characterised by children with communication and behavioural disabilities, 38% have moderate to severe learning difficulties. The majority of the children in the multiple disability clusters (9–11) have severe learning difficulties, often as a result of specific mental impairments.

Table 8.2 Children aged 5–15 assessed as having learning difficulties, analysed by clusters

Cluster	Description	Percentage with learning difficulty	Mean severity score on the OPCS intellectual functioning scale	Base
1	Mild disabilities	18	0.9	134
2	Behaviour	19	1.0	254
3	Incontinence	3	..[a]	76
4	Fits	5	0.1	41
5	Hearing and communication	11	0.6	68
6	Communication and behaviour	38	2.2	141
7	Personal care	12	0.5	52
8	Hearing and behaviour	29	1.4	68
9	Multiple disabilities	62	4.4	77
10	Multiple and severe	79	5.2	50
11	Multiple and very severe	96	8.6	28
All		**28**	**1.7**	**989**

Notes:
a .. = less than 1%.

3. Where the children in private households went to school

Table 8.3 gives details of the type of school attended by the children, analysed by clusters. For the whole sample some notable features emerge

Table 8.3 Where children (aged 5–15) living in private households received their education, analysed by clusters

Cluster	Description	Type of school						
		Special school	Special unit, ordinary school	Assessment centre	Ordinary school	Other	Total	Base
		(%)	(%)	(%)	(%)	(%)	(%)	
1	Mild disabilities	9	7	–	84	1	100	134
2	Behaviour	20	11	1	65	4	100	254
3	Incontinence	13	1	–	84	1	100	76
4	Fits	7	7	–	83	2	100	41
5	Hearing and communication	10	12	–	79	–	100	68
6	Communication and behaviour	35	16	1	48	1	100	141
7	Personal care	19	6	–	73	2	100	52
8	Hearing and behaviour	19	19	–	57	6	100	68
9	Multiple disabilities	63	3	–	31	4	100	77
10	Multiple and severe	64	8	–	24	4	100	50
11	Multiple and very severe	85	7	–	–	7	100	28
All		**26**	**10**	**..[a]**	**61**	**3**	**100**	**989**

Notes:
a .. = less than 1%.

from this analysis. First, the majority of disabled children (61%) were attending ordinary classes in ordinary primary and secondary schools. Secondly, at this time, the use of special units attached to ordinary schools was meeting the educational needs of only a small minority (10%). Special schools were the most frequent form of specialised provision, attended by just over a quarter (26%) of the total group.

When this overall picture of schooling arrangements is broken down by clusters, a number of distinct differences emerge. The children in the three multiple disability clusters (9–11) were much less likely to be attending ordinary primary and secondary schools; indeed, none of the children in the cluster of severest disability did so. They were also less likely than the group as a whole to have their needs met at special units attached to ordinary schools.

Children in two of the clusters characterised by high levels of behavioural difficulties (Clusters 2 and 6) were the next most likely groups to be educated outside the mainstream and to have been placed at special schools. There was also a higher than average likelihood that they would be attending special units attached to ordinary schools. The two clusters containing children who nearly all had moderate to severe hearing difficulties (Clusters 5 and 8) were also more likely than the average to have been receiving their education in such special units. It is perhaps not surprising that the children in Cluster 8, characterised by high levels of behavioural *and* hearing disabilities, were the most likely of all to have been attending these units. Taken together, therefore, these findings suggest that the special units attached to ordinary schools were educating children with particular types of disability; in short, that there was specialisation within this special provision.

When the pattern of the children's schooling is analysed by their ages (Table 8.4) we see that, broadly speaking, the proportion attending ordinary schools declined as they became older, whilst the proportion in special schools increased. The trend in children attending special units attached to ordinary schools is less clear, although it was a more common arrangement amongst children of secondary school age. The size of secondary schools and their greater catchment areas are likely to encourage more provision of special units than smaller, more geographically scattered, primary schools. 'Other' arrangements were also more likely to have been made for those of secondary school age than for younger children.

Table 8.4 Type of schooling arrangements for children (aged 5–15) living in private households, shown by single age bands

Age	Type of schooling arrangement				Total	Base
	Ordinary primary or secondary school	Special unit at ordinary school	Special school	Other		
	(%)	(%)	(%)	(%)	(%)	
5	83	2	13	2	100	105
6	78	7	15	–	100	73
7	69	10	19	2	100	83
8	78	7	14	1	100	76
9	71	7	20	2	100	91
10	50	13	36	1	100	84
11	53	9	37	1	100	87
12	53	18	25	5	100	90
13	48	20	30	2	100	96
14	46	9	40	4	100	97
15	53	11	31	5	100	75
All	62	10	26	2	100	956

As Table 8.4 shows, the change in the pattern of school arrangements was particularly marked at around the time of the three key transitions in the school system. At the end of the infant school period (between 7 and 8 years) the proportion in ordinary schools increased, but it then dropped sharply as the time for a move to secondary school approached. The proportion of children at special schools more than doubled between the ages of 8 and 11: from 14% to 37%. There was also a 'move back' to ordinary schools at the age of 15 – possibly in order to allow disabled young people greater opportunities to prepare for public examinations.

An analysis of the type of school attended by gender and ethnicity revealed no significant differences, although boys were twice as likely as girls to be in the 'other arrangements' category, and children from minority ethnic groups were twice as likely to experience these arrangements as 'white' children.

When the pattern of school arrangements was examined by the type of family[2] in which the children lived (Table 8.5), some quite distinct differences emerged. Children from lone-parent families were more likely than those from two-parent families to be attending ordinary primary schools. However, at the secondary level the position was reversed. This pattern is not accounted for by different age distributions, since a slightly larger proportion of children from lone-parent families were of secondary school age. This suggests that although a smaller proportion of children from lone-parent families attended special schools, those who do are older than the children from two-parent families at these schools. Children from lone-parent families were twice as likely as their two-parent peers to have been educated by some 'other arrangement'.

Table 8.5 Type of schooling arrangement for children (aged 5–15) living in private households, analysed by family type

Schooling arrangement	Family type			All children
	Two parents (%)	Lone parent (%)	Foster family (%)	(%)
Ordinary primary	36	44	15	37
Ordinary secondary	25	20	27	24
Special unit attached to primary school	4	3	–	4
Special unit attached to secondary school	5	7	15	6
Special school	27	21	34	26
Other arrangements	3	6	8	3
Total	**100**	**100**	**100**	**100**
Base[a]	773	183	26	989

a Base figures do not add up to 989 as this includes the small number of children living with non-parental relatives.

It is particularly noticeable that the pattern of school placement for foster children was markedly different from both the other two groups, although some caution must be counselled because of the small number involved. Foster children were the least likely of the three groups to be attending ordinary primary schools or special units attached to primary schools. This is partly accounted for by their age distribution, partly because some were already placed in special schools. They were three times as likely as children from two-parent families to have been attending special units attached to secondary schools, and they represented the highest proportion both at special schools and in 'other' schooling arrangements. The foster children were the only one of the three groups in which the majority of the children were not attending ordinary schools. As we shall see in Chapter 9, the children living in foster homes were, in general, more severely disabled than children living with their parents, and this might help to explain the more specialised education that they received.

4. Boarding education

The previous analyses of the schools attended by the 5–15-year-olds include a small proportion (5%) who were placed at boarding schools.[3] Although boarding away was the experience of only a small minority of disabled children, when the number of boarders identified by the survey is grossed up, the significance of this form of provision becomes apparent. The OPCS private households sample produced an estimate of 14,400 boarders, which made boarding schools the most common form of both residential provision and 'out-of-home' care for disabled children. Any consideration of the role of boarding schools in the overall pattern of services for disabled children must also take account of the cost of such placements to local authorities: with the possible exception of long-term hospital care, it is certainly the most expensive form of provision offered.

The great majority (75%) of the boarders were attending residential special schools. The next most frequent arrangement was for children to be in ordinary secondary boarding schools (12%).

Tables 8.6 and 8.7 analyse the pattern of boarding according to the clusters. It will be seen that the proportion of boarding pupils does not increase across Clusters 1–11, as was found with non-residential special school provision, although the children in the cluster with the most severe multiple disabilities do represent the second highest percentage of boarders.

As can be seen from Table 8.6, two of the clusters (2 and 6) in which the children have high levels of behavioural difficulties contain, respectively, the third highest (7%) and highest (10%) proportions of boarding pupils.

Indeed, these two clusters account for 60% of all the boarders, as Table 8.7 shows, indicating the significance of this form of specialist provision in providing for children with behavioural and emotional difficulties. Children with mild disabilities (Cluster 1) were the next largest group of boarding pupils (10%).

Table 8.6 Proportion of day and boarding pupils (aged 5–15) analysed by clusters

Cluster	Description	Day pupil (%)	Boarding pupil (%)	Total (%)	Base
1	Mild disabilities	96	4	100	134
2	Behaviour	93	7	100	250
3	Incontinence	97	3	100	76
4	Fits	97	3	100	40
5	Hearing and communication	99	1	100	68
6	Communication and behaviour	90	10	100	140
7	Personal care	96	4	100	51
8	Hearing and behaviour	95	5	100	66
9	Multiple disabilities	95	5	100	74
10	Multiple and severe	98	2	100	48
11	Multiple and very severe	92	8	100	26
All		**95**	**5**	**100**	**972**

Boys made up three-quarters of the boarding group but only 61% of all the 5–15-year-olds. Almost a third (31%) of the boarders were of primary school age (5–11 years), although most of these were 10–11-year-olds. The majority (69%) were of secondary school age (12–15 years). By contrast, only 40% of all those in the 5–15 group were in this age group.

Table 8.7 Distribution of boarding pupils (aged 5–15) analysed by clusters

Cluster	Description	Boarding pupils (%)
1	Mild disabilities	10
2	Behaviour	33
3	Incontinence	4
4	Fits	2
5	Hearing and communication	2
6	Communication and behaviour	27
7	Personal care	4
8	Hearing and behaviour	6
9	Multiple disabilities	8
10	Multiple and severe	2
11	Multiple and very severe	4
All	*Base = 52*	**100**

Only one of the boarders was from a minority ethnic group. Children from lone-parent families were more likely to be at boarding school than their peers from two-parent families; overall, children from lone-parent families comprised just under a fifth (19%) of the total 5–15 group but 27% of the boarders.

Parents were paying fees for 17% of the boarders. The largest group of fee-paying pupils (44%) attended ordinary boarding schools, a third were at special boarding schools, and the remainder received special education in units attached to ordinary boarding schools. Only three of the clusters (1, 2, and 6) contained fee-paying pupils. All of the fee-paying boarders were boys.

5. Discussion and implications

The OPCS survey of children in private households probably occurred too soon after the implementation of the Education Act 1981 to assess its impact effectively. The picture is confused because of the transitional arrangements that prevailed and the uncertainty that existed among the parents who were interviewed about the new assessment and statementing procedures. However, some priorities can be discerned. The children with the most severe disabilities, as would be expected, were the most likely to have been assessed and to have been given formal written statements. Children from the clusters characterised by high levels of behavioural difficulties also appeared to have received a high priority.

Education at ordinary primary and secondary schools was the most usual arrangement (61%) for the children in private households whom the OPCS defined as disabled. It was only amongst the children with multiple disabilities that arrangements outside the mainstream became the experience of the majority. Children from the clusters characterised by high levels of behavioural difficulties were the next most likely to receive their education in special schools and units.

Marked movements of children between the ordinary and the special education systems occurred around the time of transitions between infant, junior and secondary schools. Although this is not surprising, it does raise questions about the extent to which these transfers reflect administrative pressures rather than the needs of the children. The further question of why the use of special education tends to increase with the child's age also warrants closer investigation: although some impairments are degenerative the great majority are not.

Only a small proportion of disabled children (5%) were placed at boarding school but, when this is grossed up, the importance of boarding schools in the overall child care system becomes more clearly apparent. By the time of the OPCS survey, special boarding schools had overtaken children's homes as the most common form of 'residential care'. *The preponderance of children with behavioural difficulties at these schools suggests that special boarding schools were beginning to provide an alternative to the care offered to children with difficult social backgrounds by social services departments.* As many of the places would have been provided, or at least funded, by local education authorities it appears that a shift of responsibility for out-of-home care arrangements was occurring between local authority departments.

A common thread to emerge from the analysis of the patterns of assessments for special educational needs, provision of statements, education outside of the mainstream and placement at boarding schools was that the children from the two clusters characterised by high levels of behavioural disabilities (Cluster 2 and 6) had a higher proportional representation than might have been expected from the severity of their disabilities. *These findings suggest that behavioural difficulties raised the priority for assessment and statementing under the Education Act 1981 and were influential in diverting pupils away from mainstream education provision.* This raises the question of the ability (or willingness) of ordinary schools to cope with behavioural problems and in that respect, how far the needs of the schools are being met as opposed to those of the children.

In 1997 a major government initiative in the field of special education was launched with the Green Paper *Excellence for All Children: Meeting Special Educational Needs* (Department for Education and Employment, 1997). This placed particular emphasis on: increasing inclusion of special needs children in mainstream schools, raising their standards of attainment, introducing programmes of early identification and support for children with emotional and behavioural difficulties, and setting up new regional planning systems. *As welcome as these policy initiatives are, their impact will be hard to assess unless good routine statistical information is available to measure progress.* However, the current system of annual school statistics is not up to this task. No classification of special needs has been attempted since 1983 (Department of Education, 1983), when the old, much criticised, 'Categories of Handicap' were abandoned in the wake of the Education Act 1981. The classification of disability is certainly not a simple process, but it can be done. Without some form of classification, how can it be shown, for example, whether the number of children with emotional and behavioural difficulties is declining? Or which groups of children are more or less easily included in mainstream provision? As we have demonstrated, at the time of the OPCS survey, the degree of inclusion was heavily influenced by the nature of the children's disabilities. *Policies for children with special educational needs cannot be adequately monitored and assessed if they are treated as a homogenous group.*

In the same year as the OPCS survey, the annual education statistics for schools (Department of Education, 1985) recorded 13,961 children in special boarding schools.[4] The number of boarders steadily declined to 10,407 by 1994, which was the last year this particular statistic was published (Department for Education and Employment, 1994). Given the significance of living away from home for children and the major cost implications of these placements, this is another glaring omission from official statistics.

NOTES TO CHAPTER 8

[1] The term 'additional educational needs' is now usually preferred.

[2] The small number of children living with non-parental relatives have not been separately identified but are included in the total column of Table 8.5.

[3] Children who attended boarding schools and came home regularly were included in the private households survey. Boarding pupils who were resident at their school all year were included in the communal establishments survey (see Chapter 3).

[4] It is likely that several thousand more children were boarding in the independent sector. A total of 5819 children with special educational needs were placed by local authorities in independent schools, the majority of which were likely to be residential establishments, though this is not specified. By 1998 the number had risen to 6018 (DfEE, 1998).

9 | Children with disabilities in the care of local authorities

1. The general picture

As we pointed out in Chapter 1, nine out of ten children with disabilities were looked after by their parents at home. The most likely alternative was placement at a boarding school, from which most children returned home more or less frequently. However, 4% of all the children under the age of 16 were in the care[1] of local authorities – some 2.5% in foster homes[2] and 1.5% in communal establishments.[3] There were other children who were also in care but who did not appear in either of these categories and were, therefore, not enumerated. In particular, there were those who were 'home on trial' (in the terminology of the time)[4] as well as those who attended boarding schools but who returned to their parents in vacations rather than to foster carers.[5]

Although the various additional categories could not be identified from the survey data, we did make some 'best estimates' of their size, based on the assumption that the proportions that applied to the fostered group also applied to them. We also had to try to take account of the fact that OPCS included 16- and 17-year-olds in the adult surveys and that those of them who were in care could not be distinguished. Again, we did this by assuming that, in the various placements, the rate of disability amongst this group was the same as that found for the younger children. All these estimated additions are incorporated in the figures in Table 9.1. It will be noted that, unlike previous chapters, these figures refer only to England and Wales and not to Great Britain as a whole. This is because the child care system in Scotland is somewhat different and does not allow the 'in care' information to be merged with that for England and Wales. However, we do make reference to figures for Scotland at a number of points.

Overall, therefore, we believe that about 18,700 of the 327,000 children with disabilities in England and Wales who were recorded in the OPCS surveys were in local authority care in 1986[6] – a rate of 5.7%. The comparable rate for the child population under 18 as a whole was 0.55%

Table 9.1 Estimates of the number of children in care (under 18) who had disabilities (as defined by OPCS), analysed by the manner of their accommodation (England and Wales, 1986)

Placement	Disabled children		Non-disabled children		All children in care	
	No. in care	%	No. in care	%	No. in care	%
Foster care	9 200	49 (25)	27 807	53 (75)	37 007	52 (100)
Residential care	5 800	31 (33)	11 823	23 (67)	17 623	21 (100)
Home on trial	2 300	12 (21)	8 741	17 (79)	11 041	15 (100)
Other	1 400	7 (27)	3 848	7 (73)	5 248	12 (100)
Total	18 700	100 (26)	52 219	100 (74)	70 919	100 (100)

(Department of Health, 1988; Welsh Office, 1987). Thus, children with disabilities had a markedly greater likelihood of being in care than other children. There are, nevertheless, two provisos that should be borne in mind in connection with these figures.

In the first place, there are those who dispute the inclusion of behavioural problems in any list of disabilities. They would argue that their inclusion by OPCS led to an overestimation of the overall number of disabled children. Furthermore, since behavioural problems are known to be especially widespread amongst children in care, it would follow that any figure for the number of disabled children who were in care would be even more inflated. However, such a conclusion could be reached only with respect to children who suffered solely from behavioural or emotional problems. Certainly, their omission would have reduced the 'in care' rate, but not to such an extent as to invalidate the conclusion that disabled children ran a higher risk than other children of being in care.

The second proviso that ought to be noted is that this 'higher risk' might also have been partly accounted for by the fact that disabled children have remained 'in care' longer than other children and that their number had therefore built up. In order to explore this question, it would have been necessary to have had data about the rates of admission and the duration of the stay in care for this group of disabled children, information that the OPCS survey did not provide. However, looking at the other side of the coin, as the total number of children in care has declined since the 1980s, it may well be that those who are disabled have come to form an increasingly large proportion of the total. This will only have held true, of course, if their rate of admission to care had not fallen in step with that of other children and/or if their stay in care had become proportionately longer than that of those who are not disabled. Unfortunately, we had no way of checking on this.

Table 9.1 also shows that, once in care, it was more likely that disabled children would be placed residentially than other children in care (31% compared with 23% of other children), but that there was only a slightly reduced likelihood that they would be in foster care (49% compared with 53% of the non-disabled). Although a smaller proportion of the disabled children had been placed at 'home on trial' (12% compared with 17% of other children in care), it did appear to have been quite an important disposition, no doubt reflecting moves on the part of social services departments to re-integrate children with their families as a prelude to the discharge of the care order.

Before leaving the discussion of the estimates set out in Table 9.1, we should draw attention to the figures in brackets. Those in the first column of percentages show that 26% of all children in care in England and Wales in 1986 were disabled according to the OPCS definition, that there was a similar proportion of disabled children (25%) to be found amongst those in foster care but a somewhat greater proportion (33%) amongst the children in residential care. Figures such as these have far-reaching implications for both practice and policy, issues to which we shall return in Chapter 16.

2. Disabled children in care living in communal establishments

As we have seen, one of the most eye-catching results of our further analyses of the OPCS data was the discovery that 83% of children with disabilities living in communal establishments were also in care.[7] However, this figure referred to Britain as a whole, since in Scotland only 64% of disabled children in residential facilities were 'in care' (Gordon et al., 1994). When this is taken into account, the percentage for England and Wales rises to 86%.

As can be seen from Table 9.2, three-quarters of the children who were in care in England and Wales and living in residential establishments fell into just three of the clusters (1, 2 and 5 – those characterised by 'behavioural disabilities only'; 'behavioural disabilities together with moderate disabilities of intellectual functioning', and 'severe communication disabilities accompanied by disabilities of behaviour and intellectual functioning'. Indeed, almost half of the children who were in care fell into the first of these clusters, again emphasising the centrality of behavioural difficulties in the range of disabilities to be found amongst children who were in the care of local authorities and placed in communal facilities.

However, when we came to compare the distributions of the 'in care' and the 'not in care' groups living in communal establishments, we found

Table 9.2 Proportions of disabled children (aged 5–15) in care in each cluster compared with those children not in care (communal establishments, England and Wales, 1988)

Cluster	Description	Children in care	Children not in care	Percentage of each cluster in care	All disabled children in communal establishments
		(%)	(%)		(%)
1	Behaviour	48	16	95	42
2	Intellectual and behaviour	17	6	95	14
3	Incontinence and behaviour	5	–	100	4
4	Fits and behaviour	3	2	90	3
5	Communication and behaviour	10	8	87	11
6	Multiple disabilities	6	13	73	7
7	Multiple and severe	4	16	60	7
8	Multiple and very severe	2	13	49	4
9	Multiple and extreme	2	13	48	4
10	Multiple and very extreme	3	13	54	5
Total		**100**	**100**	**86**	**100**
		(*n* = 738)	(*n* = 120)		(*n* = 858)

pronounced differences in relation to the clustering. As Table 9.2 shows, 48% of those in care – but only 16% of those not in care – suffered from solely behavioural disabilities. By contrast, whereas just 7% of the former group fell into the three clusters (8, 9 and 10) characterised by the most severe and multiple disabilities, this proportion rose to 39% amongst those not in care. The data set out in the third column of the table highlight this difference even more clearly. Whereas children in care constituted the great majority (87–100%) in the first five clusters, they comprised about half of those in the three most severe and multiple disabilities categories – far fewer, but still a finding of considerable importance.

It was also noteworthy that 70% of the disabled children who were in care and in communal establishments were subject to compulsory orders of one kind or another. This was similar to the proportion found amongst those who were not disabled but also in care and living residentially.[8] Although we have no comparable data for disabled children in foster care, this finding reinforces the impression that there were usually factors other than their disability alone that led to the children being taken into the care of a local authority.

When we examined the legal status of the children in the survey who were in care and living residentially in relation to the clusters, we found, broadly speaking, that those suffering from severe multiple disabilities and severe mental impairments were more likely to be in care on a voluntary basis than those in the clusters dominated by behavioural disabilities.[9]

We also explored the types of establishment in which disabled children in care were accommodated and compared this with the pattern for those who were not in care (Table 9.3). Most (70%) of the 'in care' children were looked after in facilities run by social services departments, with another quarter being placed in those provided by voluntary or private bodies. Very few were in establishments administered by health or education authorities. This was in sharp contrast to the pattern for the children who were not in care, two-fifths of whom were in health authority facilities but less than a quarter in those provided by social services departments.[10]

Table 9.3 Types of establishment in which children 'in care'/'not in care' lived, and percentage of disabled children in care in each type of establishment (England and Wales, 1988)

Administrative auspices	Children in care (%)	Children not in care (%)	Disabled children in care (%)
Social services departments	70	23	95
Health authorities	2	39	25
Education authorities	2	6	70
Voluntary organisations	15	18	84
Private bodies	10	13	83
DHSS	2	–	100
Total	**100**	**100**	**86**
	(n = 736)	(n = 120)	

The final column of Table 9.3 is also illuminating. Almost all (95%) of the disabled children in social services establishments were in care, as were the great majority of those in voluntary or privately run provisions and in local education authority boarding schools. By contrast, only a quarter of those in health care facilities were in the care of local authorities.

In summary, therefore, the main points about children with disabilities who were in care and who lived in communal establishments are five-fold:

- They constituted almost 83% of all disabled children looked after residentially.
- Seven out of ten had been committed to care by the courts.
- Behavioural disabilities alone – or in conjunction with mental impairments and communication problems – characterised three-quarters of these children.
- Relatively few children suffered from the severest and most multiple forms of disability.
- By contrast, children in communal establishments who were *not* in care were much more often severely and multiply disabled and more frequently accommodated in health service facilities.

3. Disabled children in care living in foster homes

Although the number of disabled children in foster care in the OPCS private households sample was not large, it did furnish a reliable estimate of the actual number and this, as we saw in Table 9.1, exceeded the number in care and in residential settings by nearly 60%. However, as the foster care group is broken down further, the possible sampling error multiplies exponentially. We did not venture, therefore, to draw any but the broadest conclusions at these levels. Nevertheless, several results are worthy of note, although they need to be treated with due caution.

Since there were few disabled children under five in foster care in the sample, we could look at this group only in relation to the cluster analysis for the 5–15-year-olds. Of the children placed with foster carers, 40% fell into the three clusters of the most severe and multiple disabilities – compared with only 16% of the children in the private households sample as a whole. The contrast was equally marked between fostered children and those in communal establishments who were in care, only 7% of whom, as we have seen, fell into the three clusters of greatest severity that were identified in that parallel analysis.

Whereas 21% of all children with disabilities in private households were under five, this proportion fell to 4% amongst those in foster care. On the other hand, whereas another 21% of all those in the private households survey were aged 13–15, this figure rose to 36% for the fostered children. Foster carers, it seems, were not only looking after some severely disabled children but also looking after many who were older than might have been expected from the overall age distribution of disabled children in private households. However, the disabled children in foster placements were not as old, in general, as those who were in care and living in communal establishments, two-thirds of whom were between 13 and 15 years old.

In at least one respect foster carers appeared to be receiving more support than parents who looked after their own disabled children: as we noted in Chapter 6, nearly a fifth of the foster carers (19%) had benefited from respite care in the preceding year compared with only 4% of parent carers. Similarly, whereas 10% of the children looked after by their parents had had an organised 'holiday away' in the previous year, this proportion rose to 28% for the children with foster carers. It was also clear, as would be expected, that all foster carers were visited by a social worker, whereas only only one in ten of the parents received such a visit.

The picture we have, therefore, is that foster carers were:
- looking after proportionately more children with severe and multiple disabilities than either parents or the staff of communal establishments (other than hospitals);

- looking after proportionately more older children than were parents, but proportionately fewer than the residential facilities; but
- probably receiving somewhat more support than the generality of parent carers – in part doubtless reflecting the greater likelihood that they would be caring for more severely disabled children and were in contact with visiting social workers.

4. Discussion and implications

Although relatively few disabled children were in public care, they constituted a quarter of all children who were and, for reasons that we have explained, this proportion may have increased since the surveys were conducted. This represents a considerable challenge for social services departments, not only because they carry special responsibilities for children in their care but also because these responsibilities in turn call for the appropriate training and supervision of residential care staff as well as for the support of the foster carers with whom disabled children in care are placed.

Over and above these challenges there are at least two other issues. The first concerns the question of *the balance of care between residential and foster care provision.* What considerations determine which disabled children in care are looked after in one setting or the other; and is the division the most appropriate? The second issue is the question of *what precipitates disabled children into the care system?* We noted that a large proportion of those living in communal establishments had been committed to care by a court, suggesting that it had been the family circumstances of the child rather than the disability that had been the precipitating factor. Even so, that leaves unanswered the question of the relationship between these circumstances and the disability, particularly, but not exclusively, in the case of a behavioural disability. These are matters about which we should be better informed, not least through a more careful monitoring of the disabilities of children in care. Indeed, Berridge (1997) has pointed out that a 'review of foster care research 20 years ago concluded that little was known about the needs of "handicapped" children in care'. He continued: 'Unfortunately, not a great deal has altered.' In 1989 the British Agencies for Adoption and Fostering sent a short (five question) questionnaire on deaf children in local authority care to all 127 social service authorities in Great Britain. They received a positive response from 35 authorities, giving details of only 70 profoundly deaf or partially hearing children (Warr, 1990). This points to just how little information social service departments have been able to provide on disabled children in their care.

There is a danger that children in care will lose contact with their families, although many do re-establish that contact later. *However, it would seem likely that, for disabled children in care, contact will be more fragile* (some evidence for this appears in Chapter 12 in relation to the parental visiting of those in residential care). Furthermore, it will be more difficult for many of the disabled children in care to re-connect with their families after they leave care. Local authorities, therefore, have an even more exacting task in preparing the disabled child for this transition than they do for other children in their care. How will the disabled child in care be looked after as they become adult? In a good many cases, a solution will have to be found in the close co-operation with adult services for the disabled, a process that is still beset by many problems of organisation and resources.

Nonetheless, *several important changes have occurred in policies and practices* with respect to the disabled child in care since the OPCS surveys were undertaken. Two in particular should be mentioned. *First*, there has been an undoubted increase in respite care, and this may well have served to reduce the number of disabled children coming into long-term care (though we cannot be certain about this). *Secondly*, it is also likely that more of those who are in care will have been placed in foster homes or for adoption.

Thus, for reasons like these, the picture of the disabled child in care may be somewhat different from that which is outlined in this chapter. However, the reality is that we do not know the nature or the extent of any such changes because disabled children in care are not separately identified in the national statistics and rarely identified even in those available locally. In future, the *Looking After Children* materials (Parker *et al.*, 1991; Ward, 1995) that are now being used increasingly by local authorities should enable such distinctions to be made. For the moment, however, the details set out in this chapter offer the best general description we have of the disabled child in care.

NOTES TO CHAPTER 9

[1] We have employed the term 'in care' in preference to the current usage – 'looked after' – since this was how such children were described at the time of the OPCS surveys.

[2] OPCS did not specifically identify 'children in care' in its private households survey, in contrast to what had been done in the communal establishments survey. However, the information gathered in the interviews about payments to foster carers strongly suggested that virtually all the children they looked after were in care.

[3] Of course, the number of disabled children in residential care is based upon the OPCS survey, which omitted children under five on the assumption that there were so few children with disabilities of that age in communal establishments that they could safely be ignored. In England and Wales, in 1986, there were some 400 children of that age in care living in such establishments; but how many suffered from disabilities is unknown.

[4] For a fuller discussion and research about 'home on trial', see Farmer and Parker, 1991.

[5] The OPCS criteria for a child's inclusion in the communal establishments sample were designed to exclude those whose main place of residence, their 'home', was considered to be somewhere other than the establishment in which they were then residing. Thus, it was decided that children who were in care on a compulsory basis would be included, but that those whose stay had been arranged on a voluntary basis and who visited their parental home more than once a fortnight, on average, would be included in the private households survey.

[6] We have used 1986 data for children in care generally since the two OPCS surveys were undertaken in different years, namely 1985 and 1988.

[7] This represented 37% of all children aged 5–15 who were in care in Britain at the time of the survey and who were placed in residential settings – a proportion somewhat higher than the estimate of 33% in Table 9.1 because of differences in the age ranges in question.

[8] The OPCS classification of 'legal status' included children who were subject to parental rights resolutions under the 'care order' category, whereas in the national statistics these children were counted as in voluntary care. The national data do not allow the number of children who were subject to such resolutions and living in communal establishments to be calculated. However, the OPCS definition of 'care order' status can be applied to *all* children in care for the 5–15 age range, and this gives a figure of 72%.

[9] As we have seen, children with disabilities who were in voluntary care and who went home at least once a fortnight were excluded by OPCS from the survey of communal establishments because they were regarded as living in a private household. For this reason, the proportion of disabled children resident in communal establishments who were in care on a voluntary basis is likely to be higher than appears at first sight, and the proportion in compulsory care somewhat lower. But these qualifications are unlikely to alter the general conclusion: that there was an essential similarity between the disabled and the non-disabled in care with regard to their legal care status.

[10] Unfortunately, it is not possible to compare the distribution of disabled children in care and non-disabled children in care between different types of establishments, although rough calculations would suggest that fewer of the latter were in social services homes and more in local education authority boarding schools. However, the picture is, in any case, complicated because of the existence of community homes with education on the premises, some of which were run by voluntary bodies.

10 | The communal establishments survey and the children

1. Background

One of the unique features of the OPCS survey of disability was the inclusion of children who were resident in communal establishments. In earlier surveys these children have tended to be excluded, not separately identified, or were too few to permit any special analysis.[1] Although, as we have seen, the proportion of youngsters between 5 and 15 who were recorded as living in residential settings was only 1.5% of the disabled in this age range, they did constitute a rather special group, not least because the great majority of them (86%) were in the care of local authorities and because almost half were suffering from the single disability of an emotional or behavioural disorder.

Before embarking upon a discussion of some of the characteristics of the children who were living in communal establishments, as well as some of the issues surrounding their care, it is important to appreciate the considerable pains that were taken by OPCS in order to obtain a representative sample. First, it was necessary for them to identify the establishments in which children with disabilities lived. This was done by consulting the various registers held by central government departments, by combing through relevant year-books, and by contacting all local authority social services and education departments, health authorities and the headquarters of all the major voluntary child care organisations. As we saw earlier, a total of 517 authorities provided information (a 95% response rate) on 3421 establishments that offered any form of residential care for children.

The second step was to discover which of these units contained children who met the criteria for inclusion in the survey. From these data, as we explained at the outset, 687 eligible establishments were identified.[2] OPCS noted that the ones that were excluded were predominantly those where the children's stay was relatively short term (Bone and Meltzer, 1989).

Finally, all the units that looked after 11 or more children with disabilities were selected for the survey, and those with fewer children were sub-sampled. In fact, 85% of the establishments were looking after this lesser number, although, of course, they may also have been caring for other children who were not disabled. It was noteworthy that only 7% of the facilities were accommodating more than 15 children with disabilities.

In all, after the various sampling fractions had been applied, 1019[3] children between the ages of 5 and 15 in 288 units were selected. Information about them was collected by means of structured interviews conducted with members of the establishments staff.[4] Only 13 of the children were present during these interviews.

Thus, the OPCS survey was by far the most comprehensive and systematic study of children with disabilities living in communal settings ever undertaken in this country. However, the picture it produced tended to understate the importance and size of this sector of care. One reason for this, as we have seen, was that many children in boarding schools (the most frequently used form of residential provision) were included in the private households survey rather than regarded as part of the population of the communal establishments: the sample to which they were allocated depending upon how often they returned home. Granted that, for boarding pupils, 'home' is usually elsewhere, they do spend a significant proportion of their childhood away from this home.

Similarly, a large number of establishments and their residents were excluded because the children did not satisfy the 'residential status' criteria; in particular, they were not included if, on average, they went home more than once a fortnight. Although such children will have been enumerated in the private households survey (and therefore not lost to the overall estimate) their omission from the communal establishments research meant that, again, the importance of the experience of residential care in the lives of some of the children will have been missed.

These 'exclusions', together with the absence from the survey of the under-5s and the 16- and 17-year-olds, led to the scale of residential care at the time being somewhat underestimated. It also needs to be borne in mind that the study did not record details about successive admissions to communal care. In order to have obtained this fuller account of the part that residential living played in the lives of disabled children, OPCS would have had to have mounted a longer-term inquiry.

Some idea of the possible under-enumeration by OPCS of children in communal establishments may be gained from the 1991 census. This found that there were nearly 1,525,000 people in some 56,000 such establishments in Britain (OPCS, 1993a). The great majority were adults. However, almost 130,700 (or 8.6%) were children under the age of 16. Of these, 10,700 (or 8.2%) were classified as having a 'limiting long-term illness' (LLTI). By contrast, the OPCS survey estimated that there were only 5600 children with disabilities living in communal establishments.

However, a comparison between these two figures is somewhat hazardous because the census divided children who were resident into those whose 'usual address' was the establishment (but who were not the children of resident staff) and those whose 'usual address' was 'elsewhere'. Seventy-six per cent of the resident children with LLTI were assigned to this latter category, leaving just 2500 who were regarded as permanent residents. Clearly, as with the OPCS survey, a problem arises with respect to the enumeration and classification of those disabled children who were short-term admissions (probably for respite care or hospital treatment) and those who, although longer-term residents, went home from time to time and whose 'usual address' was considered by the respondents to be their home.

Thus, the upper census figure of children with LLTI living in communal establishments in 1991 was 10,700 and the lower figure was 2500 – all depending on the interpretation of 'usual address'. Even so, the upper figure does give some indication of the magnitude of the number of disabled children who might have been 'defined out' by OPCS as a result of the application of their 'residence' criteria. Obviously, were the figure of 10,700 to be substituted for the OPCS figure of 5600, the rate of disabled children living in residential establishments would rise from 1.5% to nearly 3%.

Despite these various notes of caution and the alternative figures derived from the 1991 census, the information that the OPCS survey *did* provide is of considerable importance and, in terms of its scale and range, it remains the best that we have. After offering a brief profile of the children included in the study, we discuss, in subsequent sections and chapters, some of the issues relating to their residential care to which our further analysis drew attention.

2. Profiles of the children

Age

The great majority (88%) of the children in the residential survey were between 10 and 15 years of age. Indeed, two-thirds of them (65%) were 13, 14 or 15 years old. Nonetheless, one in eight were between 5 and 9 years, emphasising that there was an important minority of younger children whose particular needs should not be overlooked.

Table 10.1 compares the ages of disabled children in communal establishments and in private households, as found by the OPCS surveys. The differences are immediately apparent and of a kind that one might expect: as some children with disabilities get older, they are likely to move into residential care. Had 16- and 17-year-olds been included, the differences would doubtless have been even more pronounced.

Table 10.1 Ages of children with disabilities (under 16) in communal establishments and in private households

Ages	Children in communal establishments 1988 (%)	Children in private households 1985 (%)
0–4	–	21
5–9	12	34
10–12	23	24
13–15	65	21
Total	100	100
Base	1000	1200

Note:
OPCS assumed that there were few, if any, children under five in communal establishments and so omitted them. It should be noted, however, that the 1991 census found a relatively large number of such children.

Taking the residential establishments' population alone, however, it was plain from the cluster analysis that the older children were to be found in greater number in those groups characterised by behavioural difficulties, either singly or in combination; indeed, in the cluster where *only* behavioural disabilities existed (Cluster 1), 95% of the children were between 10 and 15, whereas in Clusters 8, 9, and 10 (characterised by multiple severe disabilities) the proportion in this age group fell to 72%.

There was no difference in the children's ages with respect to gender or whether or not they were in care. However, as Table 10.2 indicates, children in social services department establishments tended to be older than those in facilities run by other agencies.

Table 10.2 Ages of children analysed by the organisation administering the establishment, 1988

Age	Social services department (%)	Local health organisations (%)	Voluntary agencies (%)	Privately run (%)
5–9	9	19	15	13
10–15	91	81	85	87
Total	100	100	100	100
	(n = 578)	(n = 107)	(n = 185)	(n = 103)

In sharp contrast to those cared for in private households, those who lived in communal establishments were predominantly adolescents. Nevertheless, younger children were to be found in residential provisions, most notably in those run by health authorities. However, in order to obtain a fuller picture of the influence of age on the population of children with disabilities cared for communally, we examined how old the children were at the time of their admission.

Unfortunately, OPCS only collected data on admission to the establishments in which children were currently accommodated, although they may have been transferred from other residential facilities or have experienced spells of communal care earlier in their lives. In fact, three-fifths of the children had come into the establishments from a private household,[5] the rates being similar amongst those who were or were not in care. However, proportionately more of those in care had come from social services facilities (33% compared with 11%) and more of those not in care had been transferred from a hospital (17% compared with 4%). Since, therefore, at least 40% of the children had had previous placements in a communal establishment, the ages of admission to the residential *system* would, overall, have been younger than was indicated by the data for admission to the current establishments.[6] Nevertheless, despite its limitations, the information that was gathered by OPCS is of considerable interest. Eight per cent of the children had been under five at the last admission, 22% between five and nine and 70% were ten years of age or older. Furthermore, there were significant differences between the admission ages of children who were in care and those who were not; for instance, whereas only 5% of those in care had entered the establishment under the age of five, this proportion rose to 22% amongst those who were not in care. At the other end of the age range, three-quarters of the 'in care' group, but only half of those who were not in care, were ten or older at admission.

The fact that some 1 in 12 of the children had come into the communal establishments in which they were living before they were five, rather puts into question the assumption made by OPCS (admittedly on the basis of a preliminary examination) that there were so few children under five in residential care that they could be omitted from the study. However, those children who had been admitted to the establishments under five were mainly to be found in the three clusters of severest multiple disabilities, whilst most of the rest were contained in the two clusters (6 and 7) mainly characterised by severe mental impairment. By contrast, the children who were over ten at entry were principally (79%) those allocated to the clusters where behavioural problems predominated, albeit together with other disabilities. The pattern of these differences is evident in Table 10.3 which gives the mean ages of the children at admission in each of the ten clusters selected for the communal establishments sample. There was, as can be seen, an almost completely smooth reduction in the average age of entry as the severity of the disabilities increased.

Table 10.3 Mean age at admission to present establishment analysed by clusters (1988)

Cluster	Description	Mean age in years	Base
1	Behaviour	13.03	412
2	Intellectual and behaviour	12.48	137
3	Incontinence and behaviour	11.23	41
4	Fits and behaviour	11.33	31
5	Communication and behaviour	11.29	102
6	Multiple disabilities	9.10	59
7	Multiple and severe	8.69	64
8	Multiple and very severe	7.30	34
9	Multiple and extreme	6.49	34
10	Multiple and very extreme	6.13	50
All children		**11.32**	**964**

The average age at admission to the establishments was somewhat over 11 years (although it would have been rather less for first admissions to the residential *system*). Children who were in care and those in the clusters in which behavioural problems predominated (categories that overlapped considerably) had entered at older ages than those who were not in care and those who suffered from the most severe multiple disabilities.

Gender

As OPCS pointed out, 'there was no difference in the age distribution of boys and girls'. However, 'since the prevalence of disability at all ages was greater for boys than for girls it is not surprising that 62% of the sample of children [in communal establishments] were boys' (Meltzer *et al.*, 1989, p. 74). As we have seen, almost the same figure was recorded in the private households sample. Further analysis revealed that the boys and girls in this survey were equally likely to have been in care. Nor were there any significant differences between them with respect to the clusters. In particular, there was no significant difference between the boys and girls in terms of their presence in the clusters dominated by disabilities of behaviour.

Ethnicity

Seven per cent of the disabled children living in communal establishments were from minority ethnic groups, compared with 6% of those in private households. However, both figures were slightly lower than the 9% of all children from ethnic minorities recorded in the 1988–9 Labour Force

Surveys (OPCS, 1991).[7] In general, therefore, as we saw in Chapter 3, children from these backgrounds were somewhat under-represented amongst those with disabilities discovered in both of the OPCS surveys. In terms of the children in communal care, however, those from Asian backgrounds were less numerous than might have been expected and those with African-Caribbean, African and Arab antecedents were more numerous. However, it was the group with mixed origins (which OPCS classed together with 'ethnic minorities') that was particularly over-represented (2.8% of the children in communal facilities compared with 1.3% of those in private households). However, the actual number of children from ethnic minorities in the sample was so small that conclusions should be treated with caution. Nevertheless, it is worth bearing in mind that 40% of those described by OPCS as being from ethnic minorities and living in communal establishments were classed as of 'mixed origins', whereas only 17% in total were recorded as having Indian, Pakistani, Bangladeshi or Chinese backgrounds.

These findings are broadly in line with those of other studies that have examined the ethnicity of *all* children looked after by local authorities. Although, in general, it has been found that black or ethnic minority children have been over-represented in care, in residential homes or amongst those waiting to be adopted (Baxter *et al.*, 1990), it has also been revealed that the largest single minority group is of mixed parentage and that children from Asian families have been somewhat under-represented (Kahan, 1994).[8]

Why were the children living in a communal establishment?

OPCS asked why children were living in the establishment and, of course, there was often more than one reason. The categories that they employed are listed in Table 10.4 and divided by gender.

Table 10.4 Reasons why children were living at establishments, by gender (1988)

Reason given	Boys (%)	Girls (%)	All (%)
Sexual abuse	4	15	8
Physical abuse	6	8	7
Parents unable to cope with the child's disabilities	32	31	32
Broken home	29	30	29
Reason not given	31	21	28
	(n = 615)	(n = 383)	(n = 998)

Note: The figures add up to more than 100% because of multiple responses.

Several features are of interest. First, in the case of 8% of all the children, sexual abuse was said to be a reason why they were in residential care. However, for girls the rate rose to 15%. Given the claim in several studies and in the Utting Report (1997) that disabled children are more vulnerable to abuse than others (Kennedy, 1990, Crosse *et al.*, 1993), these rates look rather low. However, in her review of the literature, Westcott (1991) argued that claims about these children's greater vulnerability were not as yet adequately supported by empirical evidence. Despite a number of recent studies, the level of risk of abuse experienced by disabled children in Britain is still unknown (Westcott, 1993; Kennedy, 1996).

A second noteworthy aspect of Table 10.4 is the large percentage of instances where no reason for admission was given. At first sight, this suggests that a large proportion of the respondents (the establishments' staff) were unable to say why about a quarter of the children were with them. However, the highest proportions of cases where no reason was given (45%, 41% and 38%) were to be found in, respectively, establishments run by private bodies, health services and voluntary organisations. This was in contrast to the facilities of social services departments where the staff were unable to provide reasons for the admission of only 19% of the children.

These are disturbing findings if they reflect a lack of information being held by the establishments about the children's backgrounds. However, because of the way in which OPCS defined and interpreted 'no reason given', such a conclusion should not be drawn hastily. It seems likely that there was some confusion between 'the reasons why a child was living in the establishment' and the reasons for their behaviour or other disabilities. Thus, although it may have been known that certain problems led to the child's admission, a coding of 'reason not given' may have been employed if the respondent's answer only described the *child's* problems. Because of this, some caution should be exercised in interpreting 'reason not given'. Even so, it is interesting that a measure of confusion could have arisen about the reasons why a child was in residential care, added to which the reasons for *admission* would not necessarily have been the same as the reasons why a child *continued* to live in the establishment. The general picture, however, is one upon which Morris (1995) has commented, claiming that not enough is known about the circumstances in which disabled children enter residential establishments. A decade after the OPCS study, she found that few local authorities had any information about why the children were living in residential care except that they were said to be 'looked after to meet family needs' – a descriptive category employed in the statistical returns that are required by the Department of Health.

A third notable feature of Table 10.4 is the rather high proportion (29%)

of cases where a 'broken home' was given as the reason for a child's residence. Again, however, this raises some definitional problems. OPCS included single parenthood and homelessness, as well as parental separation and divorce in this category, but situations where parents were unable to cope because of *their* problems were also described in this way. These included, for example, illness, drug or alcohol addiction and imprisonment. Despite these questions of classification, the fact remains that, in some three in ten instances, family disruption was given as a reason for the child's being in the establishment. This may lend some support to Quine and Pahl's (1989) evidence that a behaviourally disturbed disabled child is liable to create marital tension and breakdown. However, it was clearly the intention of OPCS to distinguish between family disruption (as a reason for admission to residential care) and those situations in which the parents were unable to cope with the child's disabilities, even though the family remained intact.

When these data were broken down by whether or not the children were in care, some clear differences emerged, as is apparent from Table 10.5.

Table 10.5 Reasons why children were living in an establishment, analysed by whether or not they were in care (England and Wales, 1988)

Reason given	In care (%)	Not in care (%)	All (%)
Sexual abuse	10	1	9
Physical abuse	9	2	8
Parents unable to cope with the child's disabilities	31	39	32
Broken home	32	24	31
Reason not given	23	35	25
	(n = 738)	(n = 118)	(n = 856).

Note:
The difference between the figures in this table and those in Table 10.4 arise because this table only covers data for England and Wales. The figures add up to more than 100% because of multiple responses.

As might be expected, proportionately more of the children in care had been abused and/or had come from broken homes (as defined by OPCS) than those who were not in care. On the other hand, 'no reason' for the child's being at the establishment was recorded more frequently for children who were *not* in care than for those who were. It would, perhaps, not be surprising, that establishments did not have as much information about the backgrounds of 'not in care' children as they did for those 'in care', but in both instances the lack would seem to be disturbing.

The proportions of both the 'in care' and 'not in care' groups, where the inability of parents to cope with the care of their child was given as a reason for their being in residence, were, one might think, on the low side, given the severity of the disabilities of many of the children. Again, this would tend to suggest that in a number of cases it was not simply the problems associated with the child's disabilities that had led to admission to residential care; rather that it was these problems combined with other factors.

When looked at in terms of the clusters, it was noteworthy that those groups characterised by multiple severe disabilities (Clusters 8, 9 and 10) contained only 3% of the children known to have been sexually and/or physically abused. By contrast, 77% of those where such abuse was known to have occurred fell into the four clusters (1–4) in which behavioural disabilities were common, albeit combined with other disabilities such as 'fits' in the case of the fourth cluster. Furthermore, as might now be expected from our earlier results, relatively large proportions of children (50%) in the two most severely disabled clusters (9 and 10) were said to be living in the establishment because their parents could not cope with their disabilities. For all other groups the proportion was about 30%. Likewise, the existence of a 'broken home' was given as a reason for residential care for only 3% of the children in the two most severely disabled clusters, but for 74% of those in the clusters characterised by behavioural disabilities. On all these counts, the clusters marked by the children's mental impairment fell approximately mid-way between these extremes.

Thus, incomplete though the OPCS data are about reasons for admission, they do draw attention to three potentially important issues. *First*, rather different reasons appear to have led to the admission of the most severely multiply disabled children than the rest, where 'social' factors seem to have played a part along with the 'disability' factors. *Secondly*, previous abuse was more likely to have been reported in the case of children in the clusters where behavioural disabilities were significant than it was amongst the other clusters. *Thirdly*, although possibly accounted for by problems of interpretation, the large number of respondents who failed to offer any reasons for a child being in their establishment must raise some doubts about just how much was known about the children's backgrounds.

3. The duration of residence

One indication of the instability in children's lives is the frequency with which they have had to move. The OPCS data gave some idea of this since they included the duration of each child's residence in the establishments up to the time of the interviews. Obviously, this was related to how old they were when they were admitted. For example, whereas 72% of those who had entered before they were five had been there for five years or more, the comparable figure for those who were between the ages of five and nine at the time of their admission was 33%. These data are displayed in Table 10.6 and the differences are significant.

Table 10.6 Duration of child's stay in present establishment, analysed by age at admission (1988)

Duration of stay	Age at admission			
	Under 5 (%)	5–9 (%)	10+ (%)	All (%)
Less than 1 year	1	14	46	35
1–3 years	15	35	47	42
3–5 years	11	18	5	9
5 years or more	72	33	1	14
Total	100	100	100	100
	(n = 79)	(n = 211)	(n = 674)	(n = 964)

Slightly more than a third of the children had been resident for less than a year, but nearly a quarter had lived in their present placement for three years or more. However, this pattern varied according to whether or not the children were in care and according to the different clusters, as can be seen from Tables 10.7 and 10.8.

Table 10.7 Duration of child's stay in present establishment, analysed by whether or not they were in care (England and Wales, 1988)

Duration of stay	In care (%)	Not in care (%)
Less than 1 year	40	18
1–3 years	45	34
3–5 years	8	13
5 years and more	8	35
Total	100	100
	(n = 717)	(n = 111)

Clearly, whereas nearly half of those not in care had been resident for three years or more, this applied to only 16% of those who were in care. Again, as we have noted earlier, this latter group was also more likely to have entered the establishments at an older age.

When we looked at the data in relation to the clusters, it was apparent that a marked difference existed as far as the length of the children's residence was concerned. The children who had been in the establishments longest were those with severe multiple disabilities (Clusters 8, 9 and 10). Those who had lived there for the shortest period were children in Clusters 1, 2 and 4, where behavioural disabilities were prominent (Table 10.8).

Table 10.8 Duration of child's stay in present establishment, analysed by cluster (1988) (*n* = 965)

Cluster	Description	Duration of stay			
		Under 1 year (%)	1–3 years (%)	3–5 years (%)	5 years or more (%)
1	Behaviour	49	44	5	2
2	Intellectual and behaviour	39	50	6	4
3	Incontinence and behaviour	21	73	4	2
4	Fits and behaviour	43	28	17	12
5	Communication and behaviour	24	39	8	19
6	Multiple disabilities	14	46	20	19
7	Multiple and severe	15	38	16	31
8	Multiple and very severe	5	35	13	47
9	Multiple and extreme	13	15	23	49
10	Multiple and very extreme	6	21	9	65

Overall, therefore, the evidence points to there having been reasonably long stays for the children in the survey, with considerable placement stability for those who were most severely and multiply disabled. As might be expected, the long-staying children were in health authority facilities, children who had arrived more recently in those run by social services.

4. Future moves

In order to obtain a more accurate picture of the degree of stability or change that the children in communal establishments were likely to have experienced, we needed to know something about what was likely to happen to them in the future. Fortunately, OPCS had asked respondents whether or not a move was being planned for the child in the next 12 months. Overall, it was reported that such a change was being contemplated for 42% of the children. This struck us as a rather large proportion. However, there was a significant difference between the children who were in care and those who were not. A move was planned for 44% of the former, but for only 27% of the latter (in England and Wales). It was also revealed that, the younger the child, the somewhat more likely it was that a move was in mind. For example, this was the case for 48% of those under 10 compared with 40% of the older children. The most significant difference with respect to 'planned moves', however, emerged in relation to how long the child had been in the present establishment. Table 10.9 sets out the results.

Table 10.9 Whether or not a move for the child was planned within the next 12 months, analysed by child's duration of stay in establishment (1988)

Duration of stay	Move planned (%)	Move not planned (%)	Don't know (%)
Less than 6 months	52	28	20
6 months, less than 1 year	52	41	6
1–3 years	42	51	7
3–5 years	28	60	12
5 years or more	16	76	8
All children	**41**	**51**	**8**
	($n = 392$)	($n = 490$)	($n = 83$)

It is clear that, the longer the child had been in residence, the considerably less likelihood there was of a move being planned – either to return home, to go to foster parents, to be adopted or to be sent to another establishment. By contrast, moves were being planned for about half of the children who had been resident for less than a year, although for one in five of those who had been resident for less than six months no plan – either to stay or move – had yet been made.

Of course, we know from earlier discussion that it was the most severely multiply disabled children who were the typical long-term residents. However, the fact that the respondents were able to say that 'no move was planned' for half of all the children does indicate that the disabled, unlike other groups of children in communal care, are likely to be (and considered by the staff to be) resident in a particular establishment on a 'permanent' basis. Again, it must be borne in mind that OPCS excluded short-term admissions from its sample.

In terms of 'planned moves', therefore, it was clear that some change in the form of the child's care was being contemplated for about two-fifths of the children within the next 12 months. It would have been valuable to have known just what kind of move was in mind and why, but this information was not available. All that could be gleaned from the OPCS data was whether or not the unit in which a child lived prepared children for adoption, not if a *particular* child was being so prepared. In fact, only 5% of the children were reported to be living in such establishments, most of whom (91%) were in care. Another indication of the likelihood of adoption was provided by the data collected about social work and volunteer visitors. Five per cent of the children, most of whom were in care (84%), had been visited by a Be-My-Parent[9] worker during the previous year. In terms of the clusters, it was apparent that a wide range of children had been seen by staff from this adoption scheme, the only exceptions being those broadly grouped as having disabilities characterised by fits (Cluster 4) and those classified as suffering from multiple and very extreme disabilities (Cluster 10). Otherwise, there was no marked pattern to the kinds of children involved.

Since no move was being considered for about half the children, it seems reasonable to conclude that there was one 'well-established' group and one for whom long-term arrangements still had to be settled. As one might expect, the 'still unsettled' group contained a disproportionate number of children who had been resident in their present establishments for a relatively short time. However, it also included a large proportion of children who were in care and whom our analysis placed in clusters characterised by behavioural disabilities or in those where behaviour, although combined with other disabilities, was a prominent feature.

5. Discussion and implications

As well as considering the matters raised in this chapter, in what follows we reiterate and integrate some of the relevant material discussed in Chapters 2 and 3.

Although the OPCS survey of disabled children in communal establishments estimated that *they accounted for 1.5% of all disabled children* in 1988, this was almost certainly a minimum figure. Various categories of short-term residents were excluded from the sample, as were most of the children who attended boarding schools. Indeed, the 1991 census figures for children with 'long-term limiting illness' (LLTI) who resided in communal establishments indicated that the proportion could have been as high as 3% if LLTI was considered to be comparable with 'disability'. Whatever the actual proportion, then or now, it remains a small fraction of all disabled children.

It is, nevertheless, an important minority, different in several ways from the majority of disabled children who are cared for in their own homes. In the first place, *children who lived in communal facilities were older* – 88% were 10 years old or more compared with 45% of those in private households. However, although adolescents predominated in the *residential units*, these *still sheltered a notable proportion of younger children. The question of age,* therefore, *should obviously be a matter of concern* in the planning and provision of residential care for disabled children. In the case of the majority, the additional problems will be those associated with adolescence and with size and weight when personal care is needed. For those younger children who may be cared for alongside more numerous older peers, there will be a risk that their particular developmental needs will be submerged by those of the majority.

A *second* way in which the children in communal establishments differed from those in private households was in *their average number of disabilities*. For those in residential facilities *the figure was 3.3*; for those living with families it was 2.6. Furthermore, whereas 20% of those in communal establishments had six or more disabilities, only 8% of the children in private households experienced this many. On the other hand, there was a substantial minority (38%) of the children in the residential sample who had *only* a behavioural disability, whereas this applied to just 13% of those in private households. Likewise, amongst all the children in residential care, *94% had a disability of behaviour*, albeit combined with other disabilities. In the case of those in private households this proportion fell to 65%. Hence, although behavioural problems were widespread, they were particularly pronounced in the residential sector. *This – along with the multiplicity of disabilities – raises major questions concerning the training of residential care staff; about the availability of appropriate therapies that address problems of behaviour; and about the relations between children* who are brought together in communal settings. It seems unlikely that issues such as these have disappeared in the intervening years.

There was, of course, a *third* difference between the children in communal establishments and those living in private households: *a significantly greater proportion* of the former *were in the care of local authorities* (86% compared with about 2.5%).[10] Hence, *social services departments had (and have) a particular and heavy responsibility* for the well-being of most of the disabled children who are looked after residentially. Furthermore, although the children who were 'in care' were found in all kinds of establishments, they formed the largest proportion in homes run by social services departments. Over and above this, these departments will have an added responsibility for the inspection and registration of many of the provisions in the voluntary and private sectors. Thus, how social services discharge this demanding mixture of responsibilities will have an especially important impact on the standard and type of residential care provided for disabled children. Of course, social services also have parallel responsibilities for the more numerous disabled children in their care in foster homes as well as for all other disabled children and their families 'in need' in the community.

Certain other issues raised in this chapter do not lend themselves to comparison with the private households sample but remain important in their own right. One revolves around *the 'reasons' given for the children being in residential settings*. Although physical and/or sexual abuse was reported to be a factor with respect to 15% of the children (with sexual abuse having been much more common amongst the girls than the boys), 'a broken home' was given as a precipitating reason for admission for 29%.[11] Admittedly, 'broken home' is a crude concept, but it offers a rough demarcation between the families from which children eventually entered residential care for reasons of 'social disruption' and those from which they entered primarily because of their disability. Of course, the figures for 'abuse' and 'broken homes' admissions will have overlapped, so they cannot simply be added together. Even so, one might conclude that *for at least three out of ten of the children, the social circumstances in their families had conspired with, or in some cases accentuated, the problems of their disability, thereby leading to their living in a communal establishment*.

This, however, is to ignore the large minority of cases where the staff were unable to give reasons as to why the child was resident. That, in itself, raised a second specific issue; namely, the question of *how well informed communal establishments were* about each child's background. This, in its turn, leads on to a third matter; that is, *the plans that should be made* for disabled children in residential care. Without full information, these will not be securely founded. We saw that a quarter of the children had been in their present placement for three years or more and, indeed, that one in seven had been resident for longer than five years. On the other hand, about a third had been in their present accommodation for less than a year. These *different durations suggest that different issues of planning for the children's futures may arise*. For example, for 20% of the newly arrived children (that is, within the previous six months) no plan about whether or not they would be moving elsewhere had yet been formulated. For those who had been in the same establishment for several years, the need to plan for their long-term future may have faded into the background as a false sense of enduring permanence began to take hold. Whatever the actual situation, the need for planning is clear, and the essential contribution to this of sufficient and accurate information is indisputable.

NOTES TO CHAPTER 10

[1] The previous OPCS surveys of disability did not include children (Harris *et al.*, 1971; Buckle, 1971). The Committee on Child Health Services had to compile its own estimate of the national prevalence of childhood disability from the results of several local studies (Court, 1976). Two studies based upon the General Household Survey did include children, but not those living in communal establishments, and the samples were much smaller than in the OPCS inquiries (Weale and Bradshaw, 1980; OPCS, 1985). Prior to the

OPCS surveys, the most comprehensive study of childhood disability was that mounted by Rutter and his colleagues on the Isle of Wight (Rutter *et al.*, 1970). The great strength of this study was that it was based upon individual medical, psychiatric and psychological examinations but, because of its restricted geographic and age coverage (9–11-year-olds), general conclusions could not be drawn with confidence.

[2] The remaining establishments were excluded for one or more of four reasons: that they had no children resident who were under the age of 16; that none of the children met the 'residence' criteria; that they contained no children who met the 'disability' criteria; or that they catered for fewer than four children.

[3] For the purposes of analysis this total was weighted down to a base figure of 1000.

[4] As OPCS pointed out, it was often necessary to approach several members of staff in order to complete a schedule for one child; knowledge about the child could be scattered (Bone and Meltzer, 1989).

[5] However, it will be recalled that children who were resident in establishments from which they went home for holidays were included in the private households survey, as were many of those in boarding schools. Likewise, those in foster homes were classified as living in private households.

[6] The OPCS finding in respect of the children's prior experience of residential care is consistent with a number of other studies of disabled and non-disabled children (Packman *et al.*, 1986; Fisher *et al.*, 1986). Indeed, in Berridge's (1985) survey of children's homes, 43% of the residents had lived in two or more residential establishments before their current placement. Some ten years later, a similar study reported that 48% of the children had had at least one previous period in communal care (Berridge and Brodie, 1997).

[7] The figures used for the comparison are derived from Table 5.30, p. 25.

[8] Shah (1992, 1997) has highlighted some of the reasons why the needs of disabled children in Asian families may fail to be identified or, if they are identified, why they fail to be met in a culturally sensitive fashion.

[9] 'Be-My-Parent' is a scheme which endeavours to find adopters for children needing adoption.

[10] However, this figure will have included some children who were in care but accommodated in boarding schools; as we have pointed out, the actual number was not recorded by OPCS.

[11] It was not absolutely clear whether the reasons given for a child's admission to the present establishment actually referred to the reasons for their being taken into care in the first place.

11 | The establishments and their finance

1. The bodies responsible for the establishments

As we have explained, the number of children in boarding schools was under-reported in the residential care survey because of its design. Thus, only 3% of them were listed as living in units run by education authorities. However, the figure does show that there was a minority who probably did not leave during the normal vacations, and there were almost certainly others who experienced 52-weeks-a-year residence in schools in the voluntary and private sectors.[1]

Likewise, very few of the youngsters in the survey lived in the establishments that were run directly by the DHSS (the youth training centres – see Bullock *et al.*, 1998). For this reason, both they and those in education authority facilities have been omitted from the subsequent discussion and from the tables that follow after Table 11.1.

Table 11.1 Administration of establishments and proportion of children with disabilities (aged 5–15) living in each (1988)

Administrative body	Percentage of children
Social services departments	58
Voluntary bodies	19
Privately run	10
Health authorities	9
Education authorities	3
DHSS (centrally)	1
Total (Base = 1000)	**100**

By far the largest proportion of the disabled children in residential care (58%) lived in local authority homes run by social services departments, 19% lived in homes provided by voluntary societies and 10% in homes that were privately run. Hospitals or other health services' units were responsible for comparatively few of the children (9%). It was also apparent that the establishments administered by the different bodies looked after a rather different age range of children, as was explained in the previous chapter (Table 10.2). In brief, older children were to be found in establishments run by social services departments and younger ones in those administered by health authorities.

These are all figures for Great Britain as a whole, but it was evident that the pattern in Scotland was different. There, more of the children were in health service establishments (22%) and in facilities run by voluntary bodies (39%). Only 26% lived in units run by social work departments. Furthermore, as we have seen in Chapter 9, a substantially smaller proportion (64%) than in England and Wales were in the care of local authorities. However, returning to the whole of Britain, another major difference between the health sector establishments and the others was to be found in relation to the time that the children had spent as residents. Of course, these data did not reflect the full duration of stay because of the different dates of admission, but, even so, as Table 11.2 demonstrates, the pattern was quite distinct.

Table 11.2 Administration of establishments analysed by duration of child's stay (1988)

Administrative body	Duration of stay (%)				
	Under 6 months	6 months, under 1 year	1–3 years	3–5 years	Over 5 years
Social services departments	11	33	44	6	5
Voluntary bodies	2	23	43	11	21
Privately run	1	15	52	16	15
Health authorities	1	11	19	13	57
All (n = 964)	7	28	42	9	14

Whereas only 5% of the children in social services run establishments had been there for five years or more, this figure rose to 57% amongst those in facilities administered by health authorities.[2] Thus, disproportionately more of the long-term residents were to be found in these establishments and, to a lesser extent, in the voluntary and private sectors as well. Nonetheless, it is important to note that social services homes were not – at least in 1988 and in respect of children with disabilities – dealing exclusively with short-term admissions: over half of the children had already been resident for a year or more. However, as we have repeatedly pointed out, OPCS omitted very short-term admissions from its study, preferring to include these children in its survey of private households.

In order to obtain a more precise picture of the differences between the sectors, we related them to the ten clusters already described. Clear distinctions emerged. For instance, whereas 52% of the children in social services homes exhibited *only* behavioural disabilities, this proportion fell to just 3% in health service facilities. Put in a different way, of the children in the first four clusters, all of which included substantial components of behavioural disturbance, 70% were in social services homes compared with only 4% in health service establishments.

In contrast to these results, it was notable that, whereas 4% of the children in social services homes were grouped in the three clusters of multiple and severe disabilities, this figure increased to 65% amongst those who were looked after in health service provisions. The voluntary and private sectors occupied intermediate positions. The data are set out in Table 11.3, where the figures in brackets give the proportion of each cluster that is looked after by the different agencies – a matter we discuss in the final section.

Table 11.3 Distribution of clusters between establishments administered by different bodies (1988) (%)

Cluster	Description	Administrative bodies									
		Social services		Voluntary		Private		Health		All	
1	Behaviour	52	(75)	31	(14)	39	(10)	3	(1)	42	(100)
2	Intellectual and behaviour	17	(74)	13	(18)	8	(6)	2	(1)	14	(100)
3	Incontinence and behaviour	5	(69)	6	(26)	2	(5)	–	–	4	(100)
4	Fits and behaviour	3	(59)	5	(31)	3	(10)	–	–	3	(100)
5	Communication and behaviour	12	(68)	13	(24)	5	(5)	3	(3)	11	(100)
6	Multiple disabilities	5	(46)	6	(17)	14	(22)	9	(14)	6	(100)
7	Multiple and severe	2	(18)	14	(39)	12	(18)	18	(25)	7	(100)
8	Multiple and very severe	2	(32)	3	(16)	4	(11)	16	(40)	4	(100)
9	Multiple and extreme	1	(16)	4	(19)	6	(16)	19	(49)	4	(100)
10	Multiple and very extreme	1	(12)	5	(18)	7	(14)	30	(56)	5	(100)
Total		**100**	**(60)**	**100**	**(19)**	**100**	**(11)**	**100**	**(10)**	**100**	
		($n = 578$)		($n = 185$)		($n = 103$)		($n = 94$)		($n = 961$)	

The picture that emerges, therefore, is of a social services sector caring mainly (but not exclusively) for active children with behavioural and emotional disabilities together with those of intellectual functioning; a health service sector providing, on a long-term basis, for children who suffered from multiple and very severe disabilities which, in a majority of cases, profoundly limited their ability to communicate, learn, walk independently and attend to their own personal care; and voluntary and private sectors that took a more mixed range of children in terms of the nature of their disabilities.

2. The pattern of financial support

The cost of the great majority of the placements was borne by public funds. Table 11.4 sets out the pattern of contributions, thereby giving some idea of the financial transfers that occurred between the different administrations. This information was not collected for the health service establishments, although contributions *from* health authorities to other bodies were recorded.

Table 11.4 Proportion of placements financially supported (in full or in part) from various sources (1988)

Financially supported by	Placements in establishments administered by:		
	Social services departments (%)	Voluntary bodies (%)	Private agencies (%)
Social services departments	96	74	79
Local health authority	..	2	4
Local education authority	2	33	48
Charitable or voluntary body	..	46	7
Parent or relative	8	2	1
Other	2	9	3
No information	3	3	1
	(n = 578)	(n = 185)	(n = 103)

Notes:
a .. = less than 0.5%.
b Placements may have been funded from more than one source, hence totals add to more than 100%.
c n overall = 866 because of the omission of the health services and other establishments.

It can be seen that social services departments contributed to the cost of three-quarters of the placements in voluntary establishments and to almost four-fifths of those in the private sector. Likewise, local education departments contributed to the cost of a third of the placements in voluntary units and to almost a half of those run privately. This would suggest that many of these latter placements were in facilities regarded as boarding schools.

However, it was not solely because the children were 'in care' that social services departments carried a financial responsibility for so many; they contributed to the support of almost three-fifths (61%) of the children in the sample who were *not* in care. Likewise, nearly a third (31%) of these children were financially supported (again, fully or partially) by education authorities and almost a fifth (19%) by contributions from charitable or voluntary bodies (either directly or indirectly).[3]

Thus, whether the children were in care or not, the cost of their placements in communal establishments was met predominantly from public monies; indeed, 88% of all placements were paid for wholly or partially from this source. In only 5% of the placements was the cost offset by parental payments. Given the large proportion of the children with disabilities in residential establishments who were in care, this suggests a widespread exemption from the requirement on their parents to make a financial contribution. This may either have been because, on assessment, they were found to be too poor or because they were not pursued for contributions that they had failed to make.

Likewise, any impression that the private sector was used by parents paying privately was shown to be unfounded. Fewer than 1% of the placements in private establishments had any part of the cost met by parents; indeed, this was the sector in which the lowest level of parental contributions was made. It was (and presumably remains) a part of the private market for the care and education of disabled children that is heavily dependent upon public funds. This pattern of financial contributions doubtless reflected a measure of 'contracting out' of services from the public to the independent sectors, a practice that will have increased since the time of the OPCS survey. However, we have no firm information about this that relates specifically to children with disabilities.

3. Discussion and implications

Although brief, this chapter highlights the general issue of the relationship between the communal provisions for disabled children that are administratively divided. For example, *whereas 86% of the children in the OPCS survey were found to be in local authority care, only two-thirds of them (67%) were living in social services establishments*. Likewise, *local authorities provided financial support not only to their own facilities but also to the majority of those in the voluntary and private sectors* as well. Although one-sided in this respect, the pattern of cross-financing and part-financing was complicated. It seems likely that questions of who pays for what, what proportion, and how much for how long will arise in such a situation, and this may influence which establishment a disabled child enters or whether they enter the residential sector at all.

Indeed, one of the issues that this chapter raises is just how the facilities offered by the different sectors vary or, equally important, what range of provision is to be found in each of them separately. How much of it is specialised and how is it distributed? We could not answer these questions but we did note (from the figures in brackets in Table 11.3) that *establishments run by social services departments looked after more children than would be expected in Clusters 1, 2, 3 and 5* (children with behavioural disabilities only; those with behavioural disabilities linked to moderate problems of intellectual functioning; those with behavioural disabilities combined with mild problems of incontinence and moderate intellectual functioning; those with severe communication disabilities together with problems of behaviour and intellectual functioning).

The voluntary sector (again, referring to the bracketed figures in Table 11.3) *also looked after more children in Clusters 3 and 5 than would be expected but also more from Cluster 4* (children with severe behavioural disabilities who also experienced fits and, in half of the cases, also faced problems of intellectual functioning). Especially, however, the voluntary establishments looked after more children from Cluster 7 than would be expected. These were children with very severe intellectual, communication, behavioural, locomotion and incontinence disabilities who required a high level of personal care. Indeed, although, overall, the voluntary sector facilities provided for only 19% of the children in the sample, it cared for 39% of this last cluster.

What was interesting about *the private and health service sectors* (again, see Table 11.3) was that their *special contributions were to the care of children in Clusters 6–10* – the clusters characterised by severe mental impairment and those covering children with the most severe and multiple disabilities. However, the private sector establishments also looked after substantially more children in other clusters than establishments run by health authorities.

These descriptions of the sectors are, of course, no more than approximations and, with the exception of the health authorities, all the agencies accommodated some children from all the clusters. Nevertheless, they do provide a broad picture of 'who did what'. It would be important to bear this overview in mind in policy developments and to elaborate it with more detailed information. Only in that way can the appropriateness of residential resources be determined in the light of the needs of disabled children.

NOTES TO CHAPTER 11

[1] Russell (1989) has drawn attention to the recent growth in the number of children with disabilities who are attending residential schools primarily for residential care. She comments: 'A number of schools in the independent sector are providing 52-weeks-a-year

facilities and whilst an educational focus in care is important, there are concerns about the quality of child care practice and the 'ordinary life' philosophy practised in schools which extend their terms to cover the whole year.'

2 One might have expected this difference to have been somewhat less pronounced given the differences in the age composition of the children in the two kinds of provision.

3 'Indirect' contributions would have been those that arose from various forms of subsidisation or 'below cost' charges.

12 Parental visits and other contacts[1]

1. Parental visits

Overall, 41% of the disabled children in the communal establishments were not visited 'nowadays' (the wording of the OPCS question) by their parents. As only four children in the survey were orphans the great majority of non-visited children did have parents, one or other of whom might have visited. In terms of the cluster analysis, the highest rates of 'non-visiting' were amongst children in Clusters 1–4, those characterised by behavioural disabilities, either singly or in combination with other disabilities. By contrast, the highest rates of visiting were found in the severely multiply disabled clusters (8–10). In general, the visiting rate rose with the severity of the disability so that, for example, in Cluster 10, almost 90% of the children had been visited. However, there was no significant difference according to the children's ages.

These findings are reflected in Table 12.1, which analyses whether or not the children were visited according to which body administered the establishment. The difference between the rate of visiting for children in social services units and that for children in health authority facilities is evident and significant and may reflect the fact that, as Russell (1995) suggested, parents feel more comfortable about visiting health (or educational) establishments because they see them as less stigmatising than those administered by social services departments.

Further light is cast on the question of visiting when we look at *who* came to see their children. Mothers visited much more than fathers: 24% of the children were visited only by their mothers. By contrast, 8% were visited only by their fathers. Both parents visited 27% of the children. These data are summarised in Table 12.2.

It follows, therefore, that 51% of the children were visited by their mothers and 35% by their fathers – singly or together. Whether or not mothers or fathers visited showed no clear pattern in relation to the clusters, although it might be noted that 19% (compared with 8% overall)

Table 12.1 Pattern of parental visiting in the previous year or since admission, analysed by the authority administering the establishment (1988)

Administering body	Percentage of children visited	Base
Local health authority	89	94
Social services department	51	578
Voluntary organisation	64	185
Private agency	60	103
Local education authority	78	26
DHSS	36	14
Overall	**59**	**1000**

Table 12.2 Pattern of parental visiting during the previous year or since admission, analysed by visitor (1988)

Who visits	Percentage of children visited
No visits	41
Mother only	24
Father only	8
Both parents	27
Total (Base = 1000)	**100**

of the 'behavioural disabilities only' cluster were visited only by their fathers and that the highest rates of both parents visiting were found amongst Clusters 6 and 7 (70% and 64%, respectively). These were the two groupings of children characterised by severe mental impairment.

The OPCS survey also asked questions about the frequency of parental visits. Table 12.3 sets out the broad result.

Table 12.3 Frequency of parental visits in the previous year or since child's admission (1988)

Frequency of parental visits	Percentage of children visited
Once a week or more often	14
Less than once a week, but at least once a month	21
Less often than monthly, but more than three-monthly	10
Less often than three-monthly	13
Never	41
Unclear	1
Total (Base = 1000)	**100**

If it is accepted that visits which are less frequent than three-monthly hardly amount to significant visiting, then it could be said that 54% of the disabled children in this residential survey were largely or completely unvisited by their parents. As a comparison, 36% of all children in residential care in Berry's (1975) study received 'virtually no parental visits' and the corresponding figure in Berridge's first study (1985) of the children in the homes that he covered was 43%. In one respect, the picture had not changed by the time of Berridge's second study (1998, p. 102) ('visits to the children's homes by residents' families were still very rare'), but there had been a substantial increase in 'contacts' of other kinds, most notably children's visits home and telephone conversations.

Although, as we have seen, the majority of the children in the communal establishments survey were in care (86% in Britain; 83% in England and Wales), it is nonetheless of interest to compare the pattern of visiting with respect to those in care and those not in care, as is done in Table 12.4.

Table 12.4 Frequency of parental visiting during the previous year or since admission: children 'in care' and 'not in care' compared (England and Wales, 1988)

Frequency of parental visits	Percentage of children visited	
	In care	Not in care
Once a week or more often	14	17
Less than once a week, but at least once a month	20	27
Less often than monthly, but more than three-monthly	8	12
Less often than three-monthly	11	21
Never	47	23
Total	**100**	**100**
	(n = 727)	(n = 119)

There was clearly a significant difference between the 'in care' and 'not in care' groups as to whether they were visited at all. However, whereas the children who were 'in care' were much more likely to have never been visited in the preceding year (47%), those 'not in care' were more likely to have been visited infrequently (33% of them less often than monthly).

Broadly speaking, the longer the child had been in the establishment, the less often they were visited by their parents. For example, weekly visiting was most likely to occur in the first six months, falling off sharply (from 37% to 17%) within the next six months. However, some one in seven of the children who had been resident for five years or more were being visited weekly. The largest proportion of those who were rarely, if ever, visited (59%) was to be found amongst the children who had lived in the establishments for between one and three years – the 'middle' duration group. The pattern, therefore, was not entirely straightforward, but the general picture appeared to be that the frequency of visiting declined over time – although it is always possible that there were ups and downs that reflected changing family circumstances.

Thus, what emerged about parental visiting was that there was a large group (41%) of unvisited children. Its relative size increased as time passed, but it did not increase as rapidly for those children who were (eventually) the longest stayers. Mothers did most of the visiting. The most severely multiply disabled children were not only the group most likely to be visited but also the most frequently visited, and this appeared to have been sustained over long periods. By contrast, the 'behavioural disabilities' clusters showed the opposite characteristics, with the 'mental impairment' categories generally falling somewhere in-between. Children in care tended to be visited either frequently or not at all. Those not in care were more likely to have received 'occasional' visits.

2. Children's visits home

The fact that some children were visited infrequently, or not at all, should not lead to the conclusion that they had no contact with their parents. Some also made visits home. Indeed, 32% of those who were visited had also been home at some time in the previous year, as had another 15% of those who had not been visited. There was also a substantial group (27%) who, although visited, had not made a home visit. Taking these facts into account reduces the 'no contact' group to 26% of all the children.

Thus, nearly half (47%) of the children had stayed with their parents at some time in the previous year or since their admission in that year. Of this group, a third had made such a visit on 12 or more occasions. If children did go home, it tended to be a frequent occurrence, probably on a regular or routine basis. Older children went home more often than younger ones (50% of those of ten or over but only 30% of those under ten) and for longer periods. By contrast, there was no significant difference with respect to whether or not a child was in care or how long they had been resident.

When we examined the data concerning the frequency of children's visits home in light of the clusters, we found little difference with respect to whether they had gone home or not (except for Cluster 9: only 31% had had a home visit by comparison with the overall rate of 47%). However, those who had gone home most often (four times or more in the last year) tended to be found in the 'behavioural disabilities' clusters (1–4) and the 'mental impairment' clusters (5 and 6), although not in the 'mental impairment plus locomotion disabilities' group (Cluster 7). What is of interest is that half of the extremely multiply disabled group (Cluster 10) had paid a visit home, 40% of them on four or more occasions in the previous year.

Our analyses of the data on children's visits home point to a number of conclusions. First, there was a fairly large overlap between parental visiting and a child also having paid a visit home. Nonetheless, about a quarter of the children were *only* visited and between one in six and one in seven *only* made visits home. That still left a quarter of all the children without any contact in the form of visits from or to their parents. Secondly, older children went home more than younger ones. Thirdly, if children went home at all then they tended to do so frequently – suggesting an established routine. Fourthly, children in care were not significantly likely to make more or fewer visits home than those who were not in care. Amongst the 44% of the children who were in care and had paid visits home, the majority, as we have seen, would have been subject to compulsory orders. Finally, similar rates of home visits applied in all our clusters except one (Cluster 9). However, the clusters characterised by 'mental impairment' (5 and 6), but without pronounced problems of locomotion, went home more often (if they went home at all) than other groups. A fifth of the group with extremely severe disabilities (Cluster 10) had stayed with their parents on four or more occasions in the last year.

Taking together the data about children's visits home and those concerning parental visiting, it is clear, as we have seen, that about a quarter of the residents had had no face-to-face contact whatsoever with their parents in the previous year. If one includes those who were visited very infrequently, the rate of 'isolated' children with disabilities in residential care could have been as high as a third. This was a worrying situation if their well-being and rights were to be fully protected and, not least, plans devised for their futures. However, before drawing too firm a conclusion on this issue, it is necessary to see what contact the children had with other 'outside' individuals who might have provided protection and championship over and above any that the establishment staff would have offered. Before doing that, however, we consider what influence distance had upon the pattern of children's contacts with their parents.

3. Travelling distances

One of the factors that may have influenced the frequency of parents' visits and children's visits home was the distance that they had to travel. Although the OPCS survey provided some information about this, it was unfortunate that the question was asked only of the parent who visited 'most often', not of the other parent or of parents who did not visit at all. Bearing in mind the limitations of these data, it did nevertheless appear that frequent parental visits were encouraged when the journeys that had to be made were not too long – the critical distance being somewhere between five and ten miles. Similarly, the least frequent visiting was associated with travelling distances of 50 miles or more, journeys that were made by a quarter of those who visited. The most distant establishments were those run by private agencies (76% of which entailed a trip of 50 miles or more for those who visited) and the next furthest were those provided by voluntary bodies (a third of which required journeys of over 50 miles). By contrast, the establishments administered by social services departments and health authorities were much closer to hand – only 12% being over 50 miles away and almost a third under five miles away. Clearly, the 'independent' sector establishments required the parents who visited to make longer journeys than those located in the public sector. This may have reflected their more specialised nature, the larger catchment areas or the geography of their distribution. However, if visiting is to be encouraged (or even not deterred) the distribution of facilities between the public and the independent sectors appears to be one of the matters that needs to be considered.

However, in contrast to these results it was found that the further away the parents lived the *more* likely it was for the child to visit and to visit frequently. Whereas 46% of those who were in establishments less than 20 miles away from their parents went home, this proportion rose to 66% for those who were further afield.

The cost and availability of transport may well have loomed rather large in determining the patterns of parental visiting. It is not clear, however, why children's visits home should have been less affected by distance, but this may have owed something to their being organised (and, perhaps, paid for) by the agencies concerned, if that was indeed the practice.

However, it must be remembered that there are other factors than 'distance' that are liable to influence parental visiting. Berridge (1985) reported that parents often found it stressful to meet their children under public scrutiny. He also suggested that feelings of guilt or inadequacy may compound anxiety based on cultural and social class expectations to the point where 'over time, there is often little currency to keep the relationship going'. Millham *et al.* (1986) also reported on the difficulties for parents visiting their children in residential placements, and Argent and Kerrane (1997) noted that disabled children may be less likely than other children to communicate with their families or make their wishes and feelings known.

4. Visits by social workers and volunteers[2]

The data that OPCS was able to gather about social worker and volunteer visits in the previous year were incomplete on two counts. First, for 13% of the children, the respondents could not supply the information; secondly, questions were not asked about the frequency of these visits. Nonetheless, as regards those children for whom information was available, it is somewhat reassuring to know that all the children who had not been visited by a parent, and most of those who had had a parental visit, had received a visit from a social worker.

Of the 700 resident disabled children in care (England and Wales) for whom the OPCS survey provided information about social worker contacts, only two were recorded as not having had a visit in the preceding year or since they had been admitted (which, for some, may have been very recently). Of course, the OPCS data give no indication of what the visits by social workers entailed – for example, whether the child was seen; whether planning meetings were held, and with whom; or what subsequent action was taken.

OPCS also asked questions about visits made to children by voluntary workers and befrienders, although it was not clear how these two categories differed. Of those children for whom information was available, 14% had had a visit from a voluntary worker and 10% from a befriender. However, there was no evidence that visits by these people compensated for the absence of parental visits. Indeed, the children who *were* visited by parents were a little more likely to be visited by a volunteer or befriender. This is rather worrying as (according to the OPCS definition) volunteer visitors included independent visitors appointed by a local authority. It was also apparent that these two groups of volunteers were more likely to visit children in the clusters containing the most severe multiple disabilities than those in clusters characterised by behavioural disabilities, alone or in combination with other disabilities. For instance, of the children in Clusters 9 and 10 combined, 65% received visits from a voluntary worker and/or a befriender, whereas, for Cluster 1 (the group characterised by behavioural disabilities alone) the comparable rate was 15%. It is also of some interest to note the related fact that children who were *not* in care were nearly twice as likely to have such visits as those who were in care. Likewise, voluntary workers and befrienders concentrated their involvement on the younger children, especially those between the ages of 8 and 11.

One of the explanations for this pattern may be found in the fact that 'volunteer' schemes are often based in, or run in association with, hospital or other health service units. Indeed, 88% of the children in these kinds of establishments received such visits. This rate fell to 38% in the voluntary sector, to 23% in the private sector and to 18% for the children in social services provisions.

5. Children's contact with general practitioners and other health service professionals

Although (after a social worker) a general practitioner was the professional person most likely to have seen the child, 14% of those who were not in a hospital had not seen their GP in the previous year (or since their admission) and that proportion was highest (18%) in privately run establishments and lowest (5%) in those run by voluntary organisations. Taking all the children together, however, 11% had not seen a GP in the preceding year (or since their admission) and another 35% had seen one only once or twice. It might be that a GP had had little time to see those recently admitted; on the other hand, one would expect an early medical examination of children soon after their arrival. Likewise, it might be argued that children in hospital were likely to have been seen by other doctors, but these may have been more specialised and may have lacked the kind of knowledge of a child's family background that a GP could be expected to have. Of course, some children will also have been seen by community paediatricians, so that the absence of contact with a GP may not be as significant as at first appears.

When we looked at the contact with GPs as experienced by children in the different clusters, we found little difference with respect to the 11% who had had no contact (although all the children in Cluster 10 had seen a GP). However, it was plain that the clusters of the most severely disabled (Clusters 7–10) had seen a GP frequently in the previous year (in the case of 45%, six times or more), whereas all the other clusters had more occasional contact (only 20% having seen a GP as often as six times or more).

In addition to the data about contacts with GPs, there was information about contacts with other health service professionals. For instance, two-thirds of the children had not seen a dentist in the previous year. Furthermore, in light of the large proportion of children included in the clusters where behavioural disabilities were dominant (72%), it was disappointing to find that only one in five of them had seen a psychiatrist in the past year (or since their admission), only 13% a clinical psychologist and only 3% a psychotherapist. This, again, suggests that a great deal of responsibility was falling upon social workers and general practitioners as 'independent' points of contact outside the establishments, for attending to both the child's specific needs and for safeguarding their general well-being.

6. Discussion and implications

About a quarter of the children in the survey were not visited by either parent nor had been home on a visit. If those who were visited only very infrequently are also taken into account, *the rate of 'isolated' children could well have been as high as a third*. This was a disturbing finding: without parental involvement, a heavy burden fell upon professionals and volunteers to oversee and safeguard the well-being and rights of these disabled children and, in particular, to make sure that appropriate and effective plans were made for their futures.

In fact, the professionals most likely to have played this role were the care staff; but often what is also needed is an 'outside' champion to pursue the child's interests, rather in the way of a partisan and energetic parent. On the face of it, the most likely people to have fulfilled this role were social workers and general practitioners for, as we have seen, most children had had contact with the former in the previous year and a majority (although by no means all) had contact with the latter. The OPCS data did not specify the frequency of the social work visits or what they involved; but what evidence we have from other sources would suggest that visiting children in residential care has not been a high priority. For example: Millham *et al.* (1986) reported that the number of social work contacts with children 'in care' declined once they were admitted to residential care; a decade later, Bilson and Barker (1995) found that the proportion of all children who saw their social worker on a regular and frequent basis fell rapidly during the first six months in care or accommodation, and that almost two-fifths of those who had been 'looked after' for over five years did not see their social worker as often as once a month unless and until a crisis arose. Thus, the fact that most children in communal establishments had had contact with a social worker in the previous year tells us very little about its quality, its consistency, its frequency or its effectiveness.

In most cases, it seems unlikely that GP contacts will have provided an alternative, consistent and committed 'championship'. Similarly, it was clear that visits by volunteers and 'befrienders' were likely to be to those children who were already being visited by their parents rather than to those we have termed the 'isolated'.

What is particularly important is the finding that *it was not the most severely disabled children who had become detached from their families* or were seen infrequently by professionals and volunteers *but those in establishments run by social services departments, those who were 'in care', and those in the clusters where disabilities of behaviour were either the most prominent problem or in a prominent combination with other disabilities*. Of course, these three categories overlapped considerably, but not completely.

One possible way in which the dangers arising from isolation from parents might have been forestalled was by the appointment of an 'independent visitor'. If there had been any at the time of the OPCS survey, they were not separately identified. However, since the Children Act 1989, local authorities have been *required* to appoint independent visitors for children who are 'looked after' and who have not been visited by a parent (or someone with parental responsibility) in the previous year. Notwithstanding this requirement, recent research (Knight, 1997) found that, in 1996, in England and Wales, it was unlikely that more than a third of authorities had any such scheme in place and that, in all, only 235 children (about half of whom were in foster homes) had been matched with an independent visitor. Furthermore, only 32 of these 235 children and young people were classified as disabled. A similar picture was painted by the Utting Report (1997) that reviewed the safeguards for children living away from home.

Therefore, *it would seem highly likely that there remains a problem* (albeit the scale may have changed) *of certain disabled children in residential care becoming 'isolated' in terms of there being no parent, or parent-like figure, to see that the utmost was done to ensure their well-being,* in whatever direction that demanded. At the very least, the scale of the actual or potential isolation from outside championship calls for examination.

NOTES TO CHAPTER 12

[1] For the sake of convenience we refer in this section to certain material broadly as it appears in the OPCS report (Meltzer *et al.*, 1989).

[2] These categories excluded 'Be-My-Parent' workers whose involvement was discussed in Chapter 10.

13 | Education and the communal establishments

1. The effects of the Education Act 1981

In Chapter 8, we saw that the Education Act 1981 introduced a new system of comprehensive assessments and also required that all children identified as having special educational needs should be provided with a formal written statement giving details of the child's needs and the provision that should be made to meet those needs.

Table 13.1 shows the proportion of children in each cluster who had been assessed for special needs and who had received a written statement. Overall, a little over a half (54%) of the children had undergone assessment, with two-fifths (42%) of the whole group being the subject of a statement. The proportion assessed and the proportion with a statement both increase across the clusters broadly in the direction that would be expected. However, in view of the extent and degree of learning difficulties

Table 13.1 Proportion of children who had been assessed for special educational needs, had been statemented and were receiving the help specified in the statement, analysed by clusters (1988)

Cluster	Description	Assessed for special needs (%)	Had/expected a written statement (%)	Base	Statemented and receiving the help specified (%)	Base
1	Behaviour	29	20	418	89	66
2	Intellectual and behaviour	64	47	142	94	58
3	Incontinence and behaviour	47	43	41	100	15
4	Fits and behaviour	57	48	31	100	12
5	Communication and behaviour	73	52	108	88	55
6	Multiple disabilities	83	60	65	100	39
7	Multiple and severe	82	73	70	98	45
8	Multiple and very severe	85	71	38	100	27
9	Multiple and extreme	76	71	37	100	25
10	Multiple and very extreme	81	69	50	95	31
All		54	42	1000	94	373

experienced by these children, the rates of assessment and statementing for both the group as a whole and, more especially, for the clusters characterised by multiple severe disabilities are surprisingly low considering that five years had passed between the implementation of the Education Act 1981 and the OPCS survey in 1988. This survey, it should be recalled, was carried out nearly three years after the private households study (see Chapter 8) and might therefore have been expected to show higher rates than were found there.

For all the clusters taken together, the proportion of children assessed for special educational needs exceeded the proportion with statements, with particularly notable differences in Clusters 2, 5 and 6. This is surprising since these children had high rates of learning difficulties. It would seem unlikely that they had been assessed and found *not* to require statements; that being so it suggests that there were administrative reasons for the difference between the proportion assessed and the proportion statemented. The highest rates of 'statementing' were found amongst the children with multiple and very severe or extreme disabilities (Clusters 7–10).

Although just 1% of the children in the cluster with behavioural disabilities alone (Cluster 1) were found to have learning difficulties, 29% of them had been assessed for special needs and a fifth had, or were expected to receive, a statement. The need for these children to have statements was likely to have arisen from a combination of two factors: first, the problems created by their behaviour within a classroom; secondly, the fact that, even though they did not have a level of learning difficulty sufficient to be classified as a disability in the OPCS survey, they nonetheless experienced sufficient problems to warrant a formal assessment.

Nearly all the children with statements, were said to be receiving the help that was specified in those statements, although some dissatisfaction was expressed by the respondents with respect to the support that was provided in two of the 'behaviour' clusters (1 and 5).

2. The extent of learning disabilities among 5–15-year-olds in communal establishments

Just over half (52%) of the children in communal establishments were found to experience a disability of intellectual functioning (see Table 13.2). The proportion rises to 89% if those in the largest cluster (1), who, with a very few exceptions, had only behavioural disabilities, are excluded. However, the most notable characteristic of the two next largest clusters

(2 and 5) is the combination of behavioural problems and learning difficulties. Nearly all the children in Clusters 6–10 have very severe learning difficulties, usually as a result of specific mental impairments.

Table 13.2 Children (aged 5–15) in communal establishments assessed as having learning difficulties, analysed by clusters (1988)

Cluster	Description	Percentage with learning difficulty	Mean severity score on the OPCS intellectual functioning scale	Base
1	Behaviour	1	..	418
2	Intellectual and behaviour	100	5.7	142
3	Incontinence and behaviour	44	2.2	41
4	Fits and behaviour	53	3.6	31
5	Communication and behaviour	80	5.8	108
6	Multiple disabilities	96	9.9	65
7	Multiple and severe	100	11.0	70
8	Multiple and very severe	100	10.9	38
9	Multiple and extreme	98	10.4	37
10	Multiple and very extreme	96	10.7	50
All		**52**	**4.5**	**1000**

3. Where the children went to school

Table 13.3 gives details of the type of school the children living in communal establishments attended, analysed by the clusters. Three particularly notable features emerge from this analysis with respect to the whole sample. First, there was little indication of integration into the ordinary school system: only a shade over a quarter (27%) received their education in an ordinary classroom in an ordinary school. Secondly, the survey found very little evidence that provision was being made for these children in special units within ordinary schools; indeed, only 3% were educated in these settings. Thirdly, a significant minority (26%) of the children were being educated somewhere other than at a school. Instead, they attended classes attached to assessment centres, children's homes, hospitals or had 'other' (undefined) arrangements made for their education.

When these three features of the overall picture of the children's education are broken down by clusters a number of distinct differences emerge between, on the one hand, the five clusters characterised by behavioural disabilities, either singly or in combination with other

Table 13.3 Where the children (aged 5–15) in communal establishments received their education, analysed by clusters (1988)

Cluster	Description	Type of school								Base
		Special school	Special unit ordinary school	Assessment centre	Class at children's home	Class at a hospital	Ordinary school	Other	Total	
		(%)	(%)	(%)	(%)	(%)	(%)	(%)	(%)	
1	Behaviour	19	3	6	18	–	49	6	100	418
2	Intellectual and behaviour	44	8	7	18	3	16	5	100	142
3	Incontinence and behaviour	34	2	10	12	–	39	2	100	41
4	Fits and behaviour	65	–	3	13	–	16	3	100	31
5	Communication and behaviour	56	7	5	14	1	15	1	100	108
6	Multiple disabilities	91	–	–	5	–	5	–	100	65
7	Multiple and severe	73	–	–	17	9	–	1	100	70
8	Multiple and very severe	87	–	–	3	8	–	3	100	38
9	Multiple and extreme	91	–	–	–	6	–	3	100	37
10	Multiple and very extreme	78	2	–	6	10	–	4	100	50
All		**45**	**3**	**5**	**15**	**2**	**27**	**4**	**100**	*1000*

disabilities (Clusters 1–5) and, on the other, the five clusters in which the children have far more profound multiple disabilities and are likely to have a specific mental impairment (Clusters 6–10). As would be expected, children in the second group of clusters were far less likely to be attending ordinary schools: there was little 'integration'. Only 5% of the cluster of children with severe learning and behavioural difficulties (Cluster 6) were attending an ordinary school. Furthermore, the only children in these multiple disabilities clusters who were provided for in special units within ordinary schools were (rather surprisingly) 2% of the cluster with the most severe disabilities (Cluster 10).

Attendance at ordinary schools was far more frequent among the children assigned to the five clusters in which behavioural disabilities were prominent, although it was only in the two which had the lowest proportion of children with learning difficulties (Clusters 1 and 3) that significant minorities attended ordinary classes in ordinary schools (49% and 39%, respectively). For children in these clusters, slightly greater use was also made of special units within ordinary schools, suggesting that such schools were prepared to make provision for children with behavioural disabilities and relatively mild learning difficulties, but not for those with more severe or a wider range of disabilities.

Taken together, children in the clusters where behavioural disabilities were common (Clusters 1–5) were more likely than the children with more severe and multiple disabilities (Clusters 6–10) to be educated somewhere other than at a school. In the two clusters characterised by children with behavioural disabilities alone and behavioural problems with learning difficulties (Clusters 1 and 2), about a third of the children were not receiving their education at a school (30% and 33% respectively). In the second group of clusters (6–10), contrary to what might be expected, the children were generally more likely to be attending a school of some kind, with the notable exception of those in the cluster with severe learning difficulties combined with a high level of physical disabilities (Cluster 7), amongst whom a significant minority (17%) were being educated in classes attached to the children's homes of voluntary organisations.

4. Education and the care status of the children

We looked at the data about learning difficulties, assessment, statementing and the type of school the children attended by whether or not they were 'in care'. The results are set out in Tables 13.4–13.7.

Table 13.4 Children (aged 5–15) assessed as having learning difficulties, analysed by whether or not they were 'in care' (England and Wales, 1988)

	In care	Not in care	All
Percentage with learning difficulty	44	84	50
Mean severity score on the OPCS intellectual functioning scale	3.5	9.1	4.5
Base	739	119	858

As Table 13.4 shows, both the proportion of children in care who were found to have learning difficulties and their mean score as a group on the intellectual functioning scale were much lower than for those children who were not in care.

Nearly half (48%) of the children 'in care' had been assessed for special educational needs and over a third (38%) had had a formal statement (Table 13.5). As would be expected, because of the more severe nature of their disabilities, both of these proportions were higher for the children not in care. Nearly all the children in both groups were receiving the provision recommended in their statements.

Tables 13.6 and 13.7 illustrate that there were important differences between the 'in care' and 'not in care' groups in the arrangements that were made for *where* they received their education. The first of the tables shows that the children in care were far more likely than those not in care to be attending an ordinary class in an ordinary school, but less likely to be receiving their education at a special school. Nearly all (93%) of the

Table 13.5 Proportion of children (aged 5–15) assessed (for statemented and special educational needs receiving the help specified in the statement), analysed by whether or not they were 'in care' (England and Wales, 1988)

	In care (%)	Not in care (%)	All (%)
Assessed for special educational needs	48	67	51
Had or expected to receive a written statement	38	54	40
Base	*739*	*119*	*858*
Proportion of those with a statement who were receiving the help specified	93	99	94
Base	*243*	*60*	*312*

Table 13.6 Where the children (aged 5–15) received their education, analysed by whether or not they were 'in care' (England and Wales, 1988)

Type of school	In care (%)	Not in care (%)	All (%)
Special school	38	83	44
Special unit in an ordinary school, full- or part-time	3	2	3
Assessment centre	6	–	5
Class attached to a children's home	16	5	15
Class attached to a hospital	1	1	1
Ordinary class in an ordinary school	31	8	28
Other	4	3	4
Total	**100**	**100**	**100**
Base	*738*	*119*	*857*

Table 13.7 Type of schooling arrangements for the children (aged 5–15), analysed by whether or not the child was 'in care' (England and Wales, 1988)

Schooling arrangement	In care (%)	Not in care (%)	All (%)
Resided all year at a special boarding school	13	22	14
Special boarding school (returning to another residential placement for vacations)	2	1	2
Class attached to children's home, hospital or assessment centre where child lives	23	6	21
Day pupil at special or ordinary school	58	69	60
Other arrangements	4	3	4
Total	**100**	**100**	**100**
Base	*738*	*119*	*857*

children who were not in care attended a school of some kind whereas this was true for less than three-quarters (72%) of the children in care; the remainder attended classes attached to the residential units in which they were living or had had 'other' arrangements made for them. None of the children who were not in care was being educated at assessment centres, which suggests that the 'assessment centres' in the OPCS classification were local authority observation and assessment establishments.

Somewhat different details about the type of schooling arrangements experienced by children in care and children not in care are set out in Table 13.7. These serve to emphasise the complex nature of the educational experience of the 'in care' group. Although the nature and severity of the pattern of disabilities which the children in care experienced were much less severe than amongst the children who were not in care, they were less likely to be attending either a special or an ordinary day school. Instead, over two-fifths (42%) of them were educated in a mixture of boarding arrangements or classes attached to the establishment in which they were living or had 'other', unspecified, arrangements made for their education.

Taken together, very few of the children enumerated in the communal establishments survey (2%) were termly boarders at special schools; but 14% were resident for the whole year. When the administration of the schools attended by 'year-round' boarders was examined, it was found that they were mainly in the private (44%) or voluntary (40%) sectors. Although these units catered for children in all of the ten clusters, just over three-quarters (76%) of their residents were in the 'behavioural disabilities' clusters (1–5). The children in the three clusters characterised by very severe multiple disabilities (Clusters 8–10) were the least likely to reside in these boarding schools. The children in the small Cluster 4, who had behavioural disabilities and experienced fits, were the most likely to be year-round boarding school residents (32% of the cluster), and there were also significant groups, 20% and 28%, respectively, from the clusters characterised by children with learning difficulties together with behavioural disabilities (Cluster 2) and severe learning as well as behavioural disabilities (Cluster 6).

5. Discussion and implications

A very high rate of learning difficulties was found among children with disabilities living in residential care. Nearly all the children with physical or sensory disabilities were also assessed as having learning difficulties.

Across all the clusters of disability *the proportion of children who had received formal statements of special needs was very low compared with the nature and severity of both their learning and their other disabilities.* This suggests that children in the communal establishments may have been accorded a low priority for 'statementing', perhaps because their needs were assumed to be self-evident or because they were thought to be met by being cared for in a residential setting.

Only minimal evidence was found of the integration of the children with disabilities living in communal establishments into the 'ordinary' school system. In only one of our clusters, that in which the children had behavioural disabilities alone, did a small majority attend ordinary schools. Amongst the clusters where the children had physical or sensory disabilities, or *any* degree of learning difficulty, the proportion attending ordinary schools was very much lower. This is in marked contrast to the children living in private households, amongst whom it was only in the multiple disabilities clusters that the majority of children did not attend an ordinary school.

Just over a quarter (26%) of the children were being educated somewhere other than at school. These alternative arrangements were particularly common amongst children who had only behavioural disabilities or behavioural disabilities combined with learning difficulties (groups in which 95% of the children were in care).

Amongst children in care the schooling arrangements were particularly complicated. Although the nature of their disabilities was far less severe than amongst the children who were not in care, they were less likely to be attending a special or ordinary day school. Instead, they experienced a variety of boarding arrangements, attended classes attached to the establishments where they were living, or had 'other' (undefined) arrangements made for their education. This pattern of schooling arrangements for the children in care raises the question of the extent to which their learning difficulties arose from, or were exacerbated by, the experience of being in care. Jackson (1989) was one of the first to study the educational experience of children in care and has argued that admission to care 'carries a high risk of educational failure', a view confirmed by a number of subsequent studies (Fletcher-Campbell and Hall, 1990; Office for Standards in Education and Social Services Inspectorate, 1995; Borland *et al.*, 1998). These studies have drawn attention to the problems, and local and central government initiatives have started to emerge (Department of Education and Department of Health, 1994; Fletcher-Campbell, 1997). However, the poor educational experience of children in residential care is a recurrent theme in the literature (for example, Berridge *et al.*, 1996).

PART TWO

Young children

14 The classification of disability in young children

1. Introduction

As we have seen, OPCS omitted the under-5s from its survey of children with disabilities living in communal establishments. Even in the private households survey, only 202 out of the 1230 interviews (one in six) were conducted for children in this age group. This relatively small number resulted from the difficulty of identifying disabilities in young children. Indeed, assessing the level (severity) of disability of children under five was one of the hardest tasks that OPCS faced.

It is obvious that the same questions cannot be used to assess disabilities in six-month-old babies and children of 15. For example, incontinence and limited communication are to be expected in a six-month-old baby but represent disabilities in a 15-year-old child. Issues of development are clearly paramount: young children cannot perform the same tasks as older children. In order to address this problem, OPCS applied the standard Denver Development Screening Test, which shows the age by which 90% of children can perform various activities. Where the Denver Test did not cover the relevant task, the Vineland Social Maturity Scale and Sheridan's 'From Birth to Five Years' were used. However, these last two scales do not show the actual ages at which 90% of children can perform tasks; instead, they employ mean ages or age ranges. When these tests were used, therefore, the ages at which nine out of ten children could be expected to have mastered the specified activities had to be estimated.

In order to assess the level of severity of disability for children of different ages under five, a separate assessment exercise was undertaken by 22 judges, 15 of whom were professionals (such as paediatricians, physiotherapists, child psychologists) and seven of whom were administrators or researchers involved in the OPCS survey. The panel was asked to assign ratings of severity to a series of age-related vignettes such as: a child of three who can walk only a few steps without help; or a child of four who can walk only a few steps without help.

Figure 14.1
*Formulae for assessing
equivalent levels of
disability for under-5s*

1 Formula for the disabilities of locomotion; holding, gripping and turning; and continence

For each of the vignette assessments in these areas:

Score for child aged x = score for 5-year-old $- A * \log \dfrac{59 - y}{x - y}$

where x = age in months

y = the normal age of attainment (months); that is, the age by which 90% of children can perform the activity

$A = 2.220$ in the case of locomotion
$A = 2.091$ in the case of holding, gripping, turning
$A = 2.885$ in the case of continence

2 Formula for the disabilities of reaching and stretching; communication; and personal care

For each of the vignette assessments in these areas:

Score for child aged x = score for 5-year-old $- B * \log \dfrac{59}{x}$

providing $x >$ the normal age of attainment and the score > 0

where x = age in months and where

$B = 2.620$ in the case of reaching and stretching
$B = 8.575$ in the case of communication
$B = 6.709$ in the case of personal care

3 Formula for the disabilities of behaviour; hearing; seeing; consciousness; intellectual functioning; eating, drinking and digestion; and disfigurement

For each of the vignette assessments in these areas:

Score for child aged x = score for a 5-year-old

Note: Discerning different levels of severity for children under five in the areas of intellectual functioning, eating, drinking and digestion and disfigurement proved to be impossible. Therefore, if these disabilities were present, a standard severity score of 0.5 was assigned.

Age-related questions like these were selected in order to represent a range of developmental 'retardation', that is, the difference between the child's age and the age at which 90% of children can perform the task. For example, 90% of children can walk a few steps by the age of 14 months and walk without help for 50 yards by 24 months. It is clear (taking the vignettes above) that a child of four who can walk only a few steps is more severely disabled than a child of three who can walk only a few steps. Therefore, all things being equal, the younger a child, the less severely disabled they can be assessed to be. That being so, a six-month-old baby cannot get a very high disability score.

The results from the judgement exercise were used to produce a series of mathematical models that related age to the severity of disability for each type of disability. The formulae allowed equivalent levels of disability for children under five to be related to the levels of children who were exactly five. For example, children of three years and two months who could not control their bowels were regarded as having an equivalent level of 'continence' disability to five-year-old children who wet themselves every day. Similarly, a child of two years and ten months who could walk a few steps, but less than 50 yards, was considered to have a similar level of 'locomotion' disability as a five-year-old who could walk at least 50 but less than 200 yards.

The calculations that were made in order to assess the equivalent levels of disability in the three groups of disability used are shown in Figure 14.1.[1]

2. The prevalence of disability by age in young children living in private households

The difficulty of distinguishing the levels of severity of disabilities in young children affected both the OPCS survey methodology and the prevalence rates of disability that it estimated from its results. (No such rates for the under-5s in the communal establishments were possible.) In the case of the survey of private households, fewer disabled young children were found than had been expected. In particular, the prevalence rates of disabilities in children under 12 months were very low. Table 14.1 shows the estimated prevalence rates of disabilities in young children, both before and after correcting for sampling bias.

Table 14.1 Estimated prevalence rates of disability in young children by age (1985)

Age (in years) (OPCS categories)	Uncorrected prevalence rates (000s)	Corrected prevalence rates (000s)
0–1	1.5	2.8
1–2	8.2	13.2
2–3	10.7	13.2
3–4	20.1	19.5
4–5	22.0	25.8
5–6	31.0	28.5
Mean rate for each year for all children aged 0–15	**23.7**	**23.7**

Even after correction, the estimated number of children with disabilities aged between one and two is almost five times as large as the estimated number of children with disabilities younger than one (that is, 13,200 for the 1–2 age group and only 2800 amongst those less than one). The rapid rise in the number of children with disabilities with increasing age is at least a partial reflection of the problems of identification and diagnosis. For instance, it is likely that some disabilities are noticed only when a child starts school.

The difficulties involved in identifying both the nature and the severity of disabilities in children under one is further illustrated in Table 14.2, which shows both the average number of disabilities for each child by age and the average OPCS disability score[2] per child by age.

Table 14.2 The average number of disabilities and the average OPCS total disability score in young children by age (1985)

Age (in years)	Average number of disabilities per child	Average total disability score
0–1	1.4	3.5
1–2	2.4	8.9
2–3	2.1	12.2
3–4	2.6	13.8
4–5	2.8	16.0
5–6	2.6	18.5
Average for all children aged 0–15	**2.6**	**18.2**

Thus, children with disabilities under one year of age were assessed as having, on average, only 1.4 different disabilities compared with 2.4 for children aged between one and two. However, it can be seen that the average number of different disabilities in children from one onwards is similar to that for all age groups (2.6). This reflects the fact that, although the *existence* of a particular disability can be adequately assessed in this age group, its severity still remains hard to determine. Table 14.2 shows that, in young children, there is a rapid rise in the average total disability score with increasing age; indeed, it doubles between the first two age bands.

3. The cluster analysis of young children with disabilities

Since it was not possible for children younger than five to have as high a severity score on the different scales of disability as older children, their disabilities were effectively being measured on a different scale. For this reason, as we explained in Chapter 2, a separate cluster analysis had to be undertaken for the under-5s. However, the same statistical procedures were used as with children aged 5–15. These showed that all solutions between 2 and 15 clusters were statistically significant. However, a seven-cluster solution was chosen as optimal for the purposes of this report. Above seven, the clusters began to be separated only by the degree of severity on specific scales, and the sample sizes of some clusters became very small. If fewer than seven clusters had been chosen, distinct clusters would have begun to merge into more heterogeneous groups. The cluster analysis results are shown as a dendrogram in Figure 14.2. The seven-cluster solution appears at the foot.

It should be noted that 72% of children under five are classified in Clusters 1 and 2, characterised, respectively, by relatively low levels of disability and mainly behavioural disabilities. Cluster 3 is associated with Cluster 2 and is characterised by mainly behavioural, continence and personal care disabilities. None of the children in these first three clusters have any disabilities of intellectual functioning. The remaining four clusters (4, 5, 6 and 7), containing 28% of the children under five, represent those with more disabilities (typically, four or more) and usually some measured or expected disabilities of intellectual functioning.

The differences between the seven clusters can be seen clearly from the analysis of the means of the number of disabilities per child, shown in Figure 14.3. The straight horizontal lines represent the overall sample mean (that is, the average number of disabilities for all the children), whilst the stepped lines show the 95% confidence intervals of that overall mean. The actual values of the overall mean and the 95% confidence intervals are given on the right hand side of the graph. The dot at the end of each vertical line marks the average number of disabilities for that cluster.

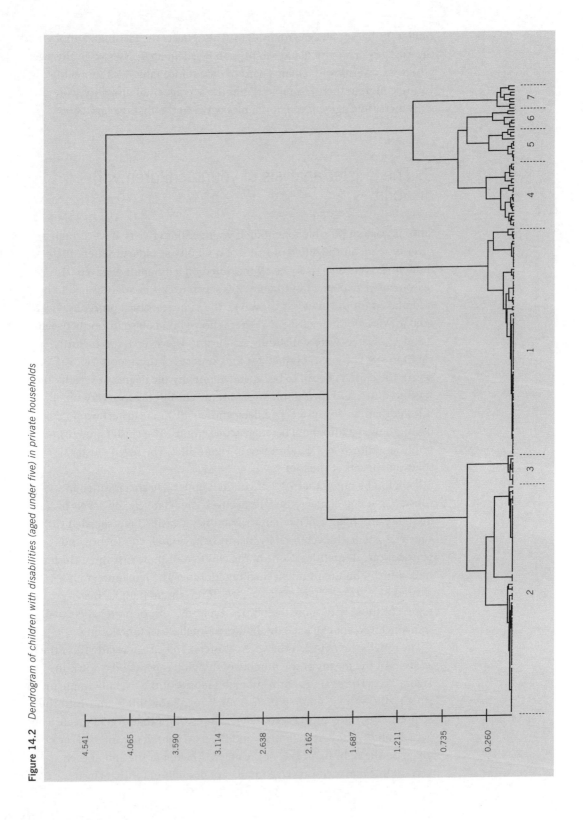

Figure 14.2 *Dendrogram of children with disabilities (aged under five) in private households*

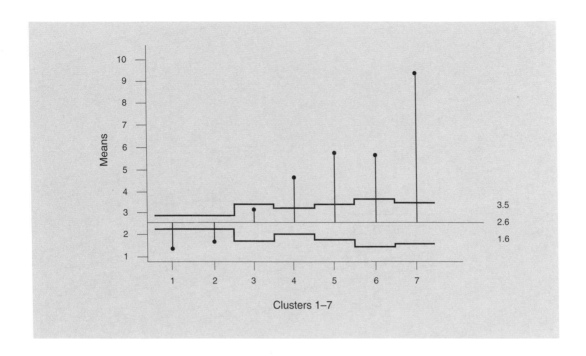

Figure 14.3
Average number of disabilities of children under five, by cluster

The average number of different disabilities experienced by children under five living in private households was 2.6, but those in Clusters 1 and 2 typically suffered from fewer disabilities than those in the remaining five clusters. They had significantly fewer disabilities than the average, whilst those children in Clusters 4–7 had significantly more. The seven clusters have been ordered so that Cluster 1 contains the children with the fewest disabilities on average (1.4) and Cluster 7 those with the most (9.4). Table 14.3 gives the details represented by Figure 14.3. As with the analysis for the 5–15 age group, we faced some difficulty in choosing short descriptive titles for the clusters but the ones we have used do reflect the predominant features of each category.

Table 14.3 Average number of disabilities of children under five, analysed by cluster

Cluster	Description	No. of children in cluster	Mean no. of disabilities	Standard deviation
1	Low levels of disabilities	73	1.4	0.86
2	Behaviour	73	1.7	0.84
3	Incontinence	10	3.2	1.32
4	Intellectual disabilities	21	4.6	1.43
5	Multiple cognitive disabilities	11	5.7	1.01
6	Multiple physical disabilities	6	5.7	1.86
7	Severe and multiple disabilities	8	9.4	0.74
All		**202**	**2.6**	**2.21**

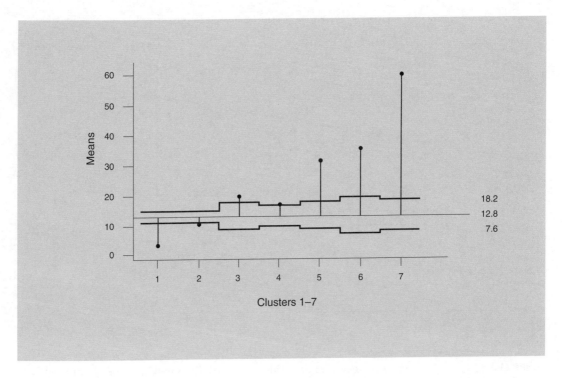

18.2

12.8

7.6

Figure 14.4
Average total disability score for children under five, by cluster

A similar pattern to that revealed by the analysis of the number of disabilities per child emerges when the average total disability scores are examined; that is, when the scores for each child in their different areas of disability are added to those of other children in the cluster and divided by the number of children. Figure 14.4 shows the analysis of these means by cluster and Table 14.4 gives the details.

Table 14.4 Mean of the total OPCS disability score assigned to children under five in each cluster

Cluster	Description	Number of children in cluster	Mean of total OPCS disability score	Standard deviation
1	Low levels of disabilities	73	3.7	4.3
2	Behaviour	73	10.5	3.7
3	Incontinence	10	19.4	6.3
4	Intellectual disabilities	21	16.2	8.1
5	Multiple cognitive disabilities	11	31.0	7.6
6	Multiple physical disabilities	6	35.5	10.0
7	Severe and multiple disabilities	8	59.9	10.9
All		**202**	**12.9**	**13.6**

Table 14.5 Frequency of different types of disability by cluster (%) amongst children under five in private households (1985)

Area of disability	Clusters						
	1	2	3	4	5	6	7
Behaviour	16	**100**	**100**	76	82	**100**	**100**
Intellectual functioning	–	–	–	**100**	**100**	33	**100**
Communication	14	8	10	52	82	17	**100**
Continence	19	14	**100**	9	**100**	17	**100**
Personal care	18	12	60	33	**100**	**100**	**100**
Locomotion	15	4	20	62	64	**100**	**100**
Seeing	5	..	–	33	–	33	37
Consciousness	30	17	10	29	9	50	**75**
Dexterity	..	..	–	24	27	50	**100**
Reaching and stretching	..	–	10	19	–	67	**100**
Hearing	16	11	10	19	9	–	25
Disfigurement	7	..	–	5	18	33	12
Eating, drinking and digestion	3	..	–	9	9	17	12
Estimated number of children (000s)	23	23	3	6	3	2	2

Notes:
a .. = less than 2%.
b The disabilities of disfigurement and of eating, drinking and digestion were not used in the cluster analysis but they are added here.

As would be expected, the children in Cluster 1 have the lowest average disability scores (3.7) and the children in Cluster 7 have the highest (59.9). There is a general trend for the overall severity scores to increase along with the increasing number of different disabilities. However, the exception is demonstrated by Clusters 3 and 4: the children in Cluster 3 have a mean total disability score that is greater than those in Cluster 4 despite the fact that Cluster 3 children suffer from fewer different disabilities on average. The explanation for this is partly to be found in the fact that the children in Cluster 4 are, on average, almost a year younger than those in Cluster 3 (the average age of Cluster 3 children is 3.3 years whilst that for Cluster 4 is 2.4 years). The method of assessing the severity of disability used by OPCS meant that, all things being equal, the younger a child, the lower the severity score for the same level of disability. Another reason why the severity scores in Clusters 3 and 4 are out of step with the general pattern may be found in the fact that all the children in Cluster 4 had, or were suspected of having, disabilities of intellectual functioning and these would only attract a flat-rate score of 0.5.

When the seven clusters are analysed by the frequency of different types of disability (Table 14.5) and by the mean scores of all the children on the OPCS severity scale for each type of disability (Table 14.6), it can be seen that, for personal care, locomotion, vision, dexterity, and reaching and stretching, disabilities tend to increase in number and severity from Clusters 1–7. In both tables, notably high rates are picked out in bold type. In Table 14.6, the large values (highlighted in bold) of severity scores are those that are significantly different at the less than the 0.5% level from the average score for all the children under five in the sample.

The pattern of disabilities within clusters is quite clear. Cluster 1 is typified by children with relatively low levels of disability, generally close to the OPCS threshold values; but no area of disability predominates. In Cluster 2, all the children have behavioural disabilities. Cluster 3 is typified by children with behavioural, continence and often personal care disabilities. All the children in Cluster 4 have, or are suspected of having, intellectual functioning disabilities in association with multiple other disabilities, typically those of behaviour, locomotion and communication. Clusters 5 and 6 contain children with different patterns of severe multiple disability and Cluster 7 is typified by children with extremely severe multiple disabilities. More detailed descriptions of the clusters are provided later in this chapter.

The seven clusters that were chosen for children under five are based on only 202 cases and some of the clusters contain only a few children (for example, Cluster 6 has only six children and Cluster 7 only eight). Furthermore, as explained above, the scores for the 11 types of disability were based on a complicated system that took account of both the children's abilities and their developmental age. For these reasons, we felt that it was important to check on the robustness of the seven-cluster classification. This could be done with the help of Fisher's Linear Discriminant Analysis. From the results of this exercise (set out in Table 14.7) we were able to confirm that 194 of the 202 children (96%) were classified correctly. All the children in Clusters 3, 4, 5 and 7 appear to be in their correct groups as are, respectively, 96% and 97% of the children in Clusters 1 and 2. The least reliable cluster is Cluster 6, where only three out of the six children are classified correctly. This poor result may arise from the small number of children in the cluster.

However, the results from linear discriminant analyses can sometimes be over-optimistic; because of a fortuitous combination of variables, they can yield a higher proportion of cases classified correctly than is warranted. In order to check this, a second series of discriminant analyses were performed using cross-validation. This gave very similar results and only reduced the overall number of children classified correctly from 194 (96%) to 190 (94%). The evidence from these second analyses, therefore, would indicate that the seven-cluster classification is quite robust.

Table 14.6 Average disability score by type of disability amongst children under five in private households, analysed by cluster (1985)

Area of disability	Clusters						
	1	2	3	4	5	6	7
Behaviour	0.5	**9.1**	**10.1**	**5.7**	**8.1**	**9.9**	**8.9**
Intellectual functioning	–	–	–	0.5	0.5	0.2	0.5
Communication	0.4	0.2	0.6	1.7	**5.0**	0.5	**8.5**
Continence	0.7	0.2	**6.2**	0.2	**6.1**	1.0	**6.4**
Personal care	0.4	0.3	1.4	1.2	**4.6**	**5.5**	**7.7**
Locomotion	0.5	..	0.7	1.8	**4.9**	**8.6**	**6.7**
Seeing	0.4	0.1	–	**2.0**	–	**3.3**	**3.2**
Consciousness	0.2	0.2	0.1	0.4	0.4	0.4	**1.9**
Dexterity	..	..	–	0.7	1.2	1.6	**6.2**
Reaching and stretching	..	–	0.1	1.0	–	**4.6**	**8.2**
Hearing	0.6	0.2	0.1	1.0	..	–	**1.8**
Estimated number of children (000s)	23	23	3	6	3	2	2

Notes:

a .. = less than 0.1.

b Possible range on severity scales for each type of disability for children aged exactly 5:

Locomotion	0.7–11.6	Continence	1.1–8.4
Reaching and stretching	1.2–10.9	Personal care	0.6–11.3
Dexterity	1.2–9.4	Intellectual functioning	0.5
Hearing	1.1–11.5	Behaviour	1.1–11.8
Seeing	1.5–11.8	Consciousness	0.5–4.0
Communication	1.8–12.5		

Table 14.7 Comparison of the classification of children with disabilities under five obtained from the cluster analysis (using Ward's method) and from Fisher's Linear Discriminant Analysis

Predicted cluster	Actual cluster						
	1	2	3	4	5	6	7
1	70	1	–	–	–	–	–
2	1	71	–	–	–	1	–
3	2	1	10	–	–	–	–
4	–	–	–	21	–	1	–
5	–	–	–	–	11	–	–
6	–	–	–	–	–	3	–
7	–	–	–	–	–	1	8
Total	**73**	**73**	**10**	**21**	**11**	**6**	**8**
Number correct	70	71	10	21	11	3	8
Proportion correct	0.959	0.973	1.000	1.000	1.000	0.500	1.000

Number of children = 202   Number correct = 194   Proportion correct = 96%

4. Fuller details of the seven clusters of disabled children under five

CLUSTER 1: Children with relatively mild disabilities

n = 73 (36% of total);
population estimate = 23,000; mean age = 2.4 years; mean number of disabilities = 1.4

This is the joint largest cluster and groups together children with a range of relatively mild disabilities. The children are, on average, younger than those in the other clusters and this in part explains the low severity scores.

Seventy-three per cent of the children have only one type of disability, and no one area of disability is predominant. However, 30% have consciousness disabilities, just under 20% mild disabilities of continence or personal care, 16% hearing disabilities and 15% locomotive disabilities. None of the children have disabilities of intellectual functioning.

Almost a third of these children had a measurable *consciousness* disability at the time of the survey. However, over 40% had had at least one fit, convulsion or 'turn' in the past.

Although the children in this group have relatively mild locomotion disabilities, 15% are unlikely to be able to walk normally at the usual age and 11% have or will have more difficulty than most children in keeping their balance.

Despite the young average age of this group, 16% could be assessed at the time of the survey as having a *hearing* disability and 14% one of *communication*. It seems likely that other children in this group may develop hearing and communications disabilities as they grow older.

The poor health of Cluster 1 children means that 40% are much more likely than most children of their age to catch ordinary infections like coughs and colds and, for 28% of them, these are especially dangerous.

CLUSTER 2: Children with behavioural disabilities

n = 73 (36% of total);
population estimate = 23,000; mean age = 3.2 years; mean number of disabilities = 1.7

This is the other joint largest cluster and groups together children who all have moderate to severe behavioural disabilities; 42% obtained the maximum score, indicating that they are 'aggressive or destructive, have temper tantrums or scream and shout *most of the time* every day'.

Fifty-one per cent of the children have behavioural disabilities alone, but all the others have behavioural disabilities in combination with one or more other disabilities: typically, disabilities of consciousness (17%), continence (14%), personal care (12%) and hearing (11%). None of these children have disabilities of intellectual functioning. However, it is unlikely or unsure whether 27% of them will be able, at the usual age, to speak so that people can understand them without difficulty.

The children in this group have a range of different *behavioural* disabilities: 54% are more aggressive, destructive, noisy or difficult to manage than most children of their age, and 56% are extremely overactive. However, their behavioural disabilities are not confined to aggression and overactivity: 47% of them are often miserable, fearful, anxious or inclined to cry much more than most children their age. Similarly, just under 60% are unusually clinging or demanding compared with children of the same age.

The poor health of these children means that 63% are much more likely than most children of their age to catch ordinary infections like coughs and colds and, for 37% of them, these are especially dangerous. Respiratory problems result in 42% of the children suffering from severe bouts of breathlessness, wheezing or coughing.

The children in this cluster are, on average, nine to ten months older than the children in Cluster 1. All are over two years old and 77% are over three. Boys are over-represented.

CLUSTER 3: Children with severe behavioural and continence disabilities, with over half having disabilities of personal care and one in five locomotion disabilities

n = 10 (5% of total);
population estimate = 3000; mean age = 3.3 years; mean number of disabilities = 3.2

All the children in this group have severe behavioural and continence disabilities – over half had the maximum behaviour score – indicating that the child is 'aggressive or destructive, has temper tantrums or screams and shouts *most of the time* every day'. None of these children have disabilities of intellectual functioning.

The *behavioural* disabilities of this group are the most severe of all the clusters. They are not only more severe than those of the children in Cluster 2, but the pattern and nature of the disabilities are also different. Cluster 3 children tend to be more clinging and lacking in interest than Cluster 2 children but do not exhibit the same levels of overactivity.

Indeed, nine out of these ten children are unusually clinging or demanding compared with children of the same age, and eight are often miserable, fearful, anxious, or inclined to cry much more than most children their age. Forty per cent also lack interest in people and things. However, only 30% are extremely overactive compared with other children of the same age, a small proportion considering that 60% of the children in this group have a maximum score on the behavioural disability severity scale.

The continence, personal care and other disabilities, together with the health problems of these children, result in 60% suffering from severe pain or itching, which is the largest proportion in any cluster. The severe pain or itching is so bad for 30% of them that this alone severely restricts their ability to lead a normal life.

The poor health of Cluster 3 children means that 60% of them are much more likely than most children of their age to catch ordinary infections like coughs and colds and, for 30% of them, these are especially dangerous. Respiratory problems result in 40% of the children suffering from severe bouts of breathlessness, wheezing or coughing.

CLUSTER 4: Children with intellectual functioning disabilities, with three-quarters having behavioural disabilities, over half disabilities of locomotion and communication, and a third visual or personal care disabilities

n = 21 (10% of total);
population estimate = 6000; mean age = 2.4 years; mean number of disabilities = 4.6

About half the children in this cluster are younger than three, and their relatively low total OPCS disability scores (see Figure 14.4 and Table 14.4) can be largely accounted for by their relatively young age. They all have, or are suspected of having, disabilities of intellectual functioning, and 82% have four or more different disabilities.

As in Cluster 7, all the children in this cluster have, or will have, severe difficulty learning or a mental handicap and, for 85% of them, it is unlikely or unknown whether they will be able, at the usual age, to speak so that people can understand them without difficulty. It is also unlikely or unsure whether 65% of these children will be able to understand what people say to them.

Over three-quarters of this group have a range of *behavioural* disabilities associated with their mental impairment. The pattern and extent of these disabilities are similar to those of the children in Cluster 3 but they are not as severe. Eight out of ten of the children are unusually clinging or demanding compared with children of the same age, and 55% are often miserable, fearful, anxious, or inclined to cry much more than most children their age. Thirty per cent show a lack of interest in people and things. However, this is the first group where a substantial proportion (a third) is considered by their parents to exhibit behaviours that are unusual, strange or odd compared with other children of the same age. Just under a third of the group (30%) is also extremely overactive compared with their peers.

These children do not have only cognitive and behavioural disabilities; the majority also have sensory and physical disabilities. Sixty-two per cent have locomotion disabilities, 33% visual disabilities, 29% disabilities of consciousness, a quarter dexterity disabilities, and just under a fifth disabilities of reaching and stretching and hearing. This is the first group where a sizeable proportion of the children can be assessed as having seeing disabilities.

The *locomotion* disabilities of this group are so severe that two-thirds of them have, or will have, more difficulty than most children in keeping their balance. It is unlikely or unsure whether 45% of them will be able to walk normally at the usual age. Although 29% of this group had a *consciousness* disability above the threshold level at the time of the survey, just under half had had at least one fit, convulsion or 'turn' in the past.

The health problems of Cluster 4 children mean that 60% of them are much more likely than most children of their age to catch ordinary infections like coughs and colds and, for 45% of them, these are especially dangerous. The multiple disabilities of these children require just under half of them to have physiotherapy, injections, dialysis, bandaging, or some other time-consuming or complicated treatment at least once a week.

CLUSTER 5: Severely multiply disabled children, predominantly with mental and learning disabilities; children with intellectual functioning, continence, personal care, behavioural and communication disabilities, with almost two-thirds having locomotion disabilities

n = 11 (5% of total);
population estimate = 3000; mean age = 3.5 years; mean number of disabilities = 5.7

The children in this group have a similar pattern, combination and range of disabilities as those in Cluster 4, but the severity of these is much greater. The children in Cluster 5 are some of the oldest in the under-five age group, with an average age of 3.5 years. They are over a year older, on average, than the Cluster 4 children, which in part explains their higher severity scores.

They are all severely multiply disabled and all have, or are suspected of having, disabilities of intellectual functioning, personal care and continence. Nine out of the eleven children also have moderate or severe communication and behavioural disabilities.

All the children have, or are suspected of having, a mental handicap or severe difficulty in learning. It is unlikely or unknown whether 90% of them will be able, at the usual age, to speak so that people can understand them without difficulty.

Just under half of these children are considered by their parents to exhibit behaviours that are unusual, strange or odd compared with other children of the same age. A similar proportion is also 'more aggressive, destructive, noisy or difficult to manage than most children of their age'. Over a third of this group (36%) is extremely overactive compared with their peers, and two-thirds have unusually clinging or demanding behaviour.

The severe cognitive and *behavioural* disabilities of this group are (as with Cluster 4 children) combined with severe physical disabilities. All the children have *locomotion* disabilities and, for 82% of cases, these result in their having more difficulty than most children their age in keeping their balance. For just under 90% of these children, difficulties in walking will affect them all or most of the time.

All the children in this group have disabilities of *continence* and none is able to control their bladder normally despite their relatively older age.

The health problems of Cluster 5 children mean that 73% of them are much more likely than most children of their age to catch ordinary infections like coughs and colds. This is the second highest proportion of all the clusters and only in Cluster 7 (the most severe of all) is a greater proportion of children more susceptible to common infections.

CLUSTER 6: Severely multiply disabled children, predominantly with physical, behavioural and sensory disabilities; children with disabilities of personal care, locomotion and behaviour, with two-thirds having disabilities of reaching and stretching and half dexterity and consciousness disabilities

n = 6 (3% of total);
population estimate = 2000; mean age = 3.0 years; mean number of disabilities = 5.7

The children in this cluster have a similar number and severity of disabilities to those in Cluster 5; however, the pattern and combination is very different. While Cluster 5 children suffer predominantly from cognitive, communication and behavioural disabilities, the children grouped in this cluster suffer predominantly from physical and behavioural disabilities. It must be noted that this is the least robust cluster, so these results should be treated with some caution.

All the children are severely multiply disabled and all have severe behavioural, locomotion and personal care disabilities, usually in combination with other physical disabilities such as those associated with dexterity and reaching and stretching. This cluster also contains the most severely visually impaired children younger than five. Only two have disabilities of intellectual functioning.

The *locomotion* disabilities of these children are also the most severe of any group. All of them have health problems that affect their legs, and it is unlikely or unsure if they will be able to walk normally at the usual age. Similarly the balance of all these children is impaired and these locomotion disabilities affect them all the time.

The physical disabilities of Cluster 6 children are not confined to their legs; five out of the six of them have disabilities that affect the use of their hands or fingers as well. Two-thirds have disabilities that affect the use of their arms and they cannot stretch both arms above their head at the same time in order to reach for something.

The high severity scores for *personal care* disability that these children obtain mainly result from the restricted use of their arms and legs, which also restricts their ability to dress, feed and wash themselves.

This cluster has the second highest severity score for behavioural disabilities amongst the under-5s. Only the children in Cluster 3 are more severely disabled in this respect. All the children exhibit extremely clinging or demanding behaviour but none is extremely overactive. The absence of overactive behaviour might be explained by their severe physical disabilities, which limit their opportunity to behave in this way. Their ability to be destructive is also reduced by their physical condition. However, two-thirds are often miserable, fearful, anxious, or inclined to cry much more than most children their age.

The multiple severe disabilities of this group require that they all have physiotherapy, injections, dialysis, bandaging, or some other time-consuming or complicated treatment at least once a week.

CLUSTER 7: Children with multiple very severe disabilities

n = 8 (4% of total);
population estimate = 2000; mean age = 3.5 years; mean number of disabilities = 9.4

These are by far the most severely disabled children in the under-five age group. All the children in this cluster have multiple very severe disabilities, with no child having fewer than eight different disabilities.

All the children have disabilities of *behaviour, intellectual functioning, communication, continence, personal care, locomotion, dexterity* and *reaching and stretching*. Six out of the eight children also have severe *consciousness* disabilities.

They all have severely restricted use of their arms and legs in conjunction with cognitive and behavioural disabilities; most also have severe sensory impairments of sight and hearing, although their severe communication disabilities make an accurate assessment of the severity of their sensory disabilities almost impossible.

In comparison with the children in all the other clusters, these children are much more severely multiply disabled. In particular, they have higher average severity scores for disabilities of communication, continence, personal care, consciousness, reaching and stretching, dexterity and sensory disabilities (seeing and hearing).

None of the children in this cluster is likely to be able to speak so that people can understand them without difficulty, and it is unlikely that they will be able to understand what is being said to them. Unsurprisingly, all these children have behaviours that are considered by their parents to be unusual, strange or odd compared with other children of the same age. Nearly two-thirds show no interest in people or things.

Although all the children in this cluster have behavioural disabilities, their average severity score is not as high as those for the children in some of the other clusters (2, 3 and 6). This is largely because of the extremely restricted abilities caused by their other disabilities. They are simply unable to exhibit many of the behavioural disabilities of which less severely multiply disabled children are capable.

The severe health problems of Cluster 7 children mean that they are more likely than any of the children in the other clusters to catch ordinary infections such as coughs and colds. Like the children in Cluster 6, all the children in this cluster have to have physiotherapy, injections, dialysis, bandaging, or some other time-consuming or complicated treatment at least once a week.

5. Discussion and implications

The measurement of disability in young children is difficult. All children are born with limited abilities and are unable to care for themselves. These conditions, which are 'normal' for a baby, would represent severe disabilities in adults or older children. In a real sense, we are all born 'disabled', and the OPCS adult disability surveys have shown that the majority of people develop a disability in old age. For this reason, some people have argued that disability should not be considered an abnormal condition but something that we all experience, both when we are young and, sometimes, in old age. Most people are only temporarily 'able' in the period between the disabilities of infancy and childhood and old age.

Disability in young children can be measured only in relation to their developmental age; for example, by comparing the child's current abilities with those that would be expected in a child of the same age. The measurement of disability in children under five is, therefore, much more complex than the measurement of disability in older children. As we have seen, OPCS made a heroic attempt to develop a single common severity scale for disability 'from the cradle to the grave'. However, this was always doomed to failure by the enormity (and, arguably, by the impossibility) of the task. The fact that OPCS made as much progress as it did is a testament to their immense expertise and professionalism.

Different types of disability in children under five are not only difficult to measure but also have complex patterns and combinations. The majority of young children in the survey (60%) had more than one disability. No simple system of classification was therefore possible. However, once again, the use of cluster analysis as a tool of classification allowed account to be taken of the number, type, severity and combination of up to 11 different types of disability. The seven resulting clusters for the under-5s not only provided far more detailed descriptions of the pattern of disability but also offered a considerable reduction in the heterogeneity and number of categories often employed.

The cluster analysis also highlighted the limitations of the measurement of the severity of disability in children younger than five. For example, the children in Cluster 7 (very severely and multiply disabled) are, as a group, probably the most severely disabled children in the private households survey, despite the fact that they have a lower average combined severity score than the 5–15-year-old children in Cluster 11 (multiply and very severely disabled). The children under five in Cluster 7 have, on average, 9.4 different disabilities and none of them has fewer than eight. By comparison, the 5–15-year-olds in Cluster 11 have, on average, 8.6 different disabilities and 21% of them have fewer than eight.

It is not surprising that amongst those living in private households there was a group of more severely multiply disabled children in the under-five age group than there was in the 5–15 category. Some of these extremely multiply disabled young children have very short life expectancies and will die before their late teens. The huge effort and expertise required to look after such a child has been well documented; for some families it proves overwhelming (Glendenning, 1983; Beresford, 1995). A number of the Cluster 7 children will be cared for in communal establishments when they are older. Their parents will simply not be able to cope with their needs.

We have explained why, at a technical level, it was necessary to carry out two separate cluster analysis exercises, one for children aged 5–15 and the other for children under five. Having done so, however, there is the advantage that both the differences and the similarities between these two age groups have been clarified, and some of the simplifications that OPCS was forced to make in their original study have been avoided. The general conclusions, however, are two-fold. First, that the measurement of the severity of disability in young children is extremely difficult and, secondly, that *it can be misleading to group all disabled children together irrespective of their age.*

NOTES TO CHAPTER 14

[1] The maximum and minimum points for each area of disability for a five-year-old are set out in Figure 1.5.

[2] That is, the disability score in each area of disability added together and then divided by the number of children.

15 Services provided for young children and their families

In Chapter 14 we have explained why it was necessary to undertake a separate analysis of children under five. In this chapter we consider the various services that were provided for them as well as the services that they were not receiving but which their parents felt were needed. However, because of the much smaller number in this group (212 after weighting), our analysis and discussion are more limited than they were for the 5–15-year-old group.

1. Domiciliary services

Overall, 78% of this age group had received, in the previous year, one or more of the domiciliary services[1] listed on the OPCS interview cards. This is a very much higher proportion than was found for the 5–15-year-olds, amongst whom the rate was 32%. However, as might be expected, this difference was attributable largely to the fact that 68% of those under five (in comparison with 14% in the older group) had had contact with a health visitor. Nevertheless, given their young ages and their disabilities, this proportion struck us as surprisingly low. However, the Manchester cohort study of families and their children with Down's syndrome (Cunningham *et al.*, 1982) noted that the number of regular visits to the home by a health visitor was highest when the child was less than three months of age, but that by the time the children were one year old only 26% of the families were visited. There was a further decline once the children reached five years of age, a reduction also found by Wilkin (1979).

Apart from health visiting, the only other services that were received by more than 5% of these children in the OPCS survey in the preceding year were physiotherapy (14%), social work (14%) and a visiting teacher (10%).[2] Physiotherapy and home teaching were, therefore, provided markedly more often for the under-5s than they were for the older age group. Even so, apart from the addition of physiotherapy, the same three domiciliary services – that is, health visiting, social work and home teaching – dominated the picture as in the 5–15 age group, although their relative significance was different.

Whereas 18% of the parents of the older children considered that their child needed a service that they were not getting, this proportion rose to 24% amongst those with younger children. The services most in demand were social work (21%), an incontinence service (also 21%), a health visitor (15%), a local authority home help (12%) and a laundry service (10%). No other domiciliary service was asked for by more than a small handful of parents. As with parents of the older children, social work help headed the list, but more of the parents of the younger children requested health visiting and home help and fewer asked for home teaching. This is a much lower proportion of parents of young disabled children expressing an unmet need than was found later by Stallard and Lenton (1992); they reported that 43% of the parents of under-5s in their study thought that they did not receive enough 'family support'.

When we looked at the seven clusters for the under-5s, we found no significant difference between the groups with respect to the provision of health visiting, but both physiotherapy and social work were more concentrated upon the 'behaviour and other disability' group (Cluster 4) and the three multiple and severe categories (Clusters 5, 6 and 7). Although the numbers were relatively small, the home teaching service also seemed to be focused upon the 'behaviour and other disability' cluster.

The small number of parents expressing the need for additional services made it hazardous to draw firm conclusions about how this was distributed amongst the clusters, but the demand for social work appeared to be greatest in those clusters where the existing provision was thin on the ground.

When we came to analyse the data about the receipt of domiciliary services by the under-5s and their families in conjunction with the socio-economic variables, we found, as with the 5–15-year-olds, that there were no sharp differences. This may have reflected the predominance of health visiting amongst the services that were provided. However, it was notable that, whereas the rate of contact with this service during the previous year clustered around 90% for the lowest four of the income quintiles, for the highest it fell dramatically to 24%. It would seem, therefore, that the families which health visitors were *not* visiting were heavily concentrated amongst the wealthiest. No comparable pattern emerged with respect to the poverty index, social class or household composition.

The number of families receiving other domiciliary services in the preceding year was much smaller, making it difficult to draw firm conclusions about socio-economic distinctions. However, what social work there was focused on the three lowest income groups (18% of them having had contact compared with 8% in the top two categories), on Social Classes III, IV and V (21% of them being seen compared with 9% in Classes I and II) and on the 'poor' (22% as against 12% of the 'not poor'). No such gradient was apparent in the case of physiotherapy.

The provision of home teaching favoured those in the higher income groups. For example, 31% of the top quintile had had this service, 24% of the second, 13% of the third, 8% of the fourth, and only 2% of the lowest. There were no similar pronounced differences in home teaching provision with respect to the poverty index or social class, once again suggesting that effective family income was the most sensitive of the socio-economic variables in accounting for unevenness in the distribution of many of the services.

Furthermore, and unlike the situation in the 5–15 age group, it is interesting to note that the proportion of parents who considered that extra domiciliary services were needed rose steeply as income fell. Whereas just 2% of those in the top quintile voiced an unmet need, this soared to 38% amongst those with the lowest fifth of incomes. A similar significant difference occurred with respect to whether or not the families were 'poor'. 'Poor' parents were some four times more likely to express the need for a domiciliary service (or more service) than the 'not poor'. However, the direction of these differences was *not* repeated when it came to social class; in fact, the lowest level of demand was found amongst the parents in Social Classes IV and V.

Once more, this suggests that class, income and a more general measure of poverty and deprivation should not be confused. Indeed, it is possible that they were and are becoming more distinct as middle class and professional unemployment becomes more common. Furthermore, for families with disabled children, the costs that the disabilities impose may well distort the widely assumed association between class, income and deprivation – even more perhaps, in 'younger' families than amongst those who are 'older'.

2. Hospital and clinic-based services

The under-5s had visited a hospital or clinic somewhat more often in the last year than children in the 5–15 age band (65% compared with 57%). Almost all of those attending a hospital or clinic as out-patients had seen a doctor (some more than one), but other professionals or services trailed far behind. Twenty-seven per cent of those who made a visit had seen a speech therapist, 25% a physiotherapist, 18% an optician and 17% a hearing therapist. (Only one family, it might be noted, had seen a hospital social worker.) This pattern is similar to that found amongst the older children, except that physiotherapy (as with the domiciliary services) was somewhat more common and the services of a psychologist less common.[3]

The average number of out-patient visits to a hospital or clinic in the preceding year (amongst those who attended), was almost exactly 15 (with a standard deviation of 25.19), a figure significantly greater than for the older group, where the mean was 10.6. When we looked at the seven clusters, different rates of hospital attendance did emerge, generally in the direction of the (multiple and severe) groups (Clusters 5, 6 and 7) being more likely to have made a visit. However, the variations were not great enough to be statistically significant.

Thus, in brief, more of the under-5s than the 5–15-year-olds attended hospital out-patient departments or clinics and those who did, did so more often. It was also clear that the younger group of children were more likely to have been admitted to hospital as in-patients in the previous year than those who were older (10% compared with 6%), but they were less likely to have been admitted than under-5s in general, amongst whom 12% had experienced an admission over the same period (OPCS, 1989).

The socio-economic characteristics of the families whose children attended or did not attend a hospital or clinic in the preceding year were somewhat different but did not present a clear or readily understandable picture. For instance, the lowest rates of hospital contact (36% and 38%, respectively) were amongst children in large families (four or more children) and those whose families fell into the highest fifth of the income divisions. However, since the number in both of these groupings was relatively small, too much should not be read into these findings. The highest rate of attendance (100%) was discovered amongst families in Social Classes IV and V. These findings are at odds with the comparable data for the 5–15 age group, suggesting that different influences begin to operate as children grow up.

None of the other socio-economic variables distinguished between the hospital attenders and non-attenders. However, certain differences were to be found amongst those who visited a hospital out-patient department or clinic during the previous year in relation to the mean number of times that they made such visits. Whereas four of the income quintiles were fairly close to the overall mean of 15 times, the average for children of parents with the lowest fifth of incomes was only five. A similar difference was found between the 'not poor' (a mean of 19 times) and the 'poor' (a mean of just over 12). There were also significant differences in the average number of attendances in relation to social class, as Table 15.1 demonstrates.

Table 15.1 Mean number of hospital or clinic attendances in the previous year (amongst those children under five making such visits), analysed by social class (1985)

Social class	Mean number of attendances
I and II	17.7
III Non-manual	22.5
III Manual	9.9
IV and V	6.7
All (n = 138)	**15.0**

We also noted that the type of household appeared to make a difference. Of the children who made a hospital or clinic visit, those living in households that comprised two adults and only the disabled child went 33.9 times, on average, in the previous year, a rate almost three times higher than any other kind of household. This suggests that the presence of two parents with only the one child to care for may enable more visits to be made than where parents are single-handed or where there are other children to be taken into account.

We pointed out earlier that, in the 5–15 age group, socio-economic factors appeared to be quite closely associated with which service a child received when they made a hospital or clinic visit. This was also the case for the under-5s, although the pattern was somewhat different. For instance, the only children who did not see a doctor during their previous year's contact with a hospital came from families in the lowest income group (92% compared with 100%). Only one child from this poorest quintile saw a physiotherapist (compared with 26% overall), none saw an occupational therapist (13% overall), only 8% saw a hearing therapist (17% overall) and only 8% saw an optician (18% overall). None of the children from the poorest fifth of families saw a psychologist or a psychotherapist (but the overall rate stood at only 9%).

It must be pointed out, however, that these figures do not mean that the children from the lowest income group of families received other hospital or clinic-based services more often. What the data reflected was that, when a child from such a family went to hospital, they had contact with fewer different kinds of service; that is, the higher contact rates for the children from better-off families arose largely from the fact that more of them visited a variety of services.

The overall impression created by our analysis of the provision of hospital or clinic-based services for the under-5s is first, that it is likely to be the nature and severity of the child's disability that mainly determines whether or not they attend these centres; but, secondly, that it is socio-economic factors which appear to influence the *number* of visits made by those who have such contact. This conclusion is again somewhat at odds with what was found in the case of the 5–15-year-old group. There, it will be recalled, factors of class, income and general deprivation appeared to influence whether or not a child had made a hospital out-patient or clinic visit in the first place, but not the number of occasions this happened. However, although the greater severity of a child's disabilities led towards a greater degree of hospital contact in both age groups, this was more pronounced amongst the older children than the younger, possibly reflecting the unfolding of the full nature and realisation of the disability.

3. Contact with general practitioners

Whereas 77% of the 5–15-year-olds had seen a general practitioner in the previous year, this proportion rose to 92% amongst the under-5s. The average number of times that they had seen a GP was 9.6 (with a standard deviation of 15.82), a significantly greater frequency than the mean of 4.5 times in the older group. Both averages were higher than the average national NHS consultations with GPs, which in 1983 were three times a year for the older group and seven times for the under-5s (OPCS, 1989, p. 116, Table 4.30). It should also be noted that GPs saw the younger age group at home more than they did the 5–15-year-olds (16% of all contacts compared with 10%).

It will be recalled that the most severely and multiply disabled group of under-5s (Cluster 7) had a surprisingly low rate of contact with hospital or clinic-based services. By contrast, as shown in Table 15.2, children in this cluster had the highest mean number of contacts with their GPs in the previous year: 16.9 contacts compared with the next highest of 10.5 (Cluster 2) and the lowest of 4.2 in the group with only somewhat less severe disabilities (Cluster 6). However, it must be borne in mind that the number of children in Clusters 6 and 7 was quite small; hence the results could be disproportionately influenced by the experience of a few children.

As with most of the other services that we have considered, there were significant differences in the pattern of GP contacts with respect to the socio-economic characteristics of the families. For example, the children whose families had incomes in the top quintile saw their GPs much less often than children in the other four income groups (a mean of 4.9 times compared with around 10 or more). Likewise, those whose families were in Social Classes I and II saw a GP less often than those in the other class groups (an average of 6.2 times a year compared with 11.0). Likewise, the children in those families that we classified as 'poor' saw their GPs a little more often on average than the 'not poor' (10.5 times compared with 8.0).

Table 15.2 Mean number of visits of under-5s to hospital out-patient departments/clinics and GPs in the previous year, analysed by clusters (1985)

Cluster	Description	Mean number of hospital visits	Mean number of GP visits
1	Low levels of disabilities	13.1	10.0
2	Behaviour	9.5	10.5
3	Incontinence	13.0	6.0
4	Intellectual disabilities	21.4	7.7
5	Multiple cognitive disabilities	32.6	6.5
6	Multiple physical disabilities	30.5	4.2
7	Severe and multiple disabilities	6.3	16.9
All (*n* = 138)		15.0	9.6

These results were more confused (and confusing) than those for the number of hospital visits, but they do tend to suggest that better-off and higher social class families did not consult their GPs about their children as often as other parents, perhaps suggesting that their children were less often ill as a result of conditions not related to their disabilities.

4. Respite care

Overall, only 4% of the families and children in the under-5 group had had respite care in the previous year, a marginally smaller proportion than amongst the 5–15-year-olds. However, 60% of the parents had not heard about the possibility (a somewhat higher rate than was found in the group of parents with older children). This lack of knowledge was steeply graded according to family income: whereas 72% of parents in the top quintile knew about short-term care, this fell to 20% amongst those in the lowest. The same pattern, though with less dramatic differences, was apparent between the 'poor' and the 'not poor' and between the social classes (63% of Social Class I and II parents were aware of the existence of respite care but only 29% of those in groups IV and V).

On the face of it, those who had had short-term care had done so frequently – the average number of times in the previous year being 7.5. However, this figure was inflated by one child who had had respite care more than 20 times in the year, whereas most of the others had only one or two such breaks. Hence, in reality, short-term care was neither common nor frequent, a finding supported by Robinson and Stalker (1989), who found that younger children received the least respite care, irrespective of which service they used.

5. Equipment, appliances and adaptations

In discussing the provision of special equipment or adaptations for the under-5s, we follow broadly the same pattern as that adopted in Chapter 7, although, again, the analysis possible with the much smaller numbers is more limited.

Mobility equipment

Only 2% of the children under five with a locomotion disability used a wheelchair, compared with 18% of the older group. Overall, a quarter of the under-5s who satisfied the OPCS criteria for a locomotion disability used a mobility aid, a slightly larger proportion than in the older group of children. The use was mainly amongst the three clusters (5, 6 and 7) of severest disability. Nevertheless, a quarter of the parents considered that their child needed a mobility aid that they did not have (compared with 14% of those with older children), and this demand was spread throughout the seven clusters. As with the older group, what parents most often wanted were special bicycles and, to a lesser extent, special pushchairs.

Of the under-5s above the OPCS threshold of locomotion disability, 34% used walking aids, a rather higher proportion than amongst the 5–15-year-olds. About a fifth of these children used callipers, walking frames or splints, but by far the most common equipment was surgical footwear, worn by 59%. Again, the use of walking aids was concentrated in the three categories of severest disability (Clusters 5, 6 and 7) but a quarter of those with low levels of several disabilities (Cluster 1) also had resort to such equipment.

Eleven per cent of the parents (a little more than in the older group) considered that their children needed walking aids that they did not have, and a surprisingly large proportion of this demand was for surgical footwear; indeed, half of all the parents of these children said that this was needed. However, it seems likely that much of this demand was for improved or better fitting surgical footwear rather than for first-time provision, not least perhaps because of the rapid growth of young children's feet.

For the purposes of our analysis of the socio-economic factors that might influence the provision of mobility equipment, we combined mobility aids and walking aids. We found no difference in their use in relation to the social class of the families or with respect to the poverty index. However, families comprising two parents and only one child showed a more pronounced usage than all other types (32% compared with 12%, although there was variation around the latter figure). The family income data revealed an even greater disparity. Whereas the first four income quintiles clustered around an 18% level of use amongst those children with a locomotion disability, this proportion fell to 4% of those in families with the lowest fifth of incomes.

Hearing and speech aids

One in eight of those reaching the OPCS threshold for a hearing disability used some form of aid to hearing, and the same proportion of parents said that their child was in need of one or in need of an improved version. Therefore, far fewer children under five with a hearing disability had an aid (or an aid that the parents thought was appropriate) than in the 5–15 age group. This would seem to be a matter of potential concern given the relationship between hearing and the development of speech, especially in the early years of life.

Incontinence aids

Altogether, 70% of the under-5s who were defined as having a disability of incontinence[4] used an incontinence aid, a much higher rate than amongst the older group. It was interesting to see that the rate only rose to 80% amongst the 'incontinence' group (Cluster 3). The most common equipment was a rubber sheet, followed by pads, but there was a good deal of use of more than one kind of aid.

Almost half (49%) of the parents wanted more by way of such equipment, but what they sought were principally bed alarms (as with the parents of the 5–15-year-olds in this category). Most of those who indicated an unmet need were already using some form of aid and what they wanted was extra or better equipment. Forty per cent of all the parents said that they had to spend more on washing clothes or bed-linen – which, again, gives some idea of the scale of the problems associated with incontinence.

Visual aids

The use of visual aids (other than glasses) amongst the under-5s was negligible, as was the demand for them.

Small aids and gadgets

Only 5% of the under-5s used small aids or gadgets and there was little demand from parents for these items – the only one of any note being for electric toothbrushes. These rates were similar to those found in the older group.

Adaptations

A quarter of the parents considered that their homes had disadvantages with respect to their child's disabilities. Indeed, only 4% of the dwellings had been adapted to take account of those disabilities, although almost one in five of the parents wanted some such improvement – chiefly the installation of a shower (or special shower) or the re-modelling of toilets and bathrooms. Compared with the parents of the older children, more homes had disadvantages, fewer were adapted and more parents expressed a need for more to be done.

Special furniture

Just over a fifth of the children had the use of special furniture, with particularly high rates amongst those in Clusters 5 and 6 (73% and 83%, respectively). It was the parents of children in these clusters, as well as in Cluster 7, who said that they lacked these kinds of equipment, although overall the rate of demand stood at 15%. The type of special furniture that was used and that which was wanted was much the same (chiefly special beds, non-slip mats and special chairs) as for the 5–15-year-olds. However, the rate of provision amongst the older group was higher (9%) and the rate of expressed unmet need lower (only a third of that found amongst the parents of the younger children).

Telephones

It was interesting to discover that the rate of telephone ownership amongst the families of the children under five was significantly lower than amongst those of the older children – 61% compared with 75% (the national rate being 85%). The rates were lowest amongst the families with young children in the 'behaviour' and 'incontinence' clusters (2 and 3) – 55% and 50%, respectively. Of those who did not have a telephone, 85% said that it was because they could not afford it, the same proportion as in the older group.

It was also interesting to see that there were significantly lower rates of telephone ownership (46% and 39%, respectively) in lone-parent and large families (that is, families with four or more children). Similarly, there was a steeply descending gradient in the proportion of families with a telephone in relationship to both income and class. Whereas 94% of those in the top fifth of the income groupings possessed a telephone, this fell by fairly regular intervals to 34% of those in the lowest fifth. Likewise, Social Classes I and II had a 93% ownership but this fell to 33% amongst those in Social Classes IV and V. The same kind of significant difference was found between the 'not poor' and the 'poor'.

When asked whether they had obtained a telephone specifically because of their child's disability, none of the top income group said that this was the case. By contrast, a quarter of those in the lowest income quintile with telephones claimed that, but for their child's disability, they would not have had one. This difference was even more pronounced with respect to the comparison between the 'not poor' and the 'poor' (2% as against 33% saying that their child's disability was the reason for their having a telephone).

6. Discussion and implications

A much higher proportion of this younger group than the 5–15-year-old group had had some form of domiciliary service in the previous year *although this was dominated by the provision of health visiting.* Even so, the rate of such visiting still seemed low – at 68% – and must prompt questions about the reported absence of this service in a third of the cases. However, the main group of families that health visitors were *not* visiting were the wealthiest fifth. Although health visiting and social work were the principal forms of domiciliary service – as they were for the older age group – both physiotherapy and home teaching were more common but, unlike social work, these services were not focused upon poorer families. Indeed, home teaching was slanted in the opposite direction. Parents of the under-5s expressed somewhat more need for domiciliary services than other parents (24% saying something was lacking compared with 18%) but what they wanted was much the same – social work and incontinence and laundry services. However, there was rather more demand for home help and less for home teaching, doubtless reflecting the ages of the children. Also, one of the sharpest differences was in the rate at which parents of the under-5s in different income groups expressed the need for additional services. For example, *whereas only 2% of the richest fifth wanted something more, this proportion rose by steady steps as income fell until, in the lowest income quintile, it stood at 38%.*

More of the under-5s than the older children had made a hospital or clinic visit in the previous year and those who had went more often. However, in both groups, the more severe the disabilities the greater likelihood there was of hospital attendance, although this was more clear cut for the older children. *There was also a much higher rate of contact with general practitioners* amongst the younger than the older children (92% compared with 72%) *and the average number of visits in the year was greater.*

In contrast to the situation for the 5–15-year-olds, socio-economic factors did not appear to have shaped a clear picture of whether the under-5s did or did not receive hospital or clinic-based services. However, one feature that is noteworthy was the low rate of contact with these services for children in families with the top fifth of incomes. Elsewhere, we have drawn attention to the significantly different position of those in the poorest fifth of the families but here, amongst the parents of the under-5s, one sees a number of analyses in which the richest fifth also stand out as different from the rest with regard to the services that their children received.

However, the under-5s show a similar pattern to the older children with regard to the frequencies of hospital visits in relation to the socio-economic variables. *Those of the poorest families who go to hospital attend significantly less often –* a mean during the previous year of five visits, compared with around 15 overall. *A similar difference existed between the 'poor' and the 'not poor' and by social class.* The type of household also appeared to be significant in this respect: *families in which there were two parents and only the disabled child attended hospitals and clinics significantly more often than any other type of family.*

When they did visit hospital, *the children from the poorest fifth of the families also had a different pattern of contact with the available services than all others – they saw almost all the services less than others, and this was largely because they saw fewer different services.* Though similar, this was a more pronounced variation than we found in the 5–15 age group.

Hence, as with the domiciliary services, it is clear that the under-5s had more contact with the health services than children in the older group, probably as a result of the often long-drawn-out process of diagnosis and treatment in the early years of a child's life. However, for whatever reason *far fewer of the younger age group had had no contact with a hospital, clinic or GP in the previous year than the older group of children –* just 3% compared with 12%.

There were certain differences that should be noted with regard to the provision of aids, adaptations and special furniture. More of the homes in which the under-5s lived had disadvantages with respect to their disabilities, fewer homes had been appropriately adapted and more parents wished that they had been. A similar pattern existed in the case of special furniture – there was a lower level of provision and higher rates of demand in the families of the younger group. These results could be interpreted in a number of ways, but there are two possible explanations. First, it may be that, *only as children grow, do parents fully appreciate the importance of supportive services* and hence only gradually articulate these needs. (Indeed, the evidence summarised in the previous paragraph suggests that a great deal of their time and energy is taken up in contacts with the medical services – much more so than later on.) Even so, there was a higher rate of expressed need for adaptations and special furniture amongst the parents of the under-5s than amongst those of the 5–15 group and that suggests a second explanation. It may have been that the provision of these services took time to materialise because of waiting lists (a factor noted by both Glendinning (1983) and Beresford (1995)) or because the nature of the child's disability and family's circumstances was still open and undecided. These are, of course, matters of conjecture but *they do raise important questions about the assumptions and practices that prevail in services for disabled children in relation to their age*, not least with respect to their size and weight, the age of the parents, the length of time that they have had to care for a disabled offspring and the possibility that some services are gradually tapered off over time.

We saw that, in the 5–15 age group, the parents' ownership of a telephone was strongly associated with income, class and the measure of poverty. Amongst the parents of the under-5s, the association was even stronger. By and large, *poor parents* (in whatever way we choose to identify that poverty) *with young disabled children had a level of telephone ownership that was barely a third of the national rate*. The problems that created hardly need to be spelt out. Moreover, when poor parents did have telephones, many of them said that they had acquired them only because of their child's disability, which accentuates the difficulties of caring for a disabled child on a low income or in deprived circumstances.

Finally, we should note *the rather different profiles of the two groups of families*. The most distinctive and significant difference is in their incomes – *families with disabled children under five were poorer*, although in social class terms there was no discernible difference. The mean effective annual income of the families with the younger children (in 1988) was £11,256, whereas that for those with older children was £13,587. As might be expected, therefore, 64% of the former were classified as 'poor' (according to the deprivation index) compared with 55% of the latter. *This probably reflects the ages and stages in the families' lives* – those with younger children were younger families with all the attendant material disadvantages. This is almost certainly reflected in the differences in the household composition of the two groups, as Table 15.3 shows.

There were significantly fewer families with more than two adult members in the under-5s group, suggesting the absence of grown-up children or older relatives. Surprisingly, perhaps, there were also rather more lone parents, but that may be because, in the older group, there had been more time for fractured families to be reconstituted as new partners were taken.

Thus, as we have argued in earlier chapters, it is important (amongst other things) to bear in mind family composition and the *general* pressures and needs that this and their stage of development create, especially in

Table 15.3 Comparison of the household composition of families with disabled children, under and over five (1985)

Family type	Under-5s (%)	5–15s (%)
Lone parent and child	1	3
Lone parent and 2 or more children	16	10
Two parents and child	14	9
Two parents and 2 children	40	29
Two parents and 3 children	19	21
Two parents and 4 or more children	7	8
More than two adults and children	3	19
All	**100**	**100**
	(n = 212)	(n = 989)

formulating priorities for the allocation of services. Again, it is important to stress that the *social factors in a family's situation need to be considered alongside the nature of a child's disability in both reviewing and determining the provision of services*. From the evidence of the brief analysis in this chapter, it may well be that this is particularly important for families with disabled children under five because they are often younger families, poorer families and less experienced families who still have to come to terms with the realities of their child's disabilities. In general, as we have suggested already, the findings raise questions about the assumptions and practices that prevail in the provision of services for disabled children in relation to their age, the age of the parents and the length of time that they have had to care for a disabled offspring.

NOTES TO CHAPTER 15

[1] There was no significant difference between the age groups in this respect, but there was some suggestion of a peaking at the age of two. In the OPCS survey, only 2% of the children under five were younger than 12 months.

[2] There were, of course, some who had more than one service.

[3] It will be recalled that OPCS did not ask parents or carers what hospital-based services they felt their children needed but were not getting, so there was no indication of what were perceived to be the deficiencies in this group of services.

[4] Note that OPCS specified carefully by age what would be considered to be a disability of incontinence, so that the usual timing of the acquisition of continence was taken into account.

PART THREE

Drawing the threads together

16 | Conclusions, implications and discussion

1. The problems and issues surrounding the definition of disability

The definition of disability is vigorously contested. Initially, DHSS had asked OPCS to design a method of assessment for the surveys based on the 'loss of faculty' approach used in adult Industrial Injuries and War Pensions schemes. However, OPCS rejected this idea as impractical for a social survey. Instead, it adopted a definition of disability that was closely related to the International Classification of Impairments, Disabilities and Handicaps (ICIDH), which utilised three different concepts to describe 'disablement'. As will be recalled, this identified:

- **Impairment:** any loss or abnormality of psychological, physiological or anatomical structure or function,
- **Disability:** any restriction or lack of ability (resulting from an impairment) to perform an activity in the manner or within the range considered normal for a human being, and
- **Handicap:** a disadvantage for a given individual, resulting from an impairment or disability, that limits or prevents the fulfilment of a role (depending on age and sex as well as upon social and cultural factors) for that individual.

The OPCS disability surveys have been criticised for using a definition of disability of this kind because it was too medical and primarily focused upon the individual. Disability was regarded as an individual phenomenon reflecting a person's identified impairments. Thus, some commentators such as Abberley (1996) considered the OPCS surveys to be inadequate because of the way in which they chose to define disability, a definition that focused on individuals rather than structures.

The current proposed revision of the International Classification of Impairments, Disabilities and Handicaps (ICIDH–2 Beta–1 Draft) has responded to such criticisms by abandoning the concepts of 'disability' and 'handicap'. In ICIDH–2:

- the concept of impairment remains,
- the concept of disability has been replaced by measures of 'activities', and
- the concept of handicap has been replaced by measures of 'participation'.

Disablement is now seen by WHO (1997) as an interaction, as a complex relationship between health conditions and contextual factors (that is, personal and environmental factors). These interact in a dynamic way to determine the level of participation of a person in his or her surroundings. Impairments, activities and participation are defined in ICIDH–2 as follows:

- Impairment is a loss or abnormality of body structure or of a physiological or psychological function.
- An activity is the nature and extent of functioning at the level of the person. Activities may be limited in nature, duration and quality.
- Participation is the nature and extent of the person's involvement in life situations in relation to Impairments, Activities, Health Conditions and Contextual factors. Participation may be restricted in nature, duration and quality (WHO, 1997).

According to WHO (1997, pp 14 and 17):

> participation deals with societal phenomena. It represents the consequence of health conditions at societal level in terms of participation in various domains, the person's degree of participation and society's response in either facilitating or hindering that participation. Participation is measured relative to the cultural norm of the society.
>
> The standard or norm against which a person's participation is compared represents the nature and extent of participation of a person without disablement in the society, culture or sub-culture.

The term 'disability' has been dropped, in part due to the risk of misunderstanding between health care professionals and disabled people. In North America and Australia people prefer to say that someone has a disability rather than that they are disabled. Similarly, they opt for the term 'person with a disability' rather than 'disabled person'. By contrast, in Europe, disability suggests the 'imposition of a disability on a person by society', people who experience disability refer to themselves as disabled people (WHO, 1997, p. 24).

In order to avoid negative attributes and stigmatisation, the definitions of disablement are moving away from trying to measure 'abilities' and towards the measurement of 'activities'. Many of the shortcomings in the OPCS surveys of children with disabilities result from the virtual impossibility of measuring the 'lack of ability' in young children compared with the 'norm'. The problems of defining what the 'normal' level of continence or intellectual ability should be in a 18-month-old child, and relating deviations from this norm to levels of adult disability, proved insurmountable. Bone and Meltzer (1989) concluded that the adult model of disability fitted the results of the children's exercise poorly. Nevertheless, the adult model was used because of the overriding need to develop a single, universal scale of severity.

There is a need to measure childhood disability using agreed international standards for health and social service planning. Unless both the number of disabled children and their service needs are measured, adequate and appropriate services are unlikely to be provided and the needs of disabled children will remain unknown and invisible.

Local authorities need to recognise that childhood disability includes many children with emotional and behavioural disabilities. In many local authorities services for disabled children are divided between services for children with physical and sensory disabilities and services for children with learning or mental disabilities. This research has clearly demonstrated that this is not a meaningful classification for service provision. Children with multiple disabilities often have physical, sensory and mental disabilities in combination. Similarly, disabled children often have emotional and behavioural disabilities, and local authorities should both recognise this and provide services to meet these needs. For example, in seven out of the ten clusters identified among children in communal establishments, virtually all had behavioural and emotional disabilities, and in the remaining three clusters, between 50% and 80% had behavioural and emotional disabilities. Although behavioural and emotional disabilities were less prevalent amongst children living in private households, in five out of the eleven clusters identified almost all the children had these disabilities. Parker (1998, p. 10) has argued that 'the incidence of behaviour problems is high in disabled children and is a cause of parental stress. Parents need help in understanding behaviour and finding ways to manage it.'

Similarly, health authorities need to provide adequate and comprehensive services to children with continence disabilities and to children with consciousness disabilities. Incontinence and fitting can be highly disabling conditions, even where the 'health' implications of these disabilities may appear small. The stigma and embarrassment that children who have these disabilities may suffer needs to be recognised and adequate information and services have to be provided.

2. The multiplicity of disability

The OPCS surveys clearly demonstrated the multivariate nature of the disability experienced by the children in private households and in communal establishments. The majority of children had more than one disability. There was no child, for instance, who was only deaf and very few who were only blind.

The complex pattern of the combination of childhood disabilities means that no simple system of classification is possible, nor will any be entirely satisfactory. We have suggested that the OPCS approach, by taking no account of the type or combination of types of disabilities nor of any number of disabilities beyond three, oversimplified a very complex picture, and in so doing grouped together children who, especially for the purposes of service planning, may have had little in common.

The method of classification developed in this study took account of the number, type, severity and combination of up to 11 areas of disability. In comparison with the OPCS groupings, the resulting clusters not only provide far more detailed descriptions of the pattern of disability but also offer a considerable reduction in the heterogeneity of the categories.

However, although this approach produced distinct and reasonably homogeneous categories, it could not take account of all the possible individual variations. There is always likely to be a conflict between the needs of *individual* planning, where classifications by type can be oversimplistic (and thereby too easily become a stigmatising label) and the need for *aggregate* planning to allow for a rational basis for the deployment of services at the local authority and health authority levels or at the national level. The OPCS approach did focus upon the limitations on activities experienced by individuals. However, when planning services, it is also necessary to have information which allows some account to be taken of the demands that a person's disabilities are likely to make upon the carers and the providers of services. This is especially true for children because, unlike adults, they are dependent upon adult care even when they do not have a disability.

The multiple nature of childhood disability has profound implications for service provision. Service planning based on impairments or specific medical conditions such as Down's syndrome or cerebral palsy will usually be inadequate. It is simply not a meaningful question to ask what services a child with cerebral palsy requires. The services a child with cerebral palsy needs will depend on their disabilities and family circumstances not on a medical diagnosis.

As disabled children have on average more than one disability, service planning that is based on dealing with one disability at a time or with the 'main' disability can also be problematic. Services (especially medical services) are often organised by specialisms and can focus on what is considered to be the primary disability. However, it may be the secondary or tertiary disability that is of greatest concern to the child or their carers. Disabilities occur in combination, and the organisation, planning and delivery of services should reflect the needs of children with combinations of disabilities. The cluster analysis results in this study demonstrate which combinations of disability occur most frequently.

3. Poverty and disability

It is clear that there are sharp differences in the prevalence of childhood disability according to the social class of the household or family. 'Working-class' children have a higher risk of suffering from a disability than children from the 'middle' and 'upper' classes. This needs to be taken into account when allocating resources for the provision of services for children with disabilities, not least because it seems likely that OPCS underestimated the additional financial costs associated with childhood disability. This finding also provides a method of checking the accuracy of local authority disability registers. There should be higher rates of childhood disability in 'poorer' neighbourhoods than in 'richer' areas.

During the 19th century a number of charitable asylums were established to care for the 'idiot children of the poor who shall appear likely by careful treatment to be capable of mental improvement' (Gladstone, 1996). It was claimed that the benefits of these asylums were 'not limited to the advantages which result to the idiots themselves, but they extend in large measure to the poverty stricken homes of their parents, to the relief of many a respectable hard working family and even to the neighbourhood where the poor lad used to wander a forlorn outcast of society' (Western Counties Asylum, 1883). There is little doubt that the modern welfare state provides better and more enlightened care and support for disabled children and their families than the Victorian charitable asylums. However, large numbers of disabled children and their families still suffer from poverty. There has been over 25 years of high-quality scientific research that has consistently demonstrated that the incomes of both disabled children and their families are often insufficient to meet even their basic needs (for example, Bradshaw, 1975; Disability Alliance, 1975; Reid, 1975;

Loach, 1976; Baldwin, 1977; Piachaud *et al.*, 1981; Baldwin, 1985; Smyth and Robus, 1989; Walker *et al.*, 1992; Beresford, 1995; Kagan *et al.*, 1998).

Almost 55% of the families with children with disabilities were living in or on the margins of poverty in 1985, using a definition of poverty that would be accepted by a large majority of people. Families with children with disabilities could be regarded as 'the poorest of the poor'. They had a greater likelihood of living in poverty than any other social group. This is important to recognise because it implies that major legislation was failing in its purported aims. Financial supplements for the families of disabled children appear to have been insufficient to put them on a par with the rest of the population, let alone cover the extra costs of disability. Current benefit levels are between 20% and 50% too low to meet the minimum essential costs of disabled children and their families (Dobson and Middleton, 1998).

Since 1992 the Disability Living Allowance (DLA) has been the main tax-free social security benefit designed to meet the extra costs of childhood disability (Sainsbury *et al.*, 1995). The claim form is 47 pages long; this, together with the complex nature of the application procedure, has resulted in poorer families being less likely to apply for the DLA, less likely to receive the DLA and more likely to receive the lower rate of benefit (Roberts and Lawton, 1998). The DLA is meant to alleviate the extra costs of disability, but Hirst (1997) has argued that the decision to award benefit is unrelated to the extra costs incurred.

The Children Act 1989 has placed a duty on local authorities to examine the barriers and difficulties that confront disabled children and to provide services to minimise these impediments. It is likely that, in many areas, more could still be done to this end, particularly with regard to helping to alleviate poverty and material and social deprivation.

Similarly, the Disability Discrimination Act 1995, which deals (to some extent) with discrimination in the provision of goods, facilities and services to disabled people, does not directly address discrimination against disabled children and their parents. In the short term, as the families of disabled children in Beresford's (1995) study explained, the greatest need is for more financial assistance through higher weekly disability benefits so that child care and development needs can be adequately met. The application procedures for disability-related benefits also need to be simplified, and proactive policies should be implemented which help families with disabled children claim the benefits to which they are entitled. Local authority disability registers could provide a mechanism for such proactive policies.

In his Beveridge Lecture on 18 March 1999, Tony Blair committed the government to 'lifting 700,000 children out of poverty by the end of the

Parliament' and 'to end child poverty for ever' over the next 20 years (Blair, 1999). He argued that: 'We have made children our top priority because as the Chancellor memorably said in his Budget "they are 20% of the population but they are 100% of the future".' Child poverty is only likely to be ended 'for ever' if the benefit levels for disabled children are increased.

In the longer term what is really needed is a more comprehensive, legally enforceable anti-discrimination policy which is relevant to all disabled children and their families (Gordon and Heslop, 1998).

4. The provision of services, unmet needs and the criteria for allocation

Of the families covered in the OPCS private households survey, only a third of the children in the 5–15 age group or their families had received a domiciliary service in the previous year and, although the rate rose to nearly four-fifths amongst the children under five, this was mainly attributable to health visiting. Furthermore, even though some two dozen different services had been provided, in the vast majority of cases only three were of any significance – social work, health visiting and home teaching – with, perhaps, the addition of physiotherapy in the case of children under five. Home help, laundry or an incontinence service were virtually absent, as were home nursing, a visiting occupational therapist, speech therapist and night sitter. Respite care had only been arranged for 1 in 25 of the families.

Domiciliary services, therefore, were thin on the ground and some of the gaps were particularly worrying. For instance, even amongst the cluster of children with the most severe and multiple disabilities in the 5–15 age group, a third had received no domiciliary service of any kind in the preceding year. None of the 5–15-year-old children whose disabilities were associated with problems of hearing and communication had had any help at home from a speech therapist, and none of the families in the cluster where enuresis was a characteristic disability had had assistance from a laundry service.

Not only were most domiciliary services few and far between but their range was extremely limited. This was more disturbing when seen alongside the data on the use of special equipment, home adaptations and telephone ownership. Generally speaking, the level of the children's use of aids appeared to be rather low when compared with their specific disabilities. For example, only one in four of those with a defined locomotion disability used a walking aid and only one in five a mobility aid. Likewise, in the clusters where hearing problems were a significant feature, only a quarter of the 5–15-year-olds used hearing aids. In some cases, the lack of services provided from outside agencies might have been offset by adaptations having been made to the home, yet only 8% of the homes of the older children had been adapted and, amongst those under five, the proportion was just 4%.

The mobilisation of help of all kinds depends upon communication and, in the present age, this relies heavily upon the telephone. However, the rate of telephone ownership amongst these families with disabled children was significantly less than that in the general population. It may still be.

We had wondered whether the lack of domiciliary services was compensated for by a greater provision of health services, especially those based in hospitals or clinics. At first sight this appeared to have been the case: overall, nearly twice as many children (58%) had had contact with a hospital or clinic in the previous year than with a service supplied to them at home. However, the range of services that children received away from home was limited. Typically, when they went to a hospital or clinic they were seen by a doctor, followed a long way behind by other services. Overall, only some one in five of those who attended had seen a speech therapist, some one in nine a hearing therapist or optician. In the older group, one in seven had seen a psychologist or psychotherapist (but hardly any of the younger children had done so); amongst the under-5s, about a quarter of those who went to hospital saw a physiotherapist (but few of the older children had such contact). No other services (for example, occupational therapy, hospital social work or dietary advice) were provided to more than a small handful of children.

However, for those children who had had contact with a hospital out-patient department or clinic the frequency of attendance was high. Amongst the older age group, the mean number of visits was 10.6; for the under-5s, it stood at 15.0. Children in some of the clusters containing those with the most severe and multiple disabilities went to hospital, on average, around 25 times in the year. Such figures must raise questions not only about *what* is provided but also *where*. The cost, disruption and time entailed for parents to take their children to services, rather than the services coming to them, ought surely to cause concern about their location. Even the GPs rarely saw children at home, although this was somewhat more common in the case of the younger age group. Beyond these considerations, one must ask what detrimental effects so many visits have upon the quality of the disabled child's life. An enormous amount of their time must have been spent being transported from place to place – not only to and from hospitals, but to and from schools as well.

Despite this pattern of contacts with hospitals, we found little evidence of any 'compensation effect' when the services they provided were compared with domiciliary services. Where the systems provided similar services, a lack of provision in one did not appear to be offset by a more ample supply in the other. However, we were unable to chart the services that the children might have received at school (for example, speech therapy), so there may have been some measure of compensation to be found here.

Nonetheless, the conclusion we draw from this review of the OPCS data is that many families and their disabled children were poorly served by organised services, in particular by those provided in their own homes. Sadly, this conclusion is echoed by Beresford in her 1995 report. She maintains that 'taken together, our findings suggest that the current levels of service provision, as well as the types of services being offered, do not adequately meet the needs of disabled children and their parents' (Beresford, 1995, p. 32).

One of the most valuable features of the OPCS survey was the collection of information about what parents considered to be lacking by way of domiciliary services. Regrettably, these questions were not asked about the hospital-based services. Nonetheless, the data are important, providing as they do an insight into 'unmet need' as experienced by the parents. Despite being shown what amounted to prompt cards in the interviews, only some one in five of the parents said they wanted a home-based service that they or their children were not getting. Given the kinds of problems which confronted them, this was a remarkably low level of demand. However, it seems likely that this is one thing that has changed over the last ten years. Certainly, Beresford's recent study suggests that there is now a greater readiness to articulate 'demand'. As she says (Beresford, 1995, p. 33): 'Less than a quarter of parents said their child had no unmet needs' and 'nine out of ten parents reported at least one unmet need' associated with their caring. Such a change in attitudes over the span of ten years may reflect a higher level of expectation as well as a growing awareness of what is available. In the OPCS study, for instance, 54% of the parents said that they had not heard of respite care, and a quarter maintained that they knew nothing of the Family Fund. It would be interesting to know what the comparable figures would be today.

According to the OPCS data, the four domiciliary services that were most in demand by parents were clear. They were: social work (asked for by one in five); home teaching (sought by one in six); an incontinence service (also requested by one in six) and a laundry service (wanted by one in seven). The demand was somewhat greater amongst parents of the under-5s, and their list also included more health visiting (one in seven) and home help (one in eight) but there was less demand for home teaching.

What exactly parents hoped for from social workers is difficult to say since OPCS did not collect that kind of material. However, it was probably a mixture of things that included counsel, information, moral support and help with tapping other services. Whatever the expectations, it is of more than passing interest to note the prominence of social work both in what little *was* provided and in the demands that parents were making, not least in the light of the rather dismissive treatment social workers are liable to receive in the media.

Requests for home teaching, incontinence and laundry services, as well as home help, are probably easier to interpret than those for social work, although, in the case of home teaching, it is reasonable to ask whether it was wanted in addition to school-based teaching or as an alternative to it.

Alongside these services, there were also various kinds of adaptations or equipment that parents said that they or their children wanted. Some one in seven sought modifications to their bathrooms or toilets, and the same proportion looked for the installation of a shower (or special shower). The aids that loomed largest in parents' demands were those to help with incontinence, followed by various others to help with their children's hearing and mobility. However, as with the domiciliary services, the extent of expressed need for such items was modest, as would have been the cost of meeting them. In view of this, the fact that only one in ten had had help from the Family Fund (although three-quarters of the parents had heard about it) is somewhat surprising.

Of course, these conclusions do not cover anything like the range of unmet needs that children or parents might have had. They relate only to the particular services about which they were asked. We could not explore more specific requirements, such as help in planning their children's long-term future or help with knowing how best to balance the needs of the disabled children and other family members. Nor were we able to consider their need for help with transport or more suitable housing. Nevertheless, the data on 'unmet need' that we were able to analyse do indicate some of the likely priorities – for sensitive and informed social work, for laundry and incontinence services, for more home teaching and for help with suitable home adaptations. Furthermore, a closer examination of just what aids children needed was obviously called for.

Leaving aside the overall level of provision of services, it is important to consider how what was available was allocated. We have noted that allocation was usually roughly in line with the severity of the child's disability; on the face of it, this would seem a satisfactory state of affairs needing little further comment. However, when we explored the question of distribution somewhat further, several important discoveries were made.

First, the data for the 5–15 age group allowed us to analyse the provision of certain services by geographical regions (but not by individual local authorities) and we found significant differences. For example, in Wales, the East Midlands and East Anglia, some two-fifths of the children and families had had some domiciliary services in the past year, but in Scotland, the north of England, the West Midlands and south-west England, only a quarter had been helped in this way. No such sharp difference was found with respect to contact with hospital or clinic-based services, except that the rate was higher in the former GLC area, perhaps reflecting the greater availability of specialist provisions. However, there were significant regional variations with respect to which services a child received when they went to hospital and in the mean number of visits made in the year. For example, physiotherapy and speech therapy were significantly more often received in East Anglia and the GLC area than elsewhere; the help of a psychologist was more common in Wales, north-west England and the Greater London area than in other regions, and no child saw a psychotherapist in 6 of the 11 standard regions. Likewise, there were enormous variations in the average number of times those children who attended a hospital or clinic did so: from a mean of 3.9 in Yorkshire and Humberside to 16.1 in north-west England.

However, none of these regional figures suggested a 'substitution effect' between domiciliary and hospital-based services, nor did they offer clues as to why such variations should have existed. What they do imply, however, is that attention needs to be paid to the nature and consequences of geographical differences in the provision of services, differences that may have become greater as a result of the changes in the organisation and financing of the National Health Service.

The second main group of conclusions that we were able to draw about the distribution of services derives from our analysis of differences between the socio-economic characteristics of the families. Principally, the variables in question were: family composition, family income, social class, a compound measure of family deprivation and, to some extent, ethnicity. Two of these are worthy of particular attention: family composition and family income.

The results show that the composition of the disabled child's family is likely to have had a bearing on whether or not services were received and, to a lesser extent, on how frequently they were provided. The weight of the evidence indicated that two types of families were likely to have fared significantly better than others in the receipt of services; two others had fared worse. The first group included two parents with just the disabled child, and foster carers. The second comprised lone-parent households and large families (four or more children).

Such a difference surprised us, since any assessment of the needs of families based upon their social circumstances rather than the child's disabilities would have been likely to have reversed this order, except perhaps for foster carers. The pattern suggests at least two explanations. First, the allocative criteria being applied by the services favoured (perversely, some might say) the families which, on the face of it, had the least *social* need and penalised those with the greatest. Secondly, it may have been that no distinctions were being made on the grounds of social need and that, as a consequence, those families who were less pressed were able to obtain more services by, for example, being better placed to make hospital visits. We do not know why the differences we found should have occurred, but the fact that they did should alert policy makers and professionals to the importance of taking into account a family's social circumstances as well as the child's disabilities. One example will suffice to make the point: whereas some one in ten of the families containing two adults and the single child had had respite care, the ratio fell to 1 in 50 amongst those families where there were two adults and four or more children, and to 1 in 20 amongst lone-parent families.

The case of foster carers is interesting even though only 2.2% of the children in the survey were looked after in this way. Foster carers had much greater contact than other carers with social workers (as might be expected) but they, and the children they looked after, were also, for example, those most likely to have had respite care. Indeed, the rate was four times that in the rest of the survey. There could have been various reasons for such variation (not least, in the case of respite care, the foster carers' greater willingness to use it). Despite that, the results may also suggest that the kind and amount of support and assistance given to foster carers could provide a yardstick against which the adequacy of what is provided for parent carers might be assessed.

Some of the most dramatic results concerning the distribution of services were obtained when we examined family incomes. Time and again we found that families with the lowest 20% of incomes received significantly less service than all other families. The examples are plentiful. For instance, whereas some 16% of children in the families in the top three income quintiles used some form of special furniture, the proportion fell to 4% amongst those in the lowest fifth. Similarly, although overall 20% of the children with defined locomotion difficulties had mobility aids, this plummeted to 5% for those in the lowest fifth. Telephone ownership provides another example: only 48% of the families in the lowest income quintile had a telephone, compared with over 70% in all the other income groups and a rate of 95% in the top income category. When it came to hospital services, the families with the lowest incomes were those most likely not to have made a visit in the previous year; if they had, they were less likely to have seen a doctor than all the others. However, there were exceptions to this common pattern. For example, no significant difference was discernible according to income in the receipt of domiciliary services.

However, because the poorest fifth of parents often obtained fewer services for their children, it did not follow automatically that it was they, above all others, who expressed high levels of unmet need. Indeed, in many instances, the opposite appeared to be the case. Again, there were exceptions; for example, with respect to requests for equipment to help deal with incontinence.

The evidence we assembled on the effect of low income on the distribution of services suggests that this was (and may still be) one of the most sensitive indicators of unmet (although not necessarily expressed) need. If guides to priorities are being sought, then particular attention should be paid to those families and their children with the lowest incomes. The fact that we know (as explained in Chapter 3) that families with disabled children are, in any case, generally poorer than other families with children lends additional weight to this conclusion.

The data on social class, and that derived from the use of the compound index of deprivation, furnished less clear-cut results, although they were generally in the same direction as those relating to income. Nevertheless, we should not assume that income, class and deprivation are interchangeable variables, at least in the case of families with disabled children. For example, whereas the 'poor' (as defined by the deprivation index) consulted their GPs significantly more often, and went to hospital less often, than the 'not poor', this did not apply to the poor as defined by their family income; nor did social class make a difference.

As the number of children in the survey from minority ethnic backgrounds was quite small (6%), conclusions in that area have to be drawn with some caution. In general, however, there were no differences between these groups and 'white' children and their families with respect to whether or not they received domiciliary services or attended a hospital or clinic. Some variations in the provision of other services were detectable but tended to indicate that it was Asian children and their families who stood out from the general pattern. For instance, whereas in the 5–15 age group the mean number of GP consultations in the previous year was 5.0 amongst white children and 4.4 amongst those of African-Caribbean background, it rose to 16.5 for Asian children. Likewise, Asian families were somewhat less likely to have obtained respite care, but their knowledge of the possibility was also significantly less than other groups (only 18% had heard about it).

Thus, to recapitulate, we would argue that, on the basis of the evidence, both policy and practice need to be scrutinised with respect to their impact upon the distribution of services. Furthermore, as well as the nature and severity of a child's disability, social factors should be considered carefully in determining priorities. In particular, the disadvantageous position of children in the families with the lowest fifth of incomes warrants careful attention. We also need to understand better how it is that, despite an element of professional 'gate-keeping', those families with the greatest social needs often appeared to have fared worst in the allocation process.

5. Disabled children in the care of local authorities

Essential profiles

We have seen that only a small proportion (4%) of the disabled children enumerated by OPCS in its two surveys were in the care of local authorities. However, this was a rate some ten times greater than that which prevailed amongst the child population as a whole. Looked at somewhat differently, disabled children (as defined by OPCS) comprised a little over one in four (26%) of all children in local authority care. Clearly, these figures raise important questions.

Do local authorities possess an adequate knowledge of the nature and extent of disabilities amongst the children for whom they have responsibility? Are these particular children appropriately monitored, their needs assessed and their care and treatment properly organised? Obviously, answers to these questions depend upon what disabilities are involved. However, the data from the OPCS surveys did not permit an exact answer to be given because of the somewhat different approaches that both the OPCS and we were obliged to adopt with respect to the analysis of the information about children in private households and those living in communal establishments. Roughly speaking, about three-fifths of those who were in care fell into the first category (foster care and 'home on trial' with parents or relatives); about two-fifths were to be found in the second.[1] However, although the results of the clusters analyses are not the same, there is enough similarity to allow us to draw certain broad conclusions; namely that, amongst *all* the disabled children in care (whatever their placement), nearly half suffered from behavioural disabilities alone; approaching a fifth presented behavioural problems together with mild intellectual disabilities; one in ten had communication problems as well as other disabilities; another one in ten were disabled by severe or very severe problems of intellectual functioning; and a further one in ten fell into the three categories covering the most severe and multiple disabilities. Thus, although behavioural problems alone, or in combination with other disabilities, certainly dominated the picture, there were also other combinations of disabilities and these did not exclude the most severe and multiple.

The above estimates are necessarily rather crude but they do give an idea of the 'balance' of disabilities amongst children in care that local authorities might have expected in the late 1980s. All social services departments ought to have a similar up-to-date profile, a profile that may change but without which the planning, mobilisation and distribution of care services will be greatly hampered.

Not only is it necessary for local authorities to possess information about the types and combinations of the disabilities suffered by children in their care, it is also necessary for them to have other basic data, such as the age distribution. From our analysis of the OPCS data about all disabled children who were in care at the time of the interviews, we found that 12% were under ten years old, and 88% were between the ages of 10 and 15.[2] Hence, although the great majority were adolescent, one in eight of the children was under ten years old, a group whose needs should not be overlooked.

However, this pattern stands in marked contrast to the age distribution of *all* children in care at about the same time, the corresponding proportions being 40% and 60%.[3] Thus, another factor that local authorities are likely to have to take into account is that disabled children in care are disproportionately older than the rest. This is probably a reflection of the preponderance of behavioural problems but also of other factors, such as a longer time having been spent in care.

Use of the *Looking After Children* materials (Parker *et al.*, 1991; Ward, 1995) – which have now been adopted by many local authorities and were adapted and revised to take account of the particular issues associated with the disabled child in care – should furnish much more accurate information and chart emerging trends.

Priorities

It is hardly surprising that the data from the OPCS surveys, and from our further analysis of them, should highlight the widespread problem of behavioural disabilities amongst children 'in care'. The fact that so few of them had had contact with mental health services is disquieting, to say the least. If such services cannot be mobilised with the aid of inter-agency agreements or through co-operation engineered through the corporate strength of a local authority acting on behalf of the children for whom it carries special responsibilities, the depth of the problem is clearly profound. This is not the place to unravel that problem, although its solution is likely to lie in a complete overhaul and expansion of the mental health services available to children and young people, services that have been reviewed by the NHS Health Advisory Service (1995).[4] However, what the inclusion by OPCS of behavioural and emotional problems within the realm of disability has done is to begin to quantify and locate them. Our cluster analyses have also shown the extent to which they accompany, or are accompanied by, other forms of disability.

Of course, behavioural problems are not unique to disabled children in care; but they are more common in that context and local authorities have an overriding responsibility to explore how best to confront them. That is obviously important not only for the children themselves but also for those who care for them or who (as, for example, potential adopters) may do so in the future. Whatever initial disabilities there may have been, the child 'in care' is likely to have gone through other experiences – of neglect, abuse, disruption and uncertainty – which have compounded and complicated their problems. If one regards children 'looked after' by local authorities as being amongst the most needful in our society, then those amongst them who are disabled are the most needful of all, not least because of the additional emotional damage that is likely to have been wrought upon them.

However, one of the risks in suggesting or choosing a 'priority' is that it can overshadow other activities that need to be maintained at the same time, many of which are often closely linked to the priority in question. In this case, for example, the recruitment, training and support of those who care for the disabled child 'in care' cannot be treated as a separate issue. The results of our further analysis emphasise just how complex and demanding such 'caring' is. Since half of all the disabled children in care were living in foster homes, and one in eight of them had been returned to parents or relatives without the care order to which they were subject having been discharged, this is much more than a matter of the quality of, and support to, residential care staff, although this remains an area of considerable concern. Yet, in order to mount training or support programmes, it is imperative that a local authority knows what kinds of disabilities children in different placements suffer, and the extent to which these differ and pose different problems.

All children are vulnerable; children in care the more so. But, as the Utting Report (1997) has so clearly pointed out, the disabled child is particularly vulnerable for many reasons. For example, they may need to be assisted with the most intimate aspects of personal care; they may well be exposed to a series of different carers, especially in the residential context; they are less likely than other children to be able to articulate a complaint or make an effective protest; and, in a mixed setting with other children, they may be especially at risk of bullying of various kinds. Such concerns – if set alongside the extent of isolation from their parents of, perhaps, as many as a third of the 'in care' children in residential establishments[5] – do suggest that there is a considerable need for a 'friend', 'visitor' or 'watchdog' to ensure the kind of scrutiny that a concerned parent would provide. The professionals involved, whether they be social workers, doctors or health visitors *may* do just that; but their responsibilities are more diverse, their visits irregular and their concerns somewhat differently focused.

Some questions

Many questions about the disabled child in care remain unanswered by our analysis of the OPCS survey data; four, in particular, should be mentioned. First, under what circumstances are disabled children admitted to care; particularly, when is this the result of a compelling court order? Furthermore, are the 'care careers' of disabled children significantly different from those of the non-disabled child who follows the same route?

Secondly, what distinguishes the disabled children who are placed in foster care from those in residential facilities? The limited information we had did not suggest that it was necessarily the severity of the disability that caused the child in care to be placed residentially. Age, though, did appear to make a difference, with the older children more likely to be living communally. However, this is based on the barest of indications. There were even fewer clues as to which disabled children in care had been returned 'on trial' to their parents, and when and why this had happened.

Thirdly, in the case of residential care, what determined the kind of establishment in which the disabled child in care was placed? There was little information about the particular characteristics of a home, school or hospital unit – whether they were specialised or mixed or whether the emphasis was upon treatment, education or day-to-day care. However, we do know that most were small and that most were run by social services departments. Nonetheless, there was a notable use of the independent sector, as well as of education department boarding schools. Who was providing what? And what determined the destination of the disabled child in care?

Finally, it is important to record that we were unable to derive any information from the OPCS material about what was likely to happen to the disabled child in care once that care status ended. How many, and which ones, returned to the care of their families? Who went on to become the responsibility of the adult services, and to what effect? Who stayed on with their foster carers? And who eventually lived independently, and with what success?

6. The residential care of disabled children

Estimating numbers

Although only 1.5%[6] of the children whom OPCS identified as disabled were classified as living in a communal establishment, their circumstances raised particular issues for both policy and practice. Furthermore, as we saw, because of the manner in which OPCS decided whether or not a child should be regarded as 'living at home', many of those who would usually have been considered to have been 'in residential care' were allocated to the private households survey. As a result, the extent and significance of residential care in the lives of disabled children was underestimated. Taking account of other data, especially those from the 1991 census, we came to the conclusion that the 'true' proportion of disabled children living in residential establishments in Britain at a particular time could have been as high as 3%, that is about 10,700, instead of the OPCS figure of 5600.

One of the disquieting facts is that there is still no reliable and agreed basis for collecting and monitoring data about this group of children. For example, the first general return of information about all children's homes recorded the situation in England in 1995 (Department of Health, 1996) but offered few details about children with disabilities, although it did give certain figures about the 'facilities' provided by different kinds of homes. Hence, it was possible to conclude that 'provision for children with disabilities was an important element in residential provisions' and that, in all, 16% of homes had facilities for children with learning and physical or sensory disabilities, 6% for children with learning disabilities alone and 1% for children with physical or sensory disabilities alone. Two years later, the figures were, respectively, 18%, 7% and 1% (Department of Health, 1997). However, these data demonstrate only that certain homes offered special facilities for these groups, not how many such children were actually resident.[7]

The paucity of information about disabled children in residential establishments contrasts rather sharply with what is collected about disabled adults. In the same year as the OPCS surveys of disabled children and adults living in communal establishments, there was, for example, a bulletin (based on local authority returns) that set out the age, sex and length of stay of all physically handicapped adults in England (Department of Health, 1989). There are also other regular statistical publications on residential accommodation for various groups of the disabled and on residential provisions in general, but none include children despite, in one case, a title that claims that the publication covers 'all client groups'

(Department of Health, 1995).[8] Doubtless, one of the reasons for the greater availability of information about adults in residential care is that they are more numerous and the cost implications much greater.[9] Whatever the full explanation for the lack of information about disabled children in residential establishments, it remains clear that the OPCS survey of the late 1980s provides the most comprehensive picture that we have, the most significant features of which deserve to be highlighted.

The 'in care' population

One of the most striking findings to emerge from the communal establishments survey conducted by OPCS was that the great majority (86%) of the resident children were in local authority care and that almost three-quarters of this group were subject to compulsory care orders or were wards of court. Looked at somewhat differently, we estimate that well over a third (37%) of children between 5 and 15 who were in care in England and Wales in 1988 and living in residential establishments would have qualified for inclusion in the OPCS survey.[10] It follows from both of these perspectives, therefore, that local authorities and the Department of Health had and still have *special* responsibilities with respect to a great many children with disabilities who were cared for residentially.

Certainly, it was clear that social services departments were playing a leading role in both the provision of residential facilities for these children and in their financing more generally. What these departments do in this field, therefore, makes a considerable impact upon the nature and extent of services. The Department of Health, in its turn, performs a crucial function in creating the national context within which social services departments must operate.

The one in seven who were not 'in care'

Despite the predominance of disabled children who were 'in care' within the residential sector, the existence of some 14% who were *not* in care should not be overlooked. This group certainly contained many children who were multiply and severely disabled (most of whom were in health service establishments), but not exclusively. There were *some* children who were not in care in all the clusters except one (Cluster 3, 'incontinence') and *some* children who were not in care in establishments run by all the different agencies (except the youth treatment centres administered by the DHSS).

Nor was 'isolation' from parents absent in this group: nearly a quarter (23%) of the children had not been visited by their parents in the previous year (or since their admission) and 45% had not made a visit home. Other points that deserve to be taken into account with respect to the children who were not in care were that they had less contact with a social worker than those who were in care; that they were more likely to have been transferred from another residential facility (primarily hospitals) rather than from a private household; and that significantly more of them had been in residential care for three years or more (partly reflecting their much younger age at admission).

If, as seems possible, the proportion of disabled children in residential care who are 'in care' has declined since the 1988 OPCS survey, the issue of the well-being of those who are not in care may actually have become a more pressing matter; it is certainly a matter warranting further exploration.

Behavioural and emotional 'problems'

Many of the children who suffered from physical or mental disabilities which were severe enough to have qualified them for inclusion in the survey would have behaved in ways that presented problems to those who were charged with their care. However, the decision of OPCS (presumably in consultation with DHSS and others) to adopt a definition of disability that allowed for the inclusion of 'behavioural problems' *as* a disability was of the utmost importance and is now somewhat at odds with what is to be found in the Children Act 1989.[11] In the first place, this decision enlarged the conventional definition of disability and, in the second place, we believe that it increased the proportion of children in the survey who were discovered to be in local authority care.

The decision of OPCS to use such an inclusive definition was, of course, in line with the concepts of disability adopted for the World Health Organisation's International Classification of Impairments, Disabilities and Handicaps (WHO, 1981). It was also in line with the approach adopted by Rutter *et al.* (1970) in their influential study of childhood 'handicap' on the Isle of Wight. In this study behavioural *problems* were considered to become *psychiatric disorders* (a) when they were of a chronic nature and (b) when they caused handicap to the child and/or distress or disturbance in the family or community. Handicap, in this sense, is taken to be a condition that impedes the child in his or her daily life.

This past reluctance to accept a definition of disability that embraced issues of behaviour may have both obscured the full extent of multiple disabilities and retarded the development of strong policy initiatives for the treatment of children with behavioural disabilities who were placed in residential care. Even so, it is surprising that so little has been done in this respect, given what is known about the extent of the abuse and emotional damage that has been and can continue to be inflicted on children in residential care, and especially on those who have been taken into care for these very reasons. That said, however, it is important to point out that, unlike the other classes of disabilities, the OPCS threshold for the inclusion of behavioural and emotional disabilities was set fairly low – at least in the light of what is known about the difficulties generally confronting those who undertake the day-to-day care of children in residential establishments.

Training

The implications of our further analysis of the OPCS data for the training of these staff are far-reaching. It is important to bear in mind, for example, that only a minority of the establishments that figured in the sample were likely to have been specialised, particularly since nearly three-fifths (58%) of the children in the survey lived in units run by social services, most of which will not have been intended to care exclusively for children with specific types or combinations of disability. Residential care staff therefore need both general skills and the particular skills required for dealing with the different kinds of disability that are often manifest in a single child. Superimposed upon this challenge is the need for staff to be able to respond appropriately to the inevitable problems of adolescence as well as to the needs of rather younger children.

Even though social services departments assumed the principal role in the provision of residential care for disabled children, the contribution of the other sectors was substantial. It would not make much sense, therefore, for staff training and development schemes to be restricted to local authority employees or to be compartmentalised in other ways. All the indications point to the need for a strong and vigorous national initiative, albeit implemented at the local level and adjusted to confirmed differences in the nature of the task.

In terms of other aspects of the development of residential child care policy, our findings concerning the duration of children's stays in the establishments were important. With a mean duration of residence approaching two and a half years (up to the time of the survey) and an average of more than ten years for children in the most disabled cluster, this 'part' of residential child care must be regarded as long term. That too has implications for the training and recruitment of staff, for the availability of appropriate accommodation, and for the harmonisation of this accommodation with the emerging emphasis upon residential services as an essentially short-term and emergency resource.

The families: isolation and protection

However, the issue of the relationship between residential care for disabled children and the situation regarding their families poses additional problems. For example, given the extent to which some children in communal establishments had returned home for short visits compared with the large number who were in local authority care on a compulsory basis, questions must arise about the likelihood or desirability of the full restoration of certain children to their families and about the possible early discharge of the outstanding orders. The answer, however, must remain a matter of speculation since the survey data did not extend to such matters. It was a pity that the OPCS question about 'future plans' asked only whether an establishment prepared children for fostering or adoption, not whether this (or restoration to their families) was intended for specific children.

The futures of some of these children may be particularly uncertain. The fact that a quarter of those in the survey neither received visits from their parents nor made visits home must give cause for concern.[12] Indeed, if the infrequently visited children are also taken into account, then up to a third of all the disabled children in residential care could be regarded as having been isolated from their parents.[13] Unfortunately, the OPCS data did not give any idea of the extent to which social workers or others were in contact with such parents, not least with a view to planning for the time to come. If one were contemplating social work priorities in this field, it may well be that the fact of 'isolation' offers a valuable indicator of where at least one priority should lie.

The absence of parental contact also raises an important question about the protection of the well-being of disabled children living in communal establishments. Potentially, parental contact provides an important means whereby this can be monitored, especially if, as is the intention of the Children Act 1989, there is an adequate system for hearing complaints and for dealing with them. Without parental contact, the welfare of disabled children in residential care relies upon the staff of the homes and a small number of professionals, particularly social workers and general practitioners. However well intentioned these 'strangers' may be, they are less likely than parents to have a strong partisan interest in the welfare of a particular child. Beyond that, there is always a risk that children's day-to-day needs will not be properly met in a communal setting and that, from time to time, there will be actual neglect or abuse.

The fact that about one in nine of all the children living in communal establishments had not seen a general practitioner in the last year (or since their admission), that two-thirds of them had not seen a dentist, that somewhat less than a fifth had contact with a community nurse, that only a fifth had seen a psychiatrist, and that a mere handful had received any psychotherapeutic help or seen a health visitor raises doubts about the extent to which the medical profession can be relied upon for purposes of *regular* monitoring, not least because many of these contacts would have taken place *outside* the residential facilities. Even these circumstances would not have permitted medical and health care staff to see the child in their day-to-day setting. The only type of contact with a professional visitor that most of the children had was with social workers; unfortunately, however, information was not collected about the frequency of such visits (unlike those of general practitioners) nor, understandably, about what they entailed.

The major role that appeared to have been played by social workers as points of 'outside contact' was further emphasised by the fact that voluntary workers of various kinds concentrated their visiting on the most severely multiply disabled, the young, those who were not in care and those already being visited by (or paying visits to) their parents. In that sense, their activities could not be regarded as an additional safeguard for the welfare of 'isolated' children although, presumably, their roles could be modified to achieve this. Certainly, the contribution of independent visitors appointed by local authorities should be especially important for this group, and priorities could be set accordingly. However, even though the Children Act 1989 requires local authorities to provide independent visitors for all children in care who are not in contact with their relatives,[14] few have so far been appointed, and even fewer have been appointed for children in residential care. In these circumstances, other innovative schemes such as the Community Service Volunteers 'Allies' befriender project become more significant.[15]

Over and above these issues, however, hovers the question of the purpose and implications of parental contact. How far and with which parents should the contact be encouraged and supported?[16] How often is it (or should it be) part of a plan to restore children to their families, to make provision for them when they have to leave care, to sustain parental commitments, or to enable their care to be better shared between parents and the caring agency? Is the visiting co-ordinated with assistance for the family[17] and with the exchange and utilisation of significant information?

Such questions assume a greater complexity when viewed against the high levels of compulsory removal that prevailed amongst these 'residential care children' and against the physical or sexual abuse that some of them had experienced. Indeed, of *all* the children in the communal establishments survey (that is, whether they were in care or not), about two-thirds were subject to compulsory orders of one kind or another. There are, therefore, at least two fundamental questions to be answered for a majority of disabled children in residential care before long-term plans can be formulated. First, what is the nature (and evolving nature) of each child's disabilities and, secondly, what were, are now and are likely to become the child's home circumstances? These are distinct questions but they are, of course, also related. For instance, some of the impairments from which children suffered will have been caused or aggravated by physical abuse at home: for example, by head injuries or by violence to the mother during her pregnancy.

The roles of the different sectors

Although, as we have said, local social services departments carried major responsibilities for the residential care of disabled children, other sectors were also important. It will be recalled, for instance, that about one in five of the children lived in establishments provided by voluntary organisations, one in ten in privately run facilities and the same proportion in health service provisions. In terms of the clusters, the groups of children that each sector cared for were rather different. Whereas social services homes looked after a large number of children where behavioural disabilities predominated (either singly or together with other disabilities), the two 'independent' sectors cared for a group of children with more mixed disabilities – not necessarily, it should be emphasised, in particular establishments but in the sector as a whole. Given that social services departments contributed to the cost of three-quarters of the placements in voluntary facilities and to four-fifths of those in the private units, it is reasonable to conclude that there was, already in 1988, a good deal of 'contracting out'. Yet the rather different cluster profiles of the children in the independent sector and those who lived in social services establishments suggested that contracting out was accompanied by a certain measure of selectivity. If that process has continued, then one might expect a widening of the differences between the groups of disabled children looked after by the public social services and those looked after by the independent sector. This would have a variety of implications for policy, both locally and nationally.

Were the use of the independent sector to expand, it is likely that there would be a number of practical implications: for example, longer travelling distances for parents wishing to visit, a more diversified task of inspection for social services departments and problems in developing co-ordinated training programmes. Clearly, the 'balance' between the sectors and the particular contribution that each makes (or might make) is a matter that needs to be explored more fully.

That is equally so with respect to the role of the health authorities in making provision for children with disabilities. As we have seen, this sector looked after a disproportionate number of the most severely disabled children, and the indications were that these children were likely to remain in health service establishments for long periods. This finding is apparently at odds with government policy. For example, in the relevant *Guidance and Regulations* to the Children Act 1989, it is emphasised that: 'The use of NHS facilities should reflect a child's needs for assessment, treatment or other services which cannot be made available in SSD provision or at home and *should in no way constitute a permanent placement*' (Department of Health, 1991, p. 39; our emphasis).

The whole question of the sequence and frequency of the placements of disabled children is a matter of concern. Why, and for what reasons, for example, were children transferred (or not transferred) from one provision to another? Why did there appear to be greater mobility within the social services sector than in any of the others? And what were the precise circumstances that led to a child being moved from a 'community' placement into residential care? Which children returned to the community to live on a permanent basis, and for what reasons? How did the provision of 'respite care'[18] in residential accommodation affect the form and development of what was undoubtedly an important area of *long-term* care?

Why residential care?

What was it that distinguished the tiny proportion of disabled children who lived in communal establishments from those who did not? One factor, as we have seen, was the severity of their disabilities. However, even amongst the most severely disabled, and especially those from Asian backgrounds, the majority continued to live outside communal establishments. A second factor associated with a child's admission to residential care was the fact that they were 'in care'. We have argued that this indicated that it was not so much their disabilities which propelled them towards residential accommodation; rather their disabilities combined with the social circumstances of their families and, related to this, their care careers. Over and above this, however, it is possible that some forms of disability, such as pronounced behavioural difficulties, or certain combinations of disabilities increased the likelihood of children being looked after residentially.

What is also of interest, of course, is that, although a substantial proportion of disabled children in care were placed residentially, the majority were not. Indeed, if, as we believe, virtually all the children enumerated in the private households survey as being in foster homes were 'in care', then their number exceeded those who were also in care but looked after in communal establishments by three to two. Again, we suspect (but are not able to verify) that it was the particular nature and mixture of disabilities that distinguished these two types of arrangements for children in care. In particular, the extent to which children in residential care suffered from *multiple* disabilities was pronounced. It will be recalled that their mean number of disabilities was 2.8, but that this rose to 8.2, 8.6 and 9.4, respectively, in the three clusters (8–10) containing children with the severest disabilities. Yet, as we have seen, the whole question of multiple disability does not seem to have received the attention that it deserves in the policy debates, possibly because of the compartmentalised nature of many of the administrative structures and interest groups, as well as the often rather fragmented nature of the literature and research. It may also be that the existence of multiple disability amongst children in residential care is so taken for granted that it has come to be ignored as a significant issue.

Finally, it must be recognised that there was and is a group of children whose disabilities were so severe and complicated that there was no other realistic option than residential care. In that respect, it should be borne in mind that the degree of severity in the 'severest' cluster in the residential care sample was usually more profound than the 'severest' cluster in the private households sample.

7. Disabled children and their families in context

Along with other studies of disabled children and their families, this study emphasises the special needs that disabilities create. Indeed, the value of our analysis lies in the clarification and quantification of what these needs are as well as in the identification of the services that are required. Nevertheless, the implication of such work is that disabled children and their families constitute a special social category. This inevitably draws attention to the *differences* between them and other families whilst obscuring the *similarities*. We should not end this report without a word to redress the balance.

All children have needs and rights that arise from the fact of their childhood: for example, with respect to protection, security, education, nourishment, play and the construction of identity. Disabled children are no exception. For this reason, their well-being depends not only on social policies that address their particular circumstances but also on those that enhance the welfare of all children. The quality of life of disabled children is, in part, a reflection of the quality of life enjoyed by children in general. Disabled children will benefit from a social, economic and political environment that is sympathetic to the rights and, therefore, to the needs of children as a whole. That must not be overlooked in the justifiable quest for those specific improvements that disabilities dictate. Of course, this applies in a similar way to the parents of disabled children. All parents have certain common needs: for adequate income and housing, for social support, and for a public recognition of the responsibilities that parenthood imposes.

Some disabled children and their families have the same kinds of needs as other distinctive social groups: for example, single parents, large families, poor families or minority ethnic families. In such cases, the adequacy of the policies that are developed to meet the special needs of these families in general will bear upon the well-being of those amongst them who care for disabled children.

As well as these rather large social groups, there are smaller ones to which disabled children may belong. Those who were looked after by the local authorities have been highlighted in this study, but there are many other children 'in care' who are not disabled. Of course, local authorities have to devise policies and practices for those with needs that spring from their disablement, but they also have to formulate policies for the generality of the children for whom they bear a responsibility. There are issues of child protection, adoption and fostering, residential care, staff training, family support, respite care and, not least, issues that concern the size of operating budgets. The welfare of those looked-after children who are disabled will be affected by the nature of the policies that prevail in these areas just as much as the welfare of those who are not disabled.

The services upon which disabled children and their families depend are not all specific to the disabilities in question. There are contacts with GPs, with dentists, with the school health service or, perhaps, with the child and adolescent mental health services. The general quality, accessibility and availability of such provisions will be an important factor in determining the standard of service that disabled children receive, with regard to both needs that arise from their disabilities and those that do not.

It is also important for it to be recognised that the support which the parents of disabled children receive from social and health services is likely to reflect their general availability and quality – for instance, with respect to incontinence or laundry services, help in the home, maternal health, or cash benefits.

All these examples underline the fact that, although the needs of disabled children and their families require a *special* response within social policies, many of the services upon which the satisfaction of those needs depends are general in their character and usage. Their *overall* quality will affect the quality of the support that disabled children and their parents receive. Thus, the problems of child disablement cannot be and should not be divorced from the wider issues of childhood and parenthood in contemporary society; they must be seen within both their specific and their general contexts.

8. Monitoring trends and providing basic information on disability in childhood

This study has shown that considerable information and insight can be gained from a re-analysis of the OPCS disability surveys despite their inadequacies and limitations. Unfortunately, the disability surveys of children are currently unique studies. Prior to 1985 all government social surveys of disability had been confined to adults, and the most recent surveys of disability (which have used the OPCS methodology) are again confined to the adult population (Craig, 1996).

None of the government's main statistical publications, such as *Social Trends*, *Regional Trends* or the *Annual Abstract of Statistics* contain a single table on disabled children. Even the special *Social Focus on Children* (Church and Summerfield, 1994), which was designed to 'fill in the gaps' in our knowledge as part of the UN's International Year of the Family, contained only one table on disabled children derived from the 1985 disability survey of children in private households. Of even greater concern, the recent *Social Focus on Families* (Pullinger and Summerfield, 1997) contained no information at all on the families of disabled children.

Even when limited information is collected on childhood disability and impairments, such as in the *General Household Survey* (OPCS, 1985) and the *Health Survey for England* (Prescott-Clarke and Primatesta, 1997), it is not considered important enough to be included in the main survey reports.

The claim by the previous director of the Central Statistical Office that 'there is a wealth of statistical information on children in the UK' (McLennan, 1994) is simply not true for disabled children. Disabled children are invisible in government statistics. We lack basic demographic information on disability in childhood, a deficiency that makes it difficult for trends in childhood disability to be adequately monitored.

We have virtually no current quantitative information about:
- the number of disabled children in Britain,
- the number, type, severity and combination of their disabilities,
- the levels of service being received by disabled children and their families,

- the adequacy of the services being received by disabled children and their families, and
- the extent of poverty and social exclusion amongst the families of disabled children.

Disabled children are one of the most vulnerable groups in our society, yet we have less statistical information about them than any other group – including the homeless. We enter the 21st century with as little quantitative knowledge about disabled children as we had at the beginning of the 20th century, albeit that great progress has been made in the understanding of certain medical conditions and their treatment. If the present government's rhetoric about the importance of combating poverty and social exclusion is to be realised, then this scandalous lack of basic information will have to be made good. Unless it is, an informed, well planned and vigorous improvement in policy and practice is unlikely to be feasible.

NOTES TO CHAPTER 16

[1] These are, inevitably, approximations for the reasons that we explained in Chapter 9.

[2] Had 16- and 17-year-olds been included in the OPCS children's surveys, the proportion of 'older' children would have been somewhat greater.

[3] The figures are for 1986 and for England and Wales only.

[4] This was based on a survey carried out in England in 1993.

[5] Forty-seven per cent had not been visited in the previous year or since their admission; 56% had not made a visit home in the same period.

[6] The percentage is the same for both England and Wales and Great Britain, although there were proportionately more children in residential care in Scotland (2.3% compared with 1.5%). However, the number in Scotland was much smaller (770).

[7] Pleas that the deficiency in statistical information be made good have been made by Morris (1995) and, more recently, by Utting (1997) in his comprehensive review of safeguards for children living away from home. Indeed, Utting calls for 'a review of the current statistical information leading to the establishment of a coherent set of data which can be used to assess and develop services for disabled children at local and central levels' (p. 85).

[8] Other regular reports include, for example, Department of Health Statistical Bulletins: *Personal Social Services, Residential Accommodation in England; Residential Accommodation: Detailed Statistics on Residential Care Homes and Local Authority Residents;* and *Residential Accommodation for Mentally Ill People and People with Learning Difficulties: the Number of Local Authority, Voluntary and Private Homes and Places.*

[9] For example, the OPCS survey of disabled adults identified six million such people (nearly 17 times more than disabled children), 7% of whom (about 420,000) lived in communal establishments (or some 75 times more than in the case of the disabled children). Obviously, it is the effect of old age that, in part, creates such differences.

[10] As explained earlier, this estimate is based upon the grossed-up figures for the survey applied to the statistics for children in local authority care in 1988.

[11] If the definitions contained in Section 17 of the Children Act 1989 are applied, children with persistent behavioural difficulties should be classed as 'children in need' but not necessarily as 'disabled'. In that legislation, a child is defined as being *in need* if:

(a) he is unlikely to achieve or maintain, or to have the opportunity of achieving or maintaining, a reasonable standard of health or development without the provision for him of services by a local authority;

(b) his health or development is likely to be significantly impaired, or further impaired, without the provision for him of such services; or

(c) he is disabled.

where 'development' means physical, intellectual, *emotional*, social or *behavioural* development; and 'health' means physical or *mental health* [our emphases].

The test for disability is, however, much narrower. Indeed, it is a similar formulation to the definition contained in the National Assistance Act 1948; namely, that:

a child is disabled if he is blind, deaf or dumb or suffers from mental disorder of any kind or is substantially and permanently handicapped by illness, injury or congenital deformity or such other disability as may be prescribed (Department of Health, 1991, p. 5).

[12] Russell (1995) points out that parents may feel depressed and guilty at being unable to care for their own child – thereby sometimes making visiting more difficult.

[13] For other relevant evidence of the scale of isolation of children in care from their parents, see Millham *et al.*, 1986.

[14] Schedule 2, Part 2, Section 17(1).

[15] The 'Allies' project is 'designed to encourage volunteers over the age of 50 to befriend for at least one year a young person in residential care' (Dartington Social Research Unit, 1997). The scheme has been instituted in three local authorities.

[16] Under Schedule 2, Part 2, Section 15(1) of the Children Act 1989, a local authority is required to promote and maintain contact between a child being 'looked after' and their family, unless 'it is not reasonably practical or consistent with his welfare'.

[17] Again, under Section 16 of the Children Act 1989, a local authority may make payments to cover the costs of travelling and subsistence in respect of a parent or relative visiting a 'looked-after' child.

[18] Geall *et al.*, 1991; Department of Health, 1991, chapters 11 and 13.

Bibliography

Abberley, P. (1992) Counting us out: a discussion of the OPCS disability surveys. *Disability, Handicap & Society*, 7 (2): 139–155.

Abberley, P. (1996) Disabled by numbers. *In* Levitas, R. and Guy, W. (Eds) *Interpreting Official Statistics*, Routledge, London.

Ahmad, W., Darr, A., Jones, L. and Nisar, G. (1998) *Deafness and Ethnicity: Services, Policy and Politics*. The Policy Press, Bristol (in association with the Joseph Rowntree Foundation).

Aldgate, J. and Tunstill, J. (1995) *Making Sense of Section 17: A Study for the Department of Health: Implementing Services for Children in Need within the 1989 Children Act*. HMSO, London.

Amin, K. and Oppenheim, C. (1992) *Poverty in Black and White: Deprivation and Ethnic Minorities*. Child Poverty Action Group, London (in association with the Runnymead Trust).

Argent, H. and Kerrane, A. (1997) *Taking Extra Care: Respite, Shared and Permanent Care for Children with Disabilities*. British Agencies for Adoption and Fostering, London.

Armstrong, G. and Race, D. (1979) *The Role and Function of the Social Services Department in the Total System of Provision for the Mentally Handicapped*. Unpublished Research Report No. 5, Evaluation Research Group, University of Sheffield.

Audit Commission (1994) *Seen but not Heard: Co-ordinating Community Child Health and Social Services for Children in Need*. HMSO, London.

Ayer, S. and Alaszewski, A. (1984) *Community Care and the Mentally Handicapped: Services for Mothers and their Mentally Handicapped Children*. Croom Helm, London.

Baldwin, S. (1977) *Disabled Children – Counting the Costs*. The Disability Alliance, London.

Baldwin, S. (1985) *The Costs of Caring: Families with Disabled Children*. Routledge & Kegan Paul, London.

Baldwin, S. and Carlisle J. (1994) *Social Support for Disabled Children and their Families: a Review of the Literature*. HMSO, Edinburgh.

Ball, M. (1998) *Disabled Children: Directions for Their Future Care*. Department of Health, London (in association with the Social Services Inspectorate and the Council for Disabled Children).

Barnes, C. (1991) *Disabled People in Britain and Discrimination: A Case for Anti-Discrimination Legislation*. Hurst and Co., London (in association with the British Council of Organisations of Disabled People).

Barolin, G.S. (1997) Further development of the ICIDH scales. *International Journal of Rehabilitation Research*, 20 (4): 393–396.

Baxter, C., Poonia, K., Ward, L. and Nadirshaw, Z. (1990) *Double Discrimination: Issues and Services for People with Learning Difficulties from Black and Ethnic Minority Communities*. Kings Fund Institute and Commission for Racial Equality, London.

Beardshaw, V. (1988) *Last on the List: Community Services for People with Physical Disabilities*. Kings Fund Institute, London.

Bennett, F. (1994) *Unequal Opportunities: Children with Disabilities and their Families Speak Out*. NCH Action for Children, London.

Ben-Shlomo, Y. and Davey Smith, G. (1991) Deprivation in infancy or in adult life: which is more important for mortality risk? *Lancet*, 337: 530–534.

Beresford, B. (1995) *Expert Opinions: A National Survey of Parents Coping with a Severely Disabled Child*. The Policy Press, Bristol (in association with the Joseph Rowntree Foundation and *Community Care*).

Beresford, B. (1996) Poverty and disabled people: challenging dominant debates and policies. *Disability & Society*, 11 (4): 553–567.

Beresford, B., Sloper, P., Baldwin, S. and Newman, T. (1996) *What Works in Services for Families with a Disabled Child?* Barnardo's, London.

Berridge, D. (1985) *Children's Homes*. Basil Blackwell, Oxford.

Berridge, D. (1997) *Foster Care: A Research Review*. The Stationery Office, London.

Berridge, D. and Brodie, I. (1997) *Children's Homes Revisited*. Jessica Kingsley, London.

Berridge, D., Brodie, I., Ayre, P., Barrett, D., Henderson, B. and Wenham, H. (1996) *Hello – is Anybody Listening? The Education of Young People in Residential Care*. University of Luton.

Berry, J. (1975) *Daily Experience in Residential Life: A Study of Children and their Care Givers*. Routledge & Kegan Paul, London.

Berthoud R., Lakey, J. and McKay, S. (1993) *The Economic Problems of Disabled People*. Policy Studies Institute, London.

Bickenbach, J.E., Chatterji, S., Badley, E.M. and Ustun, T.B. (1999) Models of disablement, universalism and the international classification of impairments, disabilities and handicaps. *Social Science and Medicine*, 48 (9): 1173–1187.

Bilson, A. and Barker, R. (1995) Parental contact with children fostered and in residential care after the Children Act 1989. *British Journal of Social Work*, 25 (3): 367–381.

Blair, A. (1999) *Beveridge Lecture by the Prime Minister at Toynbee Hall London*. Prime Minister's Office, 10 Downing Street.

Bone, M. and Meltzer, H. (1989) *The Prevalence of Disability among Children*. OPCS Surveys of Disability in Great Britain, Report 3. HMSO, London.

Borland, M., Pearson, C., Hill, M., Tisdall, K. and Bloomfield, I. (1998) *Education and Care Away from Home: A Review of Research, Policy and Practice*. Scottish Council for Research in Education, Edinburgh.

Bose, R. (1989) Innovations in care: some preliminary findings from evaluation of the Link Family Scheme. *Mental Handicap*, 17: 167–170.

Bradley, E.M. (1987) The ICIDH: format, application to different settings and a distinction between disability and handicap. *International Disability Studies*, 9: 122–125.

Bradshaw, J. (1975) *The Financial Needs of Disabled Children*. The Disability Alliance, London.

Bradshaw, J. (1980) *The Family Fund: An Initiative in Social Policy*. Routledge & Kegan Paul, London.

Bradshaw, J. and Lawton, D. (1985) 75,000 severely disabled children. *Developmental Medicine and Child Neurology*, 27: 25–32.

British Association for Community Child Health and the Department of Health (1994) *Disability in Childhood: Towards Nationally Useful Definitions*. Report of the

Working Group on Definitions of Disability in Childhood (Part 1: *Language, Definitions and Recommendations*).

Buckle, J.R. (1971) *Handicapped and Impaired in Great Britain – Part 2, Work and Housing of Impaired Persons in Great Britain*. HMSO, London.

Bullock, R., Little, M. and Millham, S. (1998) *Care Careers of Young People in Secure Treatment Units*. Ashgate, Aldershot.

Butler, N., Gill, R., Pomeroy, D. and Fewtrell, J. (1977) The handicapped child at home. *Residential Social Work*, 17 (8): 225–228.

Butler, N., Gill, R., Pomeroy, D. and Fewtrell, J. (1978) *Handicapped Children: Their Homes and Lifestyles*. Department of Child Health, University of Bristol.

Byrne, E.A., Cunningham, C.C. and Sloper, P. (1988) *Families and their Children with Down's Syndrome: One Feature in Common*. Routledge, London.

Cavalli-Sforza, L.L., Menozzi, P. and Piazza, A. (1996) *The History and Geography of Human Genes*. Princeton University Press, Princeton N.J.

Cavet, J. (1998) *People Don't Understand: Children, Young People and their Families Living with a Hidden Disability*. National Children's Bureau, London (in association with the Joseph Rowntree Foundation).

Chamberlain, A., Guthrie, S., Kettle, M. and Stowe, J. (1993) *An Assessment of Health and Related Needs of Physically Handicapped Young Adults*. University of Leeds.

Chambra, R., Ahmad, W. and Jones, L. (1998) *Improving Services for Deaf Asian Children: Parents' and Professionals' Perspectives*. The Policy Press, Bristol.

Chambra, R., Ahmad, W. and Hirst, M. (1999) *Minority Ethnic Families Caring for a Severely Disabled Child*. The Policy Press, Bristol (in association with the Joseph Rowntree Foundation).

Charlton, J., Wallace, M. and White, I. (1994) Long-term illness: results from the 1991 census. *Population Trends*, 75 (Spring): 18–25.

Cheng, Y. (1997) The Chinese: upwardly mobile. *In* Peach, C. (Ed.) *Ethnicity in the 1991 Census. Volume 2: The Ethnic Minority Population of Great Britain*. The Stationery Office, London.

Chetwynd, J. (1985) Some costs of caring at home for an intellectually handicapped child. *Australian and New Zealand Journal of Developmental Disability*, 2 (1): 35–40.

Church, J. and Summerfield, C. (Eds) (1994) *Social Focus on Children*. HMSO, London.

Cooke, K., Bradshaw, J.R. and Lawton, D. (1983) Take-up of benefits by families with disabled children. *Child Care, Health and Development*, 9 (3): 145–156.

Cooke, K. and Lawton, D. (1985) Housing circumstances and standards of families with disabled children. *Child Care, Health and Development*, 11: 71–79.

Cotterill, L., Hayes, L., Flynn, M. and Sloper, P. (1997) Reviewing respite services: some lessons from the literature. *Disability and Society*, 12 (5): 775–788.

Court, S.D.M. (1976) *Fit for the Future: Report of the Committee on Child Health Services*, 2 Vols (Cmnd 6684), HMSO, London.

Cowen, A. (1996) *Introducing the Family Fund Trust for Families with Severely Disabled Children*. York Publishing Services Ltd, York.

Craig, P. (1996) *Disability Follow-up to the Family Resources Survey: Aims, Methods and Coverage*. In-house Report 19, Department of Social Security, London.

Crosse, S.B., Kaye, E. and Ratnofsky, A.C. (1993) *A Report on the Maltreatment of Children with Disabilities*. National Centre on Child Abuse and Neglect, Washington DC.

Cunningham, C.C., Aumonier, M. and Sloper, P. (1982) Health visitor services for families with a Down's syndrome infant. *Child Care, Health and Development*, 8: 311–326.

Dale, A. and Marsh, C. (Eds) (1993) *The 1991 Census User's Guide*. HMSO, London.

Dartington Social Research Unit (1997) *A Friend in Need?* Ashgate, Aldershot.

Department for Education and Employment (DfEE) (1994) *Statistics of Education: Schools, England.* HMSO, London.

Department for Education and Employment (DfEE) (1997) *Excellence for All Children: Meeting Special Educational Needs.* HMSO, London.

Department for Education and Employment (DfEE) (1998*) Statistics of Education: Schools, England.* The Stationery Office, London.

Department of Education (1983) *Statistics of Education: Schools, England.* HMSO, London.

Department of Education (1985) *Statistics of Education: Schools, England.* HMSO, London.

Department of Education and Department of Health (1994) *The Education of Children Being Looked After by Local Authorities.* Circular 13/94 DfE and DoH LAC circular. HMSO, London.

Department of Health (1988*) Children in the Care of the Local Authorities at 31 March, 1986, England.* (A/F 86/12). HMSO, London.

Department of Health (1989*) Survey of the Age, Sex and Length of Stay Characteristics of Residents of Homes for Elderly People and Younger People who are Physically Handicapped in England at 31 March, 1988.* HMSO, London.

Department of Health (1991*) The Children Act 1989: Guidance and Regulations. Volume 6. Children with Disabilities.* HMSO, London.

Department of Health (1995) *Residential Accommodation for all Client Groups: Admissions to Local Authority, Voluntary and Private Homes, 1994, England.* HMSO, London.

Department of Health (1996) *Children's Homes at 31 March, 1995, England.* (A/F 95/22). The Stationery Office, London.

Department of Health (1997) *Children's Homes at 31 March, 1997, England.* (A/F 97/22). The Stationery Office, London.

Desai, M. (1986) Drawing the line: on defining the poverty threshold. *In* Golding, P. (Ed.) *Excluding the Poor*, Child Poverty Action Group, London.

Desai, M. and Shah, A. (1985) *An Econometric Approach to the Measurement of Poverty.* Suntory-Toyota International Centre for Economics and Related Disciplines, WSP/2, London School of Economics, London.

Disability Alliance (1975*) Poverty and Disability: The Case for a Comprehensive Income Scheme for Disabled People.* The Disability Alliance, London.

Disablement Income Group (DIG) (1988) *Not the OPCS Survey – Being Disabled Costs More than They Said.* Disablement Income Group, London.

Disablement Income Group (DIG) (1990) *Short-Changed by Disability.* Disablement Income Group, London.

Dobson, B. and Middleton, S. (1998) *Paying to Care: The Cost of Childhood Disability.* York Publishing Service, York.

Duffy, B. (1995a) *Disabled Adults in Northern Ireland: Services and Transport.* PPRU Surveys of Disability Report No. 4, PPRU, Belfast.

Duffy, B. (1995b) *Disabled Children in Northern Ireland: Services, Transport and Education.* PPRU Surveys of Disability Report No. 5, PPRU, Belfast.

Elford, J., Whincup, P. and Shaper, A.G. (1991) Early life experience and adult cardiovascular disease: longitudinal and case control studies. *International Journal of Epidemiology*, 20 (4): 833–844.

European Economic Community (EEC) (1985) *On Specific Community Action to Combat Poverty.* (Council Decision of 19 December 1984), 85/8/EEC. Official Journal of the EEC, 2/24, Luxembourg.

European Economic Community (EEC) (1991) *Final Report on the Second European Poverty Programme 1985–1989.* Office for the Official Publications of the European

Communities, Luxembourg.

Eurostat (1995) *Disabled Persons Statistical Data*, second edition. DGV and Eurostat (DG34), Luxembourg.

Farmer, E. and Parker, R. (1991) *Trials and Tribulations: The Return Home of Children from Local Authority Care*. HMSO, London.

Fisher, W., Conlon, C., Burd, L. and Conlon, R. (1986) Educating children and adults on coping with Tourette Syndrome. *Perceptual and Motor Skills*, 62 (2): 530.

Fletcher-Campbell, F. (1997) *The Education of Children who are Looked After*. National Foundation for Educational Research, Slough.

Fletcher-Campbell, F. and Hall, C. (1990) *Changing Schools? Changing People? The Education of Children in Care*. National Foundation for Educational Research, Slough.

Forrest, R. and Gordon, D. (1993) *People and Places. A 1991 Census Atlas of England*. SAUS and the Bristol Statistical Monitoring Unit, Bristol.

Geall, R., Host, N., Robinson, C., Loughran, F., Gordon, D. and Connor, D. (1991) *Sharing the Caring: Respite Care in the UK for Families and Children with Disabilities*. National Children's Home, London.

Gladstone, D. (1996) The changing dynamic of institutional care: the Western Counties Idiot Asylum 1864–1914. *In* Wright, D. and Digby, A. (Eds) *From Idiocy to Mental Deficiency: Historical Perspectives on People with Learning Disabilities*. Routledge, London and New York.

Glendinning, C. (1983) *Unshared Care: Parents and Their Disabled Children*. Routledge & Kegan Paul, London.

Gordon, D. and Heslop, P. (1998) Poverty and disabled children. *In* Dorling, D. and Simpson, L. (Eds) *Statistics in Society*. Arnold, London.

Gordon, D. and Pantazis, C. (Eds) (1997) *Breadline Britain in the 1990s*. Ashgate, Aldershot.

Gordon, D., Loughran, F. and Parker, R.A. (1994) *Children with Disabilities Resident in Communal Establishments in Scotland: A Further Analysis and Interpretation of the Office of Population Censuses and Surveys' Investigation*. University of Bristol.

Gordon, D., Parker, R.A. and Loughran, F. (1996) *Children with Disabilities in Private Households: A Re-analysis of the Office of Population Censuses and Surveys' Investigation*. University of Bristol.

Gough, G., Li, L. and Wroblewska, A. (1993) *Services for Children with a Motor Impairment and their Families in Scotland*. Public Health Research Unit, University of Glasgow.

Graham, S. (1987) The extra costs borne by families who have a child with a disability. In *SWRC Reports and Proceedings No 68*, University of New South Wales.

Halpern, P.L. (1985) Respite care and family functioning in families with retarded children. *Health and Social Work*, 10 (2): 138–151.

Harris, A.I., Cox, E. and Smith, C.R.W. (1971) *Handicapped and Impaired in Great Britain – Part 1*. HMSO, London.

Harris, A.I., Smith, C.R.W. and Head, E. (1972) *Handicapped and Impaired in Great Britain – Part 3: Income and Entitlement to Supplementary Benefit of Impaired People in Great Britain*. HMSO, London.

Heady, P., Smith, S. and Avery, V. (1996) *1991 Census Validation Survey: Quality Report*. The Stationery Office, London.

Heywood, F. (1994) *Adaptations: Finding Ways to Say Yes*. The Policy Press, Bristol.

Heywood, F. and Smart, G. (1996) *Funding Adaptations: The Need to Cooperate*. The Policy Press, Bristol (in association with the Joseph Rowntree Foundation).

Hirst, M. (1997) Variations in the administration of Disability Living Allowance. *Social Policy & Administration*, 31 (2): 136–156.

Hirst, M. and Baldwin, S. (1994) *Unequal Opportunities: Growing Up Disabled*. Social Policy Research Unit, York.

Horn, R. (1981) Extra costs of disablement: background for an Australian study. *SWRC Reports and Proceedings No 13*, University of New South Wales.

Howard, M. (1994*) Too Young to Count: The Extra Mobility Related Costs of Children under Five*. The Disability Alliance, London.

Hubert, J. (1991) *Home-bound: Crisis in the Care of Young People with Severe Learning Difficulties: A Story of Twenty Families*. King's Fund Centre, London.

Illsley, R. (1985) Occupational class, selection and the production of inequalities in health. *Quarterly Journal of Social Affairs*, 2 (2): 151–165.

Jackson, S. (1989) Education of children in care. *In* Kahan, B. (Ed.) *Child Care Research, Policy and Practice*, Hodder & Stoughton, London.

Kagan, C., Lewis, S. and Heaton, P. (1998) *Accounts of Working Parents of Disabled Children*. Family Policy Studies Centre, London (in association with the Joseph Rowntree Foundation).

Kahan, B. (1994) *Growing up in Groups*. HMSO, London.

Kennedy, M. (1989) The abuse of deaf children. *Child Abuse Review*, 3 (1): 3–7.

Kennedy, M. (1990) The deaf child who is sexually abused – is there a need for a dual specialist? *Child Abuse Review*, 4 (2): 3–6.

Kennedy, M. (1996) Sexual abuse and disabled children. *In* Morris, J. (Ed.) *Feminism and Disability*, The Women's Press, London.

Knight, A. (1997) *Valued or Forgotten? Independent Visitors and Disabled Young People*. National Children's Bureau, London (in association with the Joseph Rowntree Foundation).

Kuh, D.J.L., Wadsworth, M.E.J. and Yusuf, E.J. (1994) Burden of disability in a post war birth cohort in the UK. *Journal of Epidemiology and Community Health*, 48: 262–269.

Lawton, D. (1992) Family fund statistics special analysis. *In* Baldwin, S. and Carlisle, J. (Eds) *Social Support for Disabled Children and their Families: A Review of the Literature*, HMSO, London.

Lawton, D. (1998a) The number and characteristics of families with more than one disabled child. *Findings: Social Care 218*, Joseph Rowntree Foundation, York.

Lawton, D. (1998b) *Complex Numbers: Families with more than one Disabled Child*. SPRU, University of York.

Lawton, D. and Quine, L. (1990) Patterns of take-up of the Family Fund: the characteristics of eligible non-claimants and the reasons for not claiming. *Child Care, Health and Development*, 16 (1): 35–53.

Loach, I. (1976) *The Price of Deafness: A Review of the Financial and Employment Problems of the Deaf and Hard of Hearing*. The Disability Alliance, London.

Loughran, F., Parker, R.A. and Gordon, D. (1992*) Children with Disabilities in Communal Establishments: A Further Analysis and Interpretation of the Office of Population Censuses and Surveys' Investigation*. A report to the Department of Health. University of Bristol.

Mack, J. and Lansley, S. (1985) *Poor Britain*. Allen and Unwin, London.

Malin, N.A. (1982) Short-term care for mentally handicapped people. *Mental Handicap*, 10 (31): 77–78.

Marc, D.L. and MacDonald, L. (1988) Respite care – who uses it? *Mental Retardation*, 26 (2): 93–96.

Martin, J. and Bone, M. (1986) OPCS surveys of disabled people in Great Britain. *Survey Methodology Bulletin*, No.18. HMSO, London.

Martin, J. and Elliot, D. (1992) Creating an overall measure of severity for the Office of Population Censuses and Surveys' Disability Survey. *Journal of the Royal*

Statistical Society, 155 (1): 123.

Martin, J. and White, A. (1988) *The Financial Circumstances of Adults Living in Private Households: Report 2*. HMSO, London.

Martin, J., Meltzer, H. and Elliot, D. (1988) *The Prevalence of Disability Among Adults*. OPCS Surveys of Disability in Great Britain Report 1. HMSO, London.

Martin, J., White, A. and Meltzer, H.(1989) *Disabled Adults: Services, Transport and Employment*. OPCS Surveys of Disability in Great Britain Report 4. HMSO, London.

McClements, L. D. (1978) *The Economics of Social Security*. Heinemann, London.

McCoy, D. and Smith, M. (1992) *The Prevalence of Disability Among Adults in Northern Ireland*. PPRU Surveys of Disability Report No. 1, PPRU, Belfast.

McLennan, W. (1994) Introduction. *In* Church, J. and Summerfield, C. (Eds) *Social Focus on Children*. HMSO, London.

Meltzer, H., Smyth, M. and Robus, N. (1989) *Disabled Children: Services, Transport and Education*. OPCS Surveys of Disability in Great Britain Report 6. HMSO, London.

Millham, S., Bullock, R., Hosie, K. and Haak, M. (1986) *Lost in Care: the Problems of Maintaining Links Between Children in Care and their Families*. Gower, Aldershot.

Monteith, M., McCrystal, P. and Iwaniec, D. (1997) *Children and Young People with Disabilities in Northern Ireland. Part 1: An Overview of Needs and Services*. Centre for Child Care Research, Queen's University, Belfast.

Morris, J. (1995) *Gone Missing? A Research and Policy Review of Disabled Children Living Away from their Families*. Who Cares? Trust, London.

Morris, J. (1996) (Ed.) *Feminism and Disability*. The Women's Press, London.

Morris, J. (1997) Gone missing? Disabled children living away from their families. *Disability & Society*, 12 (2): 241–258.

Morris, J. (1998) *Still Missing? Disabled Children and the Children Act*. Who Cares? Trust, London.

Muellbauer, J. (1979) McClements on equivalence scales for children. *Journal of Public Economics*, 12: 221–231.

Muellbauer, J. (1980) The estimation of the Prais-Houthakker model of equivalence scales. *Econometrica*, 48 (1): 153–176.

NHS Health Advisory Service (1995) *Child and Adolescent Mental Health Services*. HMSO, London.

Office for Standards in Education and Social Services Inspectorate (1995) *The Education of Children Who are Looked After by Local Authorities*. OFSTED/SSI, London.

Oldman, C. and Beresford, B. (1998) *Homes Unfit for Children: Housing, Disabled Children and their Families*. The Policy Press, Bristol (in association with the Joseph Rowntree Foundation and *Community Care*).

OPCS (1985) *General Household Survey for 1985*. HMSO, London.

OPCS (1990) *General Household Survey for 1989*. HMSO, London.

OPCS (1991) *Labour Force Survey for 1988 and 1989*. HMSO, London.

OPCS General Register Office for Scotland (1993a) *1991 Census: Limiting Long-term Illness, Great Britain*. HMSO, London.

OPCS General Register Office for Scotland (1993b) *1991 Census: Communal Establishments, Parts I and II, Great Britain*. HMSO, London.

Orlik, C., Robinson, C. and Russell, O. (1991) *A Survey of Family-based Respite Care Schemes in the UK*. Norah Fry Research Centre, University of Bristol.

Packman, J., Randall, J. and Jacques, N. (1986) *Who Needs Care? Social Work Decisions About Children*. Basil Blackwell, Oxford.

Parker, G. (1998) Counting with care, a re-analysis of OPCS data. *In* Ball, M. *Disabled Children: Directions for their Future Care*. Department of Health, London (in association with the Social Services Inspectorate and the Council for Disabled Children).

Parker, R.A., Ward, H., Jackson, S., Aldgate, J. and Wedge, P. (1991) *Looking After Children: Assessing Outcomes in Child Care*. HMSO, London.

Peach, C. (1997) Black-Caribbeans: class, gender and geography. *In* Peach, C. (Ed.) *Ethnicity in the 1991 Census. Volume 2: The Ethnic Minority Population of Great Britain*, HMSO, London.

Pearce, D. and Thomas, F. (1990) The 1989 census test. *Population Trends*, 61: 24–30.

Pearce, D., Clark, A. and Baird, G. (1988) The 1987 census test. *Population Trends*, 53: 22–26.

Piachaud, D., Bradshaw, J. and Weale, J. (1981) The income effect of a disabled child. *Journal of Epidemiology and Community Health*, 35: 123–127.

Plank, M. (1982) *Teams for Mentally Handicapped People: A Report of an Enquiry into the Development of Multidisciplinary Teams*. Enquiry Paper 10. CMH (The Campaign for Mentally Handicapped People), London.

Poonia, K. and Ward, L. (1990) Fair share of the care? *Community Care*, 11 (January): 16–18.

Power, C. (1991) *Health and Class: The Early Years*. Chapman and Hall, London.

Power, C., Manor, O., Fox, A.J. and Fogelman, K. (1990) Health in childhood and social inequalities in health in young adults. *Journal of the Royal Statistical Society*, 153 (1): 17–28.

Prescott-Clarke, P. and Primatesta, P. (Eds) (1997) *Health Survey for England 1995. Volume 1: Findings*. The Stationery Office, London.

Pullinger, J. and Summerfield, C. (Eds) (1997) *Social Focus on Families*. The Stationery Office, London.

Quine, L. and Pahl, J. (1989) *Stress and Coping in Families Caring for a Child with a Severe Mental Handicap: A Longitudinal Study*. University of Kent, Canterbury.

Rahkonen, O., Lahelma, E. and Huuhka, M. (1997) Past or present? Childhood living conditions and current socioeconomic status as determinants of adult health. *Social Science and Medicine*, 44 (3): 327–336.

Reid, F. (1975) *The Incomes of the Blind: A Review of the Occupational and Financial Problems of Blind People of All Ages*. The Disability Alliance, London.

Roberts, K. and Lawton, D. (1998) Reaching its target? Disability Living Allowance for children. *Social Policy Report No 9*. Social Policy Research Unit, York.

Robinson, C. (1986) *Avon Short Term Respite Care Scheme: Evaluation Study in Final Report Part I – Summary and Discussion of Findings*. Department of Mental Health, University of Bristol.

Robinson, C. (1988) Pride and prejudice? Factors influencing 'uptake' of family based respite care services. *Mental Handicap*, 16 (4): 143.

Robinson, C. and Stalker, K. (1989) *Time for a Break. Respite Care: A Study of Providers, Consumers and Patterns of Use*. University of Bristol.

Robinson, C. and Stalker, K. (1990) *Respite Care – The Consumer's View. 2nd Interim Report*. Department of Health, London.

Robinson, C. and Stalker, J. (1991) *Respite Care – Summaries and Suggestions*. Norah Fry Research Centre, University of Bristol.

Robinson, C. and Stalker, J. (1992) *New Directions: Suggestions for Improving Take-up in Short-Term Breaks*. HMSO, London.

Robinson, V. (1997) The Indians: onward and upward. *In* Peach, C. (Ed.) *Ethnicity in the 1991 Census. Volume 2: The Ethnic Minority Population of Great Britain*. HMSO, London.

Russell, P. (1989) Handicapped children. *In* Kahan, B. (Ed.) *Child Care Research: Policy and Practice*. Hodder & Stoughton, London.

Russell, P. (1995) *Positive Choices: Services for Children with Disabilities Living Away from Home*. Council for Disabled Children.

Rutter, M., Tizard, J. and Whitmore, K. (1970) *Education, Health and Behaviour*. Longman, London.

Sainsbury, R., Hirst, M. and Lawton, D. (1995) *Evaluation of Disability Living Allowance and Attendance Allowance*. Department of Social Security Research Report No 41. HMSO, London.

Salisbury, C.L. (1990) Characteristics of users and non-users of respite care. *Mental Retardation*, 28: 291–297.

Schuntermann, M.F. (1996) The International Classification of Impairments, Disabilities and Handicaps (ICIDH) – results and problems. *International Journal of Rehabilitation Research*, 19 (1): 1–11.

Shaar, K. and McCarthy, M. (1994) Definitions and determinants of handicap in people with disabilities. *Epidemiological Review*, 16 (2): 228–242.

Shah, R. (1992) *The Silent Minority – Children with Disabilities in Asian Families*. National Children's Bureau, London.

Shah, R. (1997) Services to Asian families. *Child Care, Health and Development*, 23 (1): 41–46.

Shearer, A. (1978) The Barnardo Chorley Project. *Social Work Today*, 10 (7): 11.

Simpson, S., Fieldhouse, E. and Sandhu, A. (1993) Bias, sampling error and coverage: the preliminary validation of the sample of anonymised records from the 1991 census. Census Microdata Unit Occasional Paper 2, Manchester.

Sloper, P. and Turner, S. (1992) Service needs of families of children with severe physical disability. *Child Care, Health and Development*, 18: 250–282.

Smith, M., Robinson, P. and Duffy, B. (1992) *The Prevalence of Disability Among Children in Northern Ireland*. PPRU Surveys of Disability Report No. 2. PPRU, Belfast.

Smith, M., Duffy, B. and Robinson, P. (1993) Disability and Employment in Northern Ireland, PPRU Surveys of Disability Report No. 3. PPRU, Belfast.

Smyth, M. and Robus, N. (1989*) The Financial Circumstances of Families with Disabled Children Living in Private Households*. OPCS Surveys of Disability in Great Britain Report 5, HMSO, London.

Snowden Committee (1976) *Working Party on Integration of the Disabled* (Thorpe-Tracey, R.J., Ed.). National Fund for Research into Crippling Diseases, Horsham.

Social Services Inspectorate (1994) *Services to Disabled Children and their Families*. HMSO, London.

Stalker, K. and Robinson, C. (1991) *Out of Touch – The Non-Users of Respite Care Services*. Third Interim Report, Department of Health. HMSO, London.

Stallard, P. and Lenton, S. (1992) How satisfied are parents of pre-school children who have special needs with the services they have received? A consumer survey. *Child Care, Health and Development*, 18: 197–205.

Sturgis, P. (1999) A review of generic health measures for surveys of the general population. *Survey Methods Newsletter*, 19 (1): 4–8.

Suelze, M. and Keenan, V. (1981) Changes in family support networks over the life cycle of mentally retarded persons. *American Journal of Mental Deficiency*, 86: 267–274.

Thomas, R. (1989) Testing questions on disability and long term ill health for the 1991 census. *Survey Methodology Bulletin*, 24: 56–64.

Thomas, R. (1999) Measuring disability in the general population using sample surveys and censuses. *Survey Methods Newsletter*, 19 (1): 9–15.

Townsend, P. (1979) *Poverty in the UK*. Allen Lane and Penguin Books, London.

Townsend, P. and Davidson, N. (1988) *Inequalities in Health: The Black Report*, 2nd edn, Penguin Books, London.

Utting, W. (1997) *People Like Us: The Report of the Review of the Safeguards for Children Living Away from Home*. The Stationery Office, London.

Veit-Wilson, J. (1987) Consensual approaches to poverty lines and social security. *Journal of Social Policy*, 16 (2): 183–211.

Wadsworth, M.E.J. (1986) Serious illness in childhood and its association with later life achievement. *In* Wilkinson, R.G. (Ed.) *Class and Health: Research and Longitudinal Data*. Tavistock, London.

Walker, E., Tobin, M. and McKennel, A. (1992) *Blind and Partially Sighted Children in Britain: The RNIB Survey*. 2 volumes. HMSO, London.

Walker, L. (1991) *The OPCS Surveys of Disability in Britain: An Overall Analysis*. The Disability Alliance, London.

Ward, H. (Ed.) (1995) *Looking After Children: Research into Practice*. HMSO, London.

Warnock Committee (1978) *Report of the Committee of Enquiry into the Education of Handicapped Children and Young Persons*. HMSO, London.

Warr, B. (1990) *The Deaf Child in Care*. British Agencies for Adoption and Fostering, London.

Weale, J. and Bradshaw, J. (1980) Prevalence and characteristics of disabled children: findings from the 1974 General Household Survey. *Journal of Epidemiology and Community Health*, 34: 111–118.

Welsh Office (1987), *Children in Care or Under Supervision Orders in Wales, Year Ended 31.3.86*. Welsh Office, Cardiff.

Westcott, H. (1991) The abuse of disabled children: a review of the literature. *Child Care, Health and Development*, 17: 243–258.

Westcott, H. (1993) *The Abuse of Children and Adults with Disabilities*. NSPCC, London.

Western Counties Asylum (1883) WCA Annual Report 1883. Starcross, Devon.

Whiteford, P. (1985) *A Family's Needs: Equivalence Scales, Poverty and Social Security*. Research Paper No 27. Development Division, Australian Department of Social Security, Canberra.

Whitehead, P. (1988) *Inequalities in Health: The Health Divide*, 2nd edn, Penguin Books, London.

Wilkin, D. (1979) *Caring for the Mentally Handicapped Child*. Croom Helm, London.

Wood, P.H.N. (1975) *Classification of Impairments and Handicaps*. Document WHO/ICDO/REV CONF/75.15. World Health Organisation, Geneva.

Wood, P.H.N. (1980) The language of disablement: a glossary relating to disease and its consequences. *International Rehabilitative Medicine*, 2 (2): 86–92.

Wood, P.H.N. (1987) Malade imaginaire: some common misconceptions about the ICIDH. *International Disability Studies*, 9: 125–128.

Wood, P.H.N. (1989) Conceptual issues underlying disability research. *Survey Methods Newsletter*, Autumn, 3–4.

World Health Organisation (WHO) (1981) *International Classification of Impairments, Disabilities and Handicaps*. World Health Organisation, Geneva.

World Health Organisation (WHO) (1997) *International Classification of Impairments, Disabilities and Handicaps 2 (ICIDH–2), Beta–1 Draft for Field Trials*. World Health Organisation, Geneva.

Zarb, G. and Maher, L. (1997) *The Financial Circumstances of Disabled People in Northern Ireland*. PPRU Surveys of Disability Report No. 6, *NISRA*, Belfast.

Cluster analysis

Cluster analysis is a generic term that encompasses a large range of statistical classification procedures which, since the advent of high speed computers in the 1960s, have expanded rapidly in number. Well over 100 different clustering algorithms have been proposed; yet no adequate statistical theory exists that would allow the different advantages of these algorithms to be distinguished (Blaskfield & Aldenderfer, 1978; Blaskfield, 1980). Jardine and Sibson (1968) and Hubert (1972,1974) demonstrated that the 'single linkage' and 'complete linkage' methods of Johnson (1967) would theoretically yield the best cluster solutions. This work resulted in many researchers using these hierarchical methods although the results were often poor. More recently, a number of empirical evaluation studies by psychologists during the late 1970s and the 1980s have led to a series of recommendations on which methods have the greatest utility.

The results of Monte Carlo studies with continuous data have shown that:

1. Hierarchical algorithms generally produce more reliable cluster solutions than non-hierarchical methods. However, non-hierarchical methods can yield good results when used in combination with hierarchical methods: for example, if the cluster results from a hierarchical analysis are used as the starting point for the non-hierarchical analysis.

2. Single linkage and complete linkage algorithms generally fail to resolve cluster structure with real data sets due to their high sensitivity to chaining (cluster overlap). They are, however, very efficient at clustering ideal or perfect data sets.

3. The efficiency of cluster recovery is dependent both on the nature of the data set, as would be expected, but also on the distance measure used to construct the similarity matrix.

4. Ward's method is the most robust method using a dissimilarity matrix constructed from Euclidean distances. It is particularly good at recovering cluster structure even when considerable cluster overlap is present.

5. Average linkage is the optimal method with correlation coefficient similarity matrices. It is particularly robust to the presence of outliers in the data set.

(Bayne *et al.*, 1980; Blaskfield, 1976,1977; Blaskfield and Morey, 1980; Edelbrock, 1979; Edelbrock & McLaughlin, 1980; Milligan, 1981; Morey *et al.*, 1983; Scheibler & Schneider, 1985).

If the data set to be analysed has not been subject to multivariate tests for outliers or if there is no a priori reason to assume that outliers are not present, then it would seem wise to cluster using both Ward's method (with Euclidean distance) and average linkage (using correlation). It must be noted that Ward's method is such a robust algorithm that it will even produce a cluster solution with multivariate normally distributed data (that is, no true clusters) if there is sufficient variation along the first principal component axis (Morey *et al.*, 1983). This is not necessarily a problem since a partitioning on this basis is often as useful for classification purposes as true clusters (Morey *et al.*, 1983).

Identifying the optimum number of clusters in any given solution is one of the 'major problems of cluster analysis' (Everitt, 1979). The problem results from the lack of theoretical studies of cluster analysis as there is no agreed definition of what 'optimum solution' means (Aldenderfer and Blaskfield, 1984). Mojena (1977) has argued that a large jump in the value of the realised deviates under his Rule 1 can be used to identify an optimum solution. However, this seldom yields definitions that differ from visual inspection of a cluster dendrogram (Dunn and Everitt, 1982).

Given these findings, the most appropriate cluster analysis method for our purposes was Ward's method which is known to yield reliable solutions even where there is a considerable degree of cluster overlap. The analysis was undertaken using the Cluster algorithm available in the Clustan 3.2 package. The data used were the scores assigned on the common severity scale for 11 of 13 disability areas. The scores for disabilities of digestion and disfigurement were not used as these were a single 'weight' (of 0.5) and not a variable measure. A square Euclidean distance matrix was calculated from these scores after standardisation by range so that each disability contributed a weight of one to the analysis. The position of each case in the 11-dimensional matrix depended upon four factors: the number of disabilities each child had; the type of each disability; the severity of each disability and, where a child had more than one disability, their combination.

The optimum number of clusters was determined by examining the output statistics (including Mojena's stopping rules 1 and 2) and the dendrogram. All the 'solutions' between 2 and 15 clusters were examined. Each of these solutions was highly significant in all three analyses (see Chapters 2 and 14).

The optimum solution for our purposes was selected to be:
1. The eleven cluster solution for 5–15-year-olds in private households;
2. The seven cluster solution for children younger than five in private households; and
3. The ten cluster solution for 5–15-year-olds in communal establishments.

With more clusters than this, the groups could only be separated by small differences of severity; with fewer, the clusters began to merge into unduly heterogeneous groups.

REFERENCES

Aldenderfer, M.S. and Blaskfield, R.K. (1984) *Cluster Analysis*. Sage University Papers No. 44, London: Sage Publications.
Bayne, C.K., Beauchamp, J.J., Begovich, C.L. and Kane, V.E. (1980) Monte Carlo comparisons of selected clustering procedures, *Pattern Recognition*, 12: 51–62.
Blaskfield, R.K. (1976) Mixture model tests of cluster analysis: accuracy of four agglomerative hierarchical methods. *Psychological Bulletin*, 83: 377–388.
Blaskfield, R.K. (1977) The equivalence of three statistical packages for performing hierarchical cluster analysis. *Psychometrika*, 42: 429–431.
Blaskfield, R.K. (1980) The growth of cluster analysis: Tryone: Ward and Johnson. *Multivariate Behavioural Research*, 15: 439–458.
Blaskfield, R.K. and Aldenderfer, M.S. (1978) The literature on cluster analysis. *Multivariate Behavioural Research*, 13: 271–295.
Blaskfield, R.K. and Morey, L.C. (1980) A comparison of four clustering methods using MMPI Monte Carlo Data. *Applied Psychological Measurement*, 4: 57–64.
Dunn, G. and Everitt, B.S. (1982) An introduction to mathematical taxonomy: Cambridge Studies. In *Mathematical Biology 5*, Cambridge University Press, Cambridge.
Edelbrock, C. (1979) Comparing the accuracy of hierarchical clustering algorithms: the problem of classifying everybody. *Multivariate Behavioural Research*, 14: 367–384.
Edelbrock, C. and McLaughlin, B. (1980) Hierarchical cluster analysis using intraclass correlations: a mixture model study. *Multivariate Behavioural Research*, 15: 299–318.
Everitt, B. (1979) Unresolved problems in cluster analysis. *Biometrics*, 35: 169–181.
Everitt, B. (1980) *Cluster Analysis* (2nd edn). Gower, London.
Hubert, L. (1972) Some extensions of Johnson's hierarchical clustering algorithms. *Psychometrika*, 37: 261–274.
Hubert, L. (1974) Approximate evaluation techniques for the single-link and complete-link hierarchical clustering procedures. *Journal of the American Statistical Association*, 69: 698–704.
Jardine, N. and Sibson, R. (1968) The construction of hierarchic and non-hierarchic classifications. *Computer Journal*, 11: 117–184.
Jardine, N. and Sibson, R. (1971) *Mathematical Taxonomy*. John Wiley, New York.
Johnson, S.C. (1967) Hierarchical clustering schemes. *Psychometrika*, 32: 241–254.
Milligan, G.W. (1981) A review of Monte Carlo tests of cluster analysis. *Multivariate*

Behavioural Research, 16: 379–407.

Mojena, R. (1977) Hierarchical grouping methods and stopping rules – an evaluation. *Computer Journal*, 20: 359–363.

Morey, L.C. Blaskfield, R.K. and Skinner, H.A. (1983) A comparison of cluster analysis techniques within a sequential validation framework. *Multivariate Behavioural Research*, 18: 309–329.

Scheibler, D. and Schneider, W. (1985) Monte Carlo tests of the accuracy of cluster analysis algorithms: a comparison of hierarchical and non-hierarchical methods. *Multivariate Behavioural Research*, 20: 283–304.

Index

References to material in figures or tables are in italics

hearing disabilities
    aids 126–7
        young children 233
    communication disabilities and 31
    specialists 99
hearing/behavioural disabilities,
    communication disabilities and
    34
help received, special education needs
    and *195*
'holiday away' 157
holidays 117–18, 152, 178
'home on trial' 152
home teaching 95, 249
    young children 225
    see also education
hospitals 97–110
    contact pattern *102*
    contact rates with 97–102
        family income and *98*
        social class and *98*
    frequency of visits to *103–4*
    in-patient stays 104–5
    mean number of visits *103, 104,*
        229
    services received *99*
    young children 227–30
household composition 66–8
    short-term care and *112*
    identification/sampling 7–8
    limiting long-term illness (LLTI) and
        68
    types of, percentage of children in *67*
    see also private households
Household Sample of Anonymised
    Records 67, 68

identification of children with needs
    in communal establishments 8–9
    in private households 7–8
illness rates, limiting long-term *14*
impairment, definition of *4*
in care
    in communal establishments 154–6
    disabled children in residential care
        169, 258–66
    and duration of residence *171*
    and education *199, 200*
    and establishment types *156*
    and foster homes 157–8
    learning difficulties and education
        199
    local authority 152–9, 254–7

proportions of children in care in
    communal establishments *155*
    and schooling arrangements *200*
    and statemented needs met *200*
    status, education and 199–201
income 76–8
    adaptation to private homes and *132*
    family 252
    outpatient visits to hospital and *98*
    special furniture, use of, and *134*
independent assessors 19
independent visitors 194
individual planning 57
incontinence *see* continence disabilities
Individual Sample of Anonymised
    Records (SAR)
    age comparisons 60
    social class 70
intellectual functioning disabilities 29,
    30, 31, 143
    behavioural disabilities and 32, 34,
        48–9
    communication disabilities and 48–9,
        50
    continence disabilities and 48–9
    hearing disabilities and 34
    high personal care levels and 33, 51,
        52–3
    young children 217–19
International Classification of
    Impairments, Disabilities and
    Handicaps (ICIDH) 3, 5, 241–2,
    260
    areas of disability assessed *6*
    disability concepts *4, 5*
Isle of Wight survey 10
isolated children 193

Joseph Rowntree Foundation 134

labelling, cluster analysis and 23
Labour Force Surveys (LFS) (1988–9) 64,
    81, 166–7
    ethnic backgrounds 62, *62*
laundry service 89, 92, 94, 128–9, 249
learning difficulties
    cluster analysis *143, 197*
    education and *199*
learning disabilities
    children in communal establishments
        and 196–7
    children in private households and
        143